CATATAXIS

CATATAXIS

When More of the Same is Different

John Brodie Donald

To Aunt Elizabeth
with Love

11 / 08 / 2012

QUARTET

First published in 2011 by
Quartet Books Limited
A member of the Namara Group
27 Goodge Street, London W1T 2LD

A catalogue record for this book
is available from the British Library

ISBN 978 0 7043 7241 2

Typeset by Antony Gray
Printed and bound in Great Britain by
T J International Ltd, Padstow, Cornwall

1

For Yoko, who can endure the unendurable
For the shrub that grows only in the rocky soil
For the deep blue rainbow after the rain
And for the Golden Us

Table of Contents

CHAPTER 1

Introduction

It is the laugh that first attracts attention. A high-pitched giggle of unease and delight. A Philippina matron stands next to a man in uniform. She bends her knees into a crouch and puts her head to one side, as if to rest it on the man's shoulder. She smiles a toothy smile, both nervous and delighted at the same time. The man shows no expression and stares fixedly ahead. Her friend takes a photo and the matron bobs her head in gratitude to the man. The man ignores her. It is the twenty-seventh time this has happened in the last hour.

This is Horse Guards at Whitehall in London. The man wears a silver and brass helmet with a white horse hair plume and a plate steel cuirass. His black leather boots have large triangular wings at knee level. At first you think this is pure ostentation – like the tail fins on a 50s Cadillac. A glance at his mounted colleague shows their true propose. They cover the thighs when the knees are bent in the saddle.

The next tourist to come forward is a Turkish man. The robustness of his moustache contrasts with the anxiety lines on his forehead. He does not smile when his wife takes the shot and they both drift away together. Clumps of Italian children on a school trip are walking noisily down Whitehall. They cluster around the guardsman with excitement, laughing and posing for group photographs.

There is something strange here. It seems so unnatural. The noisiness of the children and the stillness of the guardsman go against all ingrained social behaviour. You should not be standing so close to a stranger without communicating in some way. The guardsman is silent and motionless. There is a palpable frisson in the air. In other parts of London, silent mimes and human statues are taking advantage of this sense of unease in their street theatre shows. But there is one big difference. In the end, the human statue moves, interacts with the audience and gets his tip. You think he is a statue, but it turns out he is a human being after all. That is theatre, this is different.

This Guardsman is a public monument, hardly a person at all. This is not an interaction between two people, but one between a person (the tourist) and an institution (the guardsman). The guardsman is the physical manifestation of a higher entity. Stiff, unsmiling and ceremonially antiquated he is the perfect symbol of the British establishment; a creature from another dimension. He is an alien in human form.

Comrades in arms from his foot division stood in square formations at the Battle of Waterloo in 1815. They stood for two hours being blown apart by artillery. Every time a cannon ball blew a hole in the ranks they just closed up to seal the gap. Why would someone stand there being shot at without doing something to retaliate? Here is why: had they broken their square formation the enemy cavalry waiting nearby would have slaughtered them. So why not retreat? Because, it is the job of an infantry unit to occupy ground. It is made up of people but it is more than just a gang of people. It's a unit forged by mental discipline, controlled by a general to form part of the front line. If that unit had retreated, the whole front line could have collapsed and lost the battle. So they just stood there and died until the French artillery ran out of ammunition.

That astonishing discipline is still here, distilled, condensed and made flesh in the motionless figure of the guardsman. Not a person but a symbol of an abstract concept. There are some places on earth where you sense that the veil between you and another dimension is particularly thin. That you could just reach out your finger, make a hole in the fabric and touch the other side. In most places, this is a religious experience with the other dimension being Heaven. In Whitehall, in London, at Horse Guards, the thing you touch on the other side of the fabric is the State.

Wimbledon, London

Some six miles south west of Horse Guards in another part of London is the Wimbledon Lawn Tennis Club. It is People's Sunday at the annual Tennis Championships. A week of bad weather has delayed many matches. There is a big backlog of games that must be played if the tournament is to finish on time. So the organisers have added an extra day; the Sunday in the middle of the two-week tournament. When this unusual scheduling event happens, it's known as a 'People's Sunday'. It was only announced on Saturday, so it is only the true fans that have queued up to buy all the tickets. The crowd at Centre Court is clearly different from the usual corporate hospitality types. No blazers and panama hats here today. The stands are filled with younger, more energetic types with big floppy union jack hats and St George flags. They are waiting to see their favourites play. Today there is no murmur of restrained conversations; no susurration of polite applause. Today there is chanting and some wild cheering. And what's that? Oh My God! They are doing a Mexican wave. On Wimbledon's hallowed Centre Court.

This has never happened before in this place. The ripple of excitement running around the stands is not just metaphorical but real. The spectators are standing up sequentially at just the right time to create the effect of a wave washing around the stadium. It's an extraordinary feeling. A moment of transition when the fans cease to be individuals and become a crowd. A liberating moment of empowering anonymity. All the awkwardness, the ugliness and the individualism is washed away as the whole stadium passes from the specific to the general and the wave works its way around.

It's not just the fact that this is Wimbledon that is unusual. The wave itself is an extraordinary thing. People are just moving up and down in their seats but the wave is travelling left to right around the stadium. The wave is made up of people but is also separate from them because it is moving in a different direction. Individual action vertically is causing something else to move horizontally. So what is the something else? How do you categorise the wave moving around the stadium? Is it some sort of intangible energy? In what dimension does it exist?

A scientist would say that a wave is the transport of a disturbance in space. There are many types. In an ocean wave, water molecules are moving up and down as the wave travels horizontally to the shore. In a sound wave it is the density of the air molecules that is oscillating. Some waves do not have a physical medium to travel through. For example, light is a form of electromagnetic wave. It travels from a star through the vacuum of space as a periodic oscillation of electromagnetic properties. Energy transmitted through nothingness.

Waves that do travel through a medium are known as mechanical waves. The medium through which they pass can neither be too solid nor too flexible. If a substance is perfectly stiff a wave cannot travel through it. Each particle is rigidly bound and there can be no wave motion. But this is also true if the substance is infinitely pliable: one particle cannot influence its neighbour and so again there can be no wave motion. So in order for a wave to travel, there needs to be some stickiness or linkage, but not too little and not too much.

So what is the medium that the Mexican wave in Wimbledon is travelling through? It is not the individual people but the sense of unity of the crowd. A wave needs some linkage to travel. In this case, it is the linkage of one person to another. This Mexican wave makes that linkage explicit. It turns a bunch of spectators into a crowd. That is its power. This is a wave that is made out of people, but it is separate from those people. It is an object that lives in a different dimension: at a higher level than the individual. A societal level. A meta level.

Canary Wharf, London

On the other side of London from Wimbledon, some eight miles to the east, stands Canary Wharf. Sixty years ago here were the busiest docks in the world, handling the physical imports and exports of the Empire. Now it's a key hub for global financial services. Many multinational banks have their headquarters here. On the thirtieth floor of a tower in Canada Square, a portfolio consultant is questioning a fund manager.

The fund manager invests other people's money. The performance of his fund is determined by which particular set of assets he holds over a certain time period. If he makes good choices and performs well then those who have invested in his fund will make a lot of money. The portfolio consultant advises people what funds to invest in. He needs to understand how the fund manager is coming up with his choices before he can advise others to invest in this fund.

Fund managers have certain asset classes that they are supposed to invest in: like Property or Government Bonds. In this case it is Asian Equities. Many funds also may have a stated investment style such as Income or Value. In this case, the fund manager's investment style is Growth. So, unsurprisingly, the name of the fund that he is managing is the 'Asian Equities Growth Fund'. The portfolio consultant is interviewing the fund manager. He wants to find out what stocks the fund holds. He needs reassurance that when he tells his clients to invest in this fund that they will make money. Sadly, his efforts are doomed to failure.

In the old days, you gave your savings to a 'jolly good chap' who you trusted to make money for you. But the portfolio consultant is trying to use mathematical tools to make the process more scientific. By analysing the constituent assets in a fund, he hopes to understand more about how the performance is being delivered, what level of risks are being taken and what repeatable methods are being used to beat the market. That's how he adds value. Otherwise, you might as well pick funds by throwing darts at a dartboard.

The portfolio consultant uses variety of sophisticated mathematical tools to pick apart the fund at a particular moment in time. He is taking a snapshot of the portfolio and dissecting it. You can see over a particular time period what went up, what went down and how volatile things were. Did the fund manager make his money by taking wild bets or by investing in dull but reliable performers. This is all very interesting stuff but it does not answer the most important question: how much will it go up this year? Those mathematical tools have descriptive power but no predictive power. It is a description of what has happened not what will happen.[1]

In fact, it is even worse than that because the constituent parts of the portfolio change over time. That's what you are paying the fund manager for. He is supposed to be buying and selling shares: managing the fund. Things are coming in and out of the fund all the time. So you not only need to predict how much the shares will go up by, but also which shares the fund manager will buy next week. This is a non-stationary time series and there is no statistical trick known to man that can make it surrender its secrets. This moving collection of assets is greater than the sum of its parts and cannot be comprehended through a reductionist approach. It is an evolving expression of the fund manager's sentiment. It is reacting

---

1 Some argue history is the best guide to the future. I know one fund manager who only ever reads yesterday's newspaper, never today's. He believes that observing how the market has reacted to news is more important than the news.

in a Darwinian way to the market environment. Who would have thought an inanimate collection of assets could be so complex?

The truth is no one knows how fund managers make their returns until after the fact. And it is extremely rare to find someone who can consistently beat the market. So advising people which fund manager to put your money with is pointless. You might as well go back to the 'jolly good chap' method. On second thoughts, everyone thought Bernie Madoff was a 'jolly good chap'. He raised all his money through word of mouth and ended up defrauding thousands of investors of billions of dollars.

There is only one theory of finance that has any conceptual legitimacy and that is diversity. The more you diversify the safer you are. So you should really just pick a bunch of things that are completely unrelated to each other. OK. Well . . . anyone fancy a game of darts? Or maybe put an ant on the financial section of the newspaper and see where it crawls.

Fazenda Aretuzina, Brazil

Adam Tofilski studies ants. In particular, he is interested in *Forelius pusillus*, a Brazilian ant. He spends three years videotaping a sandy patch of dirt at the edge of a sugar cane field at Fazenda Aretuzina in Brazil. Such dedication deserves a reward, and in this case it pays off. He finds something extraordinary. Some ants are deliberately sacrificing themselves for the sake of their colleagues. Ants forage in the daytime but at dusk they return to their nest. As they go back into the hole, they deposit sand particles around the entrance. This makes a flat elliptical pile of sand, partially sealing the nest. A few ants are left outside to kick sand from this pile over the entrance to disguise it. These few are left stranded outside the colony and die of cold in the night. Greater love hath no ant than to lay down its life for a friend.

Dr Tofilski, from Krakow University in Poland, publishes his paper in *The American Naturalist* in November 2008. He rightly points out that other insects show sacrificial behaviour. Bees leave their stinging barb in the flesh of attackers and then die. Some termites deliberately rupture their abdomens to release a sticky fluid that entangles enemies. But these suicidal defences are only used when the nest is under attack. The Brazilian ant, *Forelius pusillus*, is sacrificing himself pre-emptively to close the entrance of the nest each evening. Even without an enemy present, they are laying down their lives to die outside in the cold. It sounds as noble as Captain Oates[2] of the Scott Antarctic Expedition.

Ants are social insects, related to wasps and bees. Ant societies have a division of labour, communicate amongst individuals and have an ability to solve complex problems collectively. It is these similarities to human societies that make them so fascinating to the myrmecologists who study them. There are over 12,000 species of ant. They have colonised every part of the Earth and are arguably the most successful creature on it. They account for twenty per cent of the total weight of all land animals. But the most fascinating thing about them is this: they are so social that no one is sure whether to classify the individual ant or the whole colony as the key organism.

It's easy to see a colony of ants as a creature in its own right: a superorganism. Ants have specialised roles such as workers, soldiers, foragers, drones and fertile queens. This division of labour means that the ants are working for the good of the colony, rather than themselves. They are doing what the superorganism wants. The colony as a whole exhibits a form of intelligence and is able to do things that the individuals can't. It behaves like a living creature: it moves, it metabolises, it grows and reproduces. With the army ants of South America, the colony itself is constantly on the move through the jungle attacking large prey en masse. When the colony gets too big, it 'reproduces' itself by splitting in two. Leafcutter ants have four different castes of workers producing food in an elaborate chain. Leaves are cut, cleaned and fed to a special fungus that grows in gardens in their nests. The ants eat the fungus not the leaves. This is a superorganism with a complex digestive system.

Let's shift perspective and view the colony as the organism rather than the ant. What then shall we make of *Forelius pusillus*, the Brazilian ant? It is no longer a poignant story of self-sacrifice. They are just a few disposable cells sloughed off by the organism. It's a bit like exfoliating with a pumice stone in the bath or cutting your

---

2 Captain Oates was suffering from severe frostbite and knew he was slowing down his companions and putting the entire expedition at risk. On 16 March 1912, he deliberately walked out of his tent to die in the cold. His last words were, 'I am just going outside. I may be some time . . .'

finger nails. Do you shed a tear when you pull out your nail scissors? Do you feel sorry for the clippings when you throw them away? It's not really suicide . . .

Zurich, Switzerland

A pale man walks unsteadily up the stairs of a nondescript flat in a slightly shabby residential district of Zurich. He has been talking to a Swiss doctor for five months. He is paying £7,000 for this service. Two close friends, who have travelled with him from England, come up the stairs behind him. As he enters the room he is greeted by two volunteers who are setting up a video camera. They place him in the chair and point the camera at him. The pale man records a brief message on videotape. A volunteer comes in with a glass of clear liquid and puts it on the table near the pale man. The volunteer says 'If you drink this you will die. Do you understand?' The pale man nods, takes the glass and drains it while the camera records everything. The man is a suicide tourist who has come to the Dignitas clinic. He is terminally ill and has just taken an overdose of barbiturates. Five minutes later he is asleep; twenty minutes later he is dead. 'Live with dignity, die with dignity' that's the Dignitas motto. The body is taken to the morgue along with the videotape, which is evidence of informed consent. The body then goes to the crematorium and the ashes are scattered in Lake Zurich. Later still, small fragments of human bone wash up on the private beaches beneath the expensive villas that line the shore.

Euthanasia is such a hoary old chestnut. It's the question that you first learn to express an opinion about. It's probably the topic that you wrote your first essay about. I remember it being on exam papers when I was at school forty years ago. My father remembers it on his. It has been a staple issue in the newspapers and surfaces at least once each generation into the spotlight of public debate. There were strong pro euthanasia movements at the very beginning of the twentieth century. They were resurgent in the 1930s but at that time yoked to the evil of eugenics and Nazi ideas of racial hygiene. In the 1960s, voluntary euthanasia – the 'right to die' – began to attract many advocates. This was a response to dramatic medical advances that could prolong life for coma patients almost indefinitely. In the early 1990s Dr Jack Kevorkian became infamous for assisted suicides in Michigan. These days the papers are full of stories about Dignitas in Switzerland.

Let's quickly summarise the arguments. Those against euthanasia point out that it goes against the cornerstone of medicine as enshrined in the Hippocratic Oath of the Ancient Greeks. Morally, euthanasia is either murder or assisted suicide both of which are forbidden in most religions. On the other hand, those who support euthanasia highlight the fundamental principle of individual choice when the quality of life has deteriorated to an unbearable extent. An economic argument for euthanasia is also sometimes proposed. The budgets for healthcare are always under pressure. Why waste scarce resources on those who want to die. Should this money not be spent on those who want to live? Or those who can be cured?

Why does euthanasia stir up such passion? The glib answer is that it is literally 'a matter of life and death'. But underneath that, it is an issue that sits right at the junction point of two tectonic plates. Euthanasia generates passion just as those geological sub-duction zones throw up volcanoes. The plate of state is grinding against the plate of individual rights. It is the friction between these two levels that causes the heat. The individual believes that he 'owns' his own life and should therefore be able to do with it as he wishes. But in order for the state to recognise that, there would need to be some sort of institutionalised system of killing even if it is only a form of state sponsored suicide. Such a 'ministry of death' is inconceivable. So euthanasia is an individual right that can never be recognised by the state. The two tectonic plates can never be fused together.

European liberal democracies believe it is wrong for the State to kill, and especially wrong for a doctor to kill. These views were reinforced in the moral furnace of World War II by the revulsion felt towards concentration camps and the medical 'experiments' of the Nazis. The state believes voluntary euthanasia compromises the professional role of health care employees.

The religious arguments, the fact that Islam, Christianity and Judaism all proscribe euthanasia, at first glance seem to concern individual conviction and not the state. In fact, they are state level arguments. They proscribe what other people can and can't do. A person with strong religious convictions would never personally assist in voluntary euthanasia. But if he wants to stop someone else doing it he needs to encode his convictions in some form of legal system operated by the state.

The individual replies, 'Why should my mother continue to suffer unnecessarily?' or 'What right do you have to tell me what I can or can't do with my own life?' There are no easy answers to either question. The debate will probably never be resolved. There will just be a slow shifting of the boundary as it is moulded by the variable heat of public opinion. Some believe that societies gradually oscillate between authoritarianism and individual liberty and that it takes several generations to complete the cycle. If so, then attitudes to euthanasia are a good yardstick. We should monitor them, much as volcanologists listen to the faint grumblings of the San Andreas Fault waiting for the next destructive quake.

Ben Tre, Vietnam

It is one of the best-known quotes of the Vietnam War. When commenting on the indiscriminate bombing of civilians in the town of Ben Tre in 1968, an unnamed US Army Major said, 'It became necessary to destroy the village in order to save it'. At first glance, this is a perfect encapsulation of the insanity of the Vietnam War. However, on reflection, it can also be seen as profoundly wise. It becomes necessary to destroy something in order to save it when issues that belong at a certain level are dealt with on another level. It is the warning signal of a case of level confusion: of catataxis.

What does 'level' mean? In this case, there are many levels that make an ascending hierarchy. Each is made from an accumulation of the things on the level beneath. First, there is the individual human level. Above that, there is the community or village level. The next one up is the level of the nation state. The Vietnam War, as with most wars, purports to be a war between two nation states. Above that is the political or conceptual level. The Vietnam War can also be read as an ideological war against communism. Each step up to the next meta level becomes more abstract. So this conflict has many ways in which it can be viewed or analysed: individuals taking each other's lives, communities being destroyed, nation states expressing their imperialism or global political dogmas in contention. Your perspective depends on the level that you pick.

Let's go back to the quote: 'It became necessary to destroy the village in order to save it'. Its poignancy derives from the collision between two levels. The thing that was destroyed (the village) belongs on level two. The thing that was saved belongs on level four; the populace was saved from communism. So something can be saved and destroyed at the same time as long as they are on different levels. The village really was both destroyed and saved. It is not an idiotic quote. It is a profound one. It is an example of level confusion. It encapsulates catataxis.

There are other examples of destroying something in order to save it. A good one is the plight of the rhino. The rhinoceros is on the edge of extinction because of the value of its horn. This is used in traditional Asian medicine and for dagger handles in Yemen. Though most nations (including China) have signed the CITES treaty banning the trade in Rhino horns, poaching of these animals remains rife. Constraints on supply merely push up the market price. This is a positive incentive for more poaching. There is a radical solution to this seemingly insolvable problem: dehorn the rhinos in the wild. The poachers then have nothing of value to poach. The rhino are still alive but without horns. However, some would argue that a rhino without a horn is not really a rhino. So it has been destroyed in order to save[3] it. The level confusion here is between the natural world and economics.

Another example, but the other way around, concerns food aid. One of the basic rules of community life is sharing. Imagine I have a full plate of food and you are sitting next to me hungry. If you have an empty plate, I will of course share my food with you. It would be unnatural, or extremely selfish, not to. By the same token, if there is a famine in Ethiopia the Western World should donate food, right? Actually, this is wrong. In fact, it is maybe the worst thing to do.

In October 2009, Oxfam publishes a report titled *Band Aids and Beyond*. It is timed to coincide with the twenty-fifth anniversary of the Ethiopian Famine that triggered Band Aid and the Live Aid concerts. The report criticizes the knee-jerk reaction of sending

3 Actually rhino dehorning does not really work. First, the horns have to be cut each year as they grow back. This is very expensive and causes a lot of stress on the animal. They are sometimes killed accidentally during this process. Second, a poacher who has spent 24 hours tracking a rhino and then finds it has no horn kills it anyway – so he won't make the same mistake next time.

food aid to famine areas. It recognizes that this saves lives in the immediate short term, but there is a problem. Dumping free food destroys the local economy. Since the price of free food is zero, there is no incentive for local farmers to grow any. The long term solution to the crisis is for local farmers to grow food. So the crisis cannot be solved by giving food, it can only be made worse. Some 70% of humanitarian aid to Ethiopia comes from the United States. Of that, 94% is in the form of food grown in the USA and dumped for free in the local market. Again, we are destroying something in order to save it. In this case, destroying an economy to save lives.

You would have to be very hard hearted not to believe that this is a good trade off. A human life is real (level 1) and an economy is an abstract thing (level 2). On the other hand, despite twenty-five years of continuous aid there are still regular famines in Ethiopia. If a major famine relief agency publishes a report criticizing food aid then there is clearly something to debate. It will trigger many heated arguments. The source of the heat is the level confusion between the individual perspective and the economic perspective.

Catataxis

You may be wondering by now what is the point. What do the six stories above have in common? The answer is this: they are all examples of catataxis, of confusion between levels. Each story is remarkable because you have a hierarchical conflict. Each level is composed of the things beneath. The state is a collection of individuals. A crowd is a group of sports fans. A portfolio is a collection of stocks. An ant colony is a nest of ants. But they are all also more than that, more than just the sum of their parts. In aggregating, them together something new is created which exists at a different level.

The key point is this. There is a moment, when things get big enough, that you need to view them in a new context. More of the same is different. The object in question has become different from its component parts. It is made of the same substance but it has a different essence. It is substantially the same but essentially different. This necessitates a shift in perspective. It is the conflict between those two perspectives that causes the emotion and the heat. This confusion between the two levels, two incompatible arguments couched in different frames of reference, is what I call cataxis. This neologism comes from the fusion of Greek words. The first *kata* means down or through, as in catastrophe or cataclysm. The second *taxis* means hierarchy or rank.[4] So cataxis is a 'collapse in the hierarchy', a confusion of levels. You could also call it a disorder of magnitude. That's what this book is all about.

If you look closely you will probably find a cataxic seed behind every contentious topic in public debate. Today's newspaper has articles about the following issues in the first few pages: global warming, euthanasia, political correctness, terrorism, media independence, financial regulation, celebrity culture, EU membership, illegal downloading and spin-doctors. Every one of these is an example of cataxis. Throughout the book we will explore these different examples, but first we need to focus on the underlying concept of cataxis: how, why and when does more of the same become different?

---

4 If you are ever waiting in a queue for a cab, you can amuse fellow strangers by telling them that 'taxi rank' literally means 'rank rank'. Then watch them shuffle nervously away from you.

CHAPTER 2

More of the Same is Different

A whole heap of trouble

Consider a pile of sand. Now take away a few grains from it. Has it changed? Not really. It may be infinitesimally smaller because it its missing a few grains, but its still a pile of sand. What happens if you repeat the process? The pile will gradually get smaller and smaller until there are only a few grains left. Clearly, it is no longer a pile of sand now; just a scattering of grains on the ground. But when exactly did that change from pile to non-pile occur? Is a million grains of sand still a pile? If so, then we can take away a few grains and start the process again. How about a thousand grains? In fact, it is not possible to pick an exact number of grains and call that a pile. Whatever number we pick, we can always add and subtract a few grains without making a substantial change.

This pile of sand problem is known as the Sorites paradox, from the Greek word for 'heap'. It is first formulated by Eubulides of Miletus, a Greek philosopher in the fourth century BC. The problem revolves around the vagueness of a word like 'pile' or 'heap'. There is no precise definition, but everyone knows what it means. It is also a good example of how a gradual change in the amount of something can lead to a change in the nature of that thing. In other words, a quantitative change sooner or later becomes a qualitative change. In the end, more of the same is different.

The Renaissance physician Paracelsus (1493–1541) makes a similar observation. He phrases it like this 'the dose is the poison'. By this he means that some substances can be beneficial in small quantities but poisonous at larger ones. Belladonna, also called deadly nightshade, is a good example. The berries of this plant are highly toxic and used as a poison by the Ancient Romans. But a very dilute tincture can be used for cosmetic purposes; to dilate the pupils and make a woman's eyes more attractive – hence the name, *Belladonna*, or 'beautiful woman' in Italian. Today, *botulism toxin*, a poison created by bacteria in spoilt meat is injected in small quantities into rich, spoilt women: a Botox facelift. The dosage is critical. As Paracelcus points out, it's not the substance that is poisonous, but the amount. Again, more of the same is different.

The notion that a quantitative change becomes a qualitative one next surfaces in the writings of the German philosopher G. W. F. Hegel (1770–1831). In his book, *The Science of Logic*, Hegel uses the example of water freezing: A change in quantity, in this case the temperature, results in a change in quality; the water becomes ice. Hegel's writings, particularly his dialectic method (which we will discuss in Chapter 7), are a strong influence on two other young Germans, Karl Marx (1818–83) and Friedrich Engels (1820–95), who write *The Communist Manifesto* together. Marx only briefly mentions the quantity to quality shift in his magnum opus, *Das Kapital*. He muses about how much money a man must have before he becomes a capitalist.[5] Engels is much more taken with the idea. He is the first to codify it explicitly as his second law in his book, *The Dialectics of Nature*. This establishes the 'law of transformation of quantity into quality' as one of the cornerstones of his theory of dialectical materialism.

Engels uses a number of examples to illustrate this concept. One comes from organic chemistry. He observes that if you add carbon and hydrogen to an organic compound like methane (CH_4), its properties will change. The structure of the molecule means that you can keep adding a carbon atom and two hydrogen atoms as a unit to make an extra link in the chain. This gives you a series of chemicals: methane (CH_4), ethane (C_2H_6), propane (C_3H_8), butane (C_4H_8), and so on. The early compounds in this series are flammable gasses, then come the liquids like hexane (C_6H_{14}) and octane (C_8H_{18}) and finally the solids like paraffin wax ($C_{25}H_{52}$). So by steadily changing the quantity of carbon and hydrogen atoms you can transform some lighter fuel into Vaseline. A change in quantity results in a change in quality.

---

5 As a lifelong Dylan fan, I am sad he didn't manage to squeeze a lyric like this into 'Blowin' in the Wind'. But then again almost every line in the song is already catataxic: 'How many roads must a man walk down before they call him a man?' How many grains of sand make a pile? This is the Sorites paradox in song.

For his second example, Engels quotes a comment by Napoleon about the relative strengths of Turkish and French cavalry. Turkish cavalry, or mamluks, are superb riders but not very disciplined. In small numbers, mamluks have the upper hand; two mamluks can take on three French cavalrymen. As the numbers increase, discipline becomes more important than individual prowess. So a thousand French cavalry can easily defeat twice that number of mamluks. They charge as a disciplined mass and cut down the fragmented, individualistic Turkish cavalry. A change in scale leads to a change in the balance of power.

Communism's catataxic fall

Lenin (1870–1924) studies the writings of Marx and Engels at University and is greatly inspired by them. He also goes back to read Hegel's *Science of Logic*. His notebooks, filled with annotations to that text, still exist. When he gets to the part where Hegel discusses the Sorites paradox and the transformation of water into ice, he triple underlines it and writes 'Leaps!' in the margin. For Lenin, the phase transitions from solid to liquid to gas are metaphors for revolution. Lenin believes in sudden change; in discontinuous leaps forward, catalysed by a small vanguard of professional revolutionaries. Capitalism can never be overthrown by gradual change from within. It must be forcefully deposed through revolution, in order to establish the dictatorship of the proletariat.

There are two types of change in quality because of a change in quantity: the sudden version and the hazy version. The first is best summed up in the proverb about the straw that broke the camel's back. An eager merchant keeps adding to the burden on his camel. Finally, adding just one straw to the load breaks the camel's back. A small inconsequential addition causes a catastrophic change. A phase transition is like this too. A small change in temperature and suddenly the whole pond freezes over. This is the type of change that Lenin believes in – a sudden, dramatic, revolutionary transformation. The second type of change is much more vague. The point of the Sorites paradox is that you cannot pinpoint the moment where the pile of sand ceases to be a pile. At one extreme it is a pile, at the other extreme it is a few grains of sand. Somewhere in the middle a transition occurs. Also, the one does not replace the other, it is composed of the other. Inside the pile of sand, you can focus on a few grains and just consider those. Then you can zoom out and contemplate the pile as a whole.

Lenin seized on the first type of change, but it was the second type of change that was his undoing. The eventual failure of the Communist ideal is linked to the Sorites paradox. Here's why. A commune is a great idea. Everybody who has lived in one can feel it. A small group of people sharing what they have – from each according to their ability, to each according to their need. Who can argue with that? But it only works at a small scale. An idea which is perfect for a small community is no good when you scale it up and use it to run an enormous empire. Human nature does not scale up well.

This principle is summed up in the motto, 'two's company, but three's a crowd'. Once things get beyond a certain size they change; people begin to focus on different things. Not on what they can give, but what they can get. You may have noticed it when you are in a restaurant with a bunch of friends. Settling the bill when there are only two of you is easy; just split it down the middle. Arguing over the bill when there are twelve of you dining is often a night-mare, because suddenly everyone is worrying about who had what. Who had the really expensive starter? Someone claims he didn't drink any wine. Someone else only had a salad. Does this sound familiar? Beyond a certain size, selfishness kicks in. Everyone thinks about themselves more than the group. You also see this in the 'bystander effect'. The more people watching an accident the less likely it is that one person will help. It becomes a spectacle, not a tragedy. Somehow more people dilute the individual sense of responsibility. More of the same is different.

So Lenin knew all about the Sorites paradox, but never properly grasped its implications. A few grains of sand become a pile at a certain indistinct moment. A group of people become dominated by self interest once the group gets beyond a certain size. The vector of history points from a commune to a capitalist economy, from selfless to selfish, as things get bigger. Lenin mistakenly believed the vector pointed the other way around. That communism would inevitably arise from capitalism.

Stalin also knew about the Sorites paradox. He famously said, 'the death of one man is a tragedy; the death of a million is just a statistic'. It sounds callous, but it does encapsulate the concept that more of the same is different. An individual death affects us at a personal level, but when the numbers get too big it is difficult to respond emotionally. Big numbers belong on a different level. They require a political response rather than an emotional or personal one.

That's where Orwell got it wrong in *Animal Farm*. Things did not become corrupt because of the fundamentally evil nature of the pigs, but because of scale. It was just too damn big. The farm was never really a farm, more of a vast agro-industrial combine: a factory farm collective. The very words, *The Communist Internationale*, are an oxymoron. How can you be a commune and international? One is a small collective of several families, the other a globe-spanning supranational entity. (We will pick up on this theme in Chapter 6 on Democracy.) For now, we conclude that though many people have been credited with causing the fall of communism, (Reagan, Pope John Paul II, etc., etc.) the underlying reason may just have been one of scale. Even though Lenin knew that 'more of the same is different,' he made a catataxic error. He tried to apply the sentiments of a commune at an inappropriately large scale.

What is Catataxis?

So now you can see that the idea of a quantitative change turning into a qualitative change has a respectable historical lineage: from Eubulides, through Paracelsus, Hegel and Engels to Lenin. Catataxis is the inability to recognise that such a change has occurred. It is a confusion between levels. A misapplication of rules, when a change in scale has shifted the whole paradigm. This tends to be less of a problem in science than it is the humanities. Scientists change their names as the levels change. You can arrange the scientific disciplines into a notional ascending order: physics, chemistry, biology, psychology, and so on. Physics studies atoms, chemistry looks at the molecules made from those atoms. Biology focuses on one particular molecule, DNA, and the creatures that arise from it. Psychology studies the brains and behaviours of those creatures. It would be wrong to think of biology as merely a subset of chemistry, or of chemistry as just 'applied physics'. Each discipline has its own distinct theories, laws and methodologies which are appropriately tailored to its field of study.

Picture this. You walk in to see a shrink. She asks you to lie down on the couch. You start talking about your relationship with your father. She goes to the bookshelf and pulls out a Physics textbook. As she flips through the diagrams of electrons and other subatomic particles, you ask her what she is doing. 'Don't worry,' she replies, 'I'm just getting right back to first principles . . . ' This is cataxis.

If you take a very pedantic view then the shrink might be right. Your actions and thoughts are controlled by your brain. Your brain is a mass of neurons firing electrical pulses to each other. Electrical pulses are a flow of electrons, hence the physics text-book. In practice, it is impossible to understand your emotions by contemplating the interaction of electrons. A psychiatrist has his own set of tools and techniques for analysing that problem and they operate at a far higher level. The answer to the question, 'Why did you do that?' is not 'because neuron X triggered neuron Y to fire'. That may be literally true, but it does not really answer anything. The proper answer will refer to thoughts, feelings and motivations, the proper language of psychiatry. Applying the rules of physics to a psychiatric problem is a cataxic blunder.

Scientists understand that paradigms shift as things get bigger. The names of the disciplines change with scale. This is true in the applied sciences too. Economics has two different disciplines: micro-economics and macroeconomics. One looks at the interaction of individuals, the other at the national economy as a whole. They are two different approaches dependant on the scale of the topic being examined. Other applied sciences like engineering, architecture, systems design and IT know all about hierarchical levels. Their whole approach is based on the analysis of systems and subsystems, ensuring they interact properly with each other.

The problem lies with the humanities not with sciences. This is mainly because, as the name suggests, humanities observe the world from a human perspective. But the world has become so big, and the scale of human institutions so large that sometimes you are required to take a different perspective, higher or lower than the individual human rung on the ladder. A simple example is encapsulated in the popular bumper sticker that reads, 'You are not stuck in traffic. You *are* traffic'. This message is inviting a shift in perspective from the individual level to the collective level. Traffic is not something that is inflicted on you – you are part of the problem. We should also note in passing that traffic jams are a good example of the 'more of the same is different' maxim. A few extra cars on the road and everything comes to a standstill.

Traffic jams are an example of an emergent phenomenon, (which we discuss in more detail in Chapter 4). Right now, it may be worth briefly summarising the issues we will be examining in the rest of the book. I will use a number in brackets (x) to indicate which is the relevant chapter. A good place to start is with biological hierarchies (4). If you contemplate systems involving living things you can see that there are a whole set of rungs on a conceptual ladder that goes from DNA at the bottom to the complete ecosystem at the top. This is a compositional hierarchy. In other words, each level is made from the things on the level beneath, but needs to be viewed as a system in its own right. The traffic bumper sticker invites a shift upward in perspective: from individual to group. The 'selfish gene' concept, as expounded by Richard Dawkins, requires a shift downwards. His theory attempts to explain things from a genetic viewpoint. Many problems in biology can be better explained by viewing evolution as a competition between genes rather than between individuals. But at the other end of the spectrum, there is Gaia theory which views the whole planet as one system. These are two contrasting viewpoints: the selfish gene view approaches things from the bottom up, whereas the Gaia approach views things top down. Above Gaia theory is the ultimate top-down view – religion. So the fight between atheists and believers, between Richard Dawkins and the Church, can be cast as a catataxic struggle between different rungs on the same ladder.

Another catataxic issue concerns free will and choice (5). Shopping can be seen as a celebration of both. But though we believe we chose the goods we want, we are heavily influenced at a subconscious level by advertising: we make emotional rather than rational decisions. So branding is a type of catataxic warfare, targeted one level below our conscious selves. In this sense, branding is the cousin of terrorism, which is catataxic warfare aimed up one level, at the nation state.

Several steps up from the individual, on the societal ladder, stands the nation state (7). This is a venerable institution which may be on its last legs. Many problems facing the world are no longer national but global: climate change, piracy, overfishing, terrorism, AIDS, immigration, global banking regulation, and GM foods. These problems are generally problems of scale and nations find it hard to come together to solve them. Their solution probably requires a stronger form of supranational entity setting regulations for CO_2 emissions and bank reserve requirements.

Sovereignty seems to be leaking away from the nation state in all directions: upwards to supranational entities, like the EU or the UN; sideways to multinational corporations and downwards to the individual consumer. And that consumer seems more and more disenchanted with politics (6). Voters have disengaged from the democratic process. The elected government, supposedly an expression of the will of the people, is seen more as a 'them' than an 'us' these days.

Meanwhile, the quality of life in the modern world seems to be degraded by an excess of bureaucracy (8) and spin (9); too much red tape and too little sincerity. In fact, both these much maligned phenomena are unfairly vilified. They get a bad press from people who are unable to make the mental shift to the next level. Both are essential, in fact, they are beneficial. They are the necessary response to the change in scale that the world has witnessed in the last one hundred years.

The vertical flip

All these issues have a catataxic root. They are disorders of magnitude; frictions in a compositional hierarchy. Most of them concern the humanities because of an insistence on a human scale viewpoint. We are often reluctant to make the shift in perspective required to understand the way things work. Our default setting is small scale and local, based on common sense and a personal viewpoint. Alexander Pope (1688–1744) opens his *Essay on Man* with the couplet:

> Know then thyself, presume not God to scan,
> The proper study of mankind is Man.

This was written in an earlier time. These days, man is *not* the measure of all things. Anybody who has worked in a large company will have scratched their head, at some time, over a particularly idiotic corporate decision. What seems ridiculous to them as an individual may make perfect sense at a corporate level. Of course, companies are not always right, and using common sense is often a useful reality check. But that instinct to grab a human-sized yardstick to measure the truth can be equally dangerous, particularly now the scale of everything is so much bigger.

When Pope wrote his poem, there were ten times fewer people on the planet. Almost all were agricultural workers, living in small villages and never travelling more than a few miles from where they were born. They knew everything about their neighbours and nothing much about everything else. A human-sized yardstick may have been appropriate then, but that is not today's world. In a global economy, driven by multinationals, connected by the internet and with no place on earth more than twenty-four hour's travel away, things have changed dramatically. Large scale institutions have emerged which follow their own rules. I am not saying that they are right or wrong, just that they are different. To use the old yardstick is a mistake. That is catataxis.

The point of this book is to try to flip the normal axis of debate on its head. We are very familiar with a 'horizontal' argument. Many dilemmas can be couched in terms of equal and opposite forces. Here are some classic dualisms: left *v.* right, good *v.* evil, hot *v.* cold, male *v.* female, dark *v.* light, yin *v.* yang. These arguments are like a seesaw. There are two sides that are linked together, balancing each other out. The debate is framed in horizontal space. In contrast, catataxis is all about the vertical axis; hierarchical levels above and below.

In the West, postmodern relativism has extended this horizontal metaphor. Before, there was a see-saw of right and wrong, balancing on the fulcrum of objective truth. But postmodern relativism means that the single fulcrum of truth is dead – that there are no facts, only interpretations. There is no universal perspective or any coherent sense of objective truth. It all depends on your viewpoint. This is the sentiment behind the old adage 'beauty is in the eye of the beholder'. Relativists believe everyone is entitled to her own view: you should not judge other cultures by the standards of your own. I think a bacon sandwich is heavenly . . . you are a vegan . . . he thinks eating pork is against the will of God. All views are equally valid. The seesaw has been replaced with an endless flat horizontal plain. No one position on that plain has a superior perspective to any other.

Surely this is the end of the line for the horizontal argument. It is hard to see how it could be extended any further. The interesting dimension is now vertical; the catataxic dimension. The arguments on the vertical axis are stimulating: real *v.* abstract, mind *v.* body, reductionist *v.* holistic, hardware *v.* software and top down *v.* bottom up.

We will spend the rest of this chapter examining these vertical arguments. But before we do, one last thought on the horizontal. Moral relativism means believing that 'you have no right to tell other people what to do'. If we move up one level there is an interesting twist when viewing diplomatic relations between countries. China is a good example. The Chinese government is a strong believer in non-interventionism between nation states. At the same time, the regime is very repressive of individual rights. In contrast, the West believes that intervening in other countries' affairs is often justified, but at the level of the individual is very permissive. So China is a moral relativist at the nation level, but not at the individual level. The West is the exact opposite.

Real *v.* Abstract

In 1671, a prisoner languishing in Bedfordshire County Gaol is inspired to start writing a novel. When published, it becomes one of the most influential books of all time. It is translated into two hundred languages, and has never been out of print since. It gives inspiration to a host of later writers: Dickens, Thackeray, Twain, Buchan and Steinbeck. It is the favourite novel of Hong Xiuqan who led the Taiping Rebellion against the Qing Dynasty in China. The prisoner's name is John Bunyan. The novel is *The Pilgrim's Progress*.

The Pilgrim's Progress is an allegory. The protagonist, Christian, journeys through many difficult places on his trip to the Celestial City (i.e., heaven). Some of these places are now so well known that the allegorical intent is almost forgotten. For example, 'The Slough of Despond' and 'Vanity Fair' are common phrases. Others sound very laboured today: The Giant called Despair who lives in Doubting Castle. To a modern audience, this seems childish, clunky and unsubtle. In its time, this blatant allegory was the reason for its phenomenal success. It makes the abstract real.

Of course, the Greeks were there first, as always. Their allegorical Muses were the embodiment of the creative arts in female form. They had nine of them, each depicted with their relevant symbol. So you can tell Clio, the muse of History, by the scrolls she holds in her hand, or Euterpe, the muse of Music, by her flute. The personification of virtues has continued since then right up to modern times. Look at any Victorian public building and you will see a statue of Fortitude or Prudence gracing the front portal. State Seals in the USA are likely to show something similar. Two interlocked figures representing Freedom defeating Tyranny, or some such stirring scene.

Allegories are popular because they make the abstract concept flesh. There is a double meaning. The character is both a person and an idealistic virtue. This duality is entertaining. It still is, but these days mutated to a less idealistic double entendre:[6] Think of the Bond Girls (Pussy Galore, Holly Goodhead, etc.)

An allegory is a type of catataxis. Let's call the real world 'level one' and the abstract world, 'level two'. An allegory is something from level two depicted as a level one being, in other words, a confusion between two levels – a concept in human form. The existence of this level two is an unresolved debate among philosophers. It is known as the Problem of the Universals and asks the question, 'In what realm do concepts exist?'

Let's take the example of chairs. There are lots of types of chair. They come in all shapes and sizes, but they all have something in common: their chair-ness. They all belong to the category of things called 'chairs'. The chairs exist in the real world, but where does the 'universal chair category' exist? Does it exist separate from the chairs? This is where the disagreement comes in: the *Realists* say 'yes'; the *Nominalists* say 'no'; the *Idealists* say 'yes', but only in our heads.

In the fourth century BC, Plato is the first to try and answer this question. He is a Realist. He believes that universals are real entities and exist in the ideal realm of perfect forms. He explains this with the Allegory of the Cave. It goes like this. We are cave dwellers seeing shadows on the wall. We believe these shadows to be reality but, in fact, there is another realm outside the cave. This is where real and perfect things exist. We only see shadows and therefore we cannot ever really know anything.

In the fourteenth century, William of Ockham is the founding

---

6 It can also be seen in 'moe gijinka' characters in Japanese manga comics. A good example is XP-Tan. The Windows XP operating system anthropomorphized into a cute female cartoon character. Nerd heaven!

father of the Nominalist school. He is best remembered for the famous maxim known as 'Ockham's Razor'. This is the principle that the simplest explanation is most likely to be the correct one. If you apply this to the problem of the universals, then you must cut out the complexity of having a mystical, separate realm outside of space and time where ideal forms exist. It is simpler just to say that there is no such separate realm. Some three hundred years later, a more considered rebuttal to Plato's Allegory comes from Rene Descartes, in his seminal work, *Discourses*, which is published in 1637.

Cartesian Dualism

Descartes was a French philosopher who spent most of his adult life in the Dutch Republic. He was the first thinker to articulate a mechanistic worldview. Descartes argues in his *Discourses* that the world is a machine that can be understood by taking its pieces apart and studying them. He also fuses together algebra and geometry for the first time by inventing Cartesian co-ordinates. But the book is most famous for the phrase *cogito, ergo sum*, which splits the world into two domains: the mental and the physical.

Plato's conclusion is that we only see shadows and therefore we cannot ever really know anything. Descartes argues that there is something we can know. *Cogito, ergo sum*. If I am capable of thinking then I self evidently must exist. So the physical world may well be just an illusion, but the mental world must be real, because I am thinking. This split between mind and matter is known as Cartesian Dualism.

By drawing this line between mind and matter, Descartes triggers a host of other debates that still resound today. He argues that God must exist in the realm of mind not matter. God is separate from the material world, which must run on its own rules like a clockwork mechanism. God may have originally set up the rules. In other words, he wound up the clock. But God does not make every single thing happen in the world, the clockwork mechanism does. Dimensions rule the physical world: Cartesian co-ordinates. So, through measurement and observation it should be possible to understand the mechanism of the clock.

The split between mind and matter has other consequences. It strikes a deathblow to belief in witchcraft. Casting a magic spell is impossible in the Cartesian world. A spell belongs in the immaterial realm and therefore cannot have an influence on the material world. Therefore no sane person can believe in witchcraft. It took some time, but this view did prevail: witchcraft ceased to be a legal offence in Britain in 1735. A more problematic issue is transubstantiation. How is it possible for bread and wine to be converted into the body and blood of Christ during the consecration of the Eucharist? This debate continues today.

Taking this one step further brings us to the problem of inter-actionism. If mind and matter are separate then how am I able to raise my arm just by thinking about it? Clearly my mind does influence my body, so there must be a link between the two. Descartes himself struggled with this problem. He eventually suggested that the communication mechanism was the pineal gland. This small, reddish-grey endocrine gland is the size of a grain of rice and located in the centre of the brain between the two hemispheres. We now know that it produces melatonin, which regulates our sleep/wake cycles. Descartes believed that it was a secret keyhole (that only humans had) that allowed the realms of mind and matter to communicate.

As above, so below

Descartes is expressing a mechanistic view of the universe in the language of philosophy. Newton expresses it in maths fifty years later, demonstrating the inner workings of the clock. He does this through his laws of motion, put forward in his *Principia Mathematica*, published in 1687. This introduces the concept of gravity and provides the scientific grounding for predictions of the motions of the planets.

Newton has one thing in common with Paracelsus, he of 'the dose is the poison' fame. They are both hermeticists; they subscribe to the occult doctrines of Hermes Trismegistus – a fusion of the Greek god, Hermes and the Egyptian god, Thoth. These are translated into Latin in the Renaissance and the book *Corpus Hermeticum* is so popular it goes through thirty editions by 1641. The book has a profound influence on Renaissance philosophers, and becomes a standard text for alchemists. The underlying con-cept of hermetic thought can be summed up in the phrase: 'As above, so below'. As you can see, this esoteric world view has a vertical axis. It asserts that what happens at one level is directly linked to another level. The world is divided into the microcosm (often oneself) and the macrocosm (the universe). Only through understanding one can you understand the other.

This idea of a link between the celestial and the human goes way back into our prehistoric past. It is probably in the minds of the builders of Stonehenge and seems to be present in all early societies; think of the Olmec and Mayan long count calendars, feng shui astrolabes in Han dynasty China. Most cultures have a tradition of astrology and their own local version of the signs of zodiac. It seems a basic human impulse to see patterns where there are none: to make stories by connecting dots in the random distribution of stars in the sky.

Newton is both the last esoteric mage and the first scientist. He is a keen alchemist and writes extensively about the occult. To begin with, many colleagues view his scientific works in the same category as his esoteric writings. The Cartesian philosophers at Newton's college (Trinity in Cambridge) are very dismissive of his theory of gravity. They see it as a violation of Descartes' philosophy. The whole notion of 'action at a distance' (i.e., gravity) sounds like witchcraft to them. The Cartesians believe that matter can only influence other matter if they touch. A billiard ball can make another ball move if it collides with it. But a mystical force called gravity that influences things some distance away sounds like superstitious nonsense. They believe that some sort of fluid must be keeping the two bodies in contact and that Newton must be wrong.

Reductio ad absurdum

Newton is not wrong. By explaining the motions of the planets, he creates a split between astronomy and astrology; between science and superstition. Having solved the problems of the heavens, he opens the door for scientists to solve the problems on earth, through the close observation of nature. After Newton, science develops its multi-layer hierarchy as new disciplines are created each with its own rules and laws. There is faith in the scientific method and a belief that all problems will fall to the disciplined application of an analytical mind.

The main change is from deductive to inductive reasoning. Deductive reasoning views ancient wisdom as being correct. It tries to deduce solutions to the problems of today from that received corpus of knowledge. Inductive reasoning works the other way around. Its starting point is the observation of nature. From those observed specifics, a general law is proposed. The cornerstone of this new scientific method is reductionism. This views a complex system as the sum of simpler parts. So by breaking things down into smaller components, the whole can be understood. Scientists take this reductionist method and apply it to the question: 'What are the building blocks of matter?' Gradually, throughout the eighteenth century, alchemy becomes the science of chemistry.

Alchemists reading the *Corpus Hermeticum* have been exploring the secrets of matter. They are trying to understand what things were made of and how they transformed. Ancient wisdom holds all things are made from fundamental elements. The Greeks believe there are four: air, earth, fire and water. The Hindus believe there are five to match the five senses: earth, air, water, fire and aether. The Chinese also believe there are five, but a different five: wood, fire, earth, metal and water. But they all believe that everything is a combination of these basic elements. By altering the blend of these basic elements you can transmute substances and, say, turn lead into gold.

The new scientific method is based on the observation of nature. John Dalton begins to measure the weights of different chemical substances and, in 1803, publishes a list of the atomic weights of six elements: hydrogen, oxygen, nitrogen, carbon, sulphur and phosphorus. Other scientists follow suit with patient observational science. By 1863 there are fifty-six known elements with atomic weights. But no one is sure how to group them. There are gasses, metals, non-metals and earths. There are elements that share similar properties but there does not seem to be any pattern to the way in which their weights differ.

When Mendeleev publishes his periodic table of elements 1869 it can be seen as another triumph of the reductionist method. What Newton did to the heavens, Mendeleev does to the workings of matter on earth. As above, so below. Newton's work enables the prediction of planetary motion, Mendeleev's work predicts elements that have not even been discovered yet.

Mendeleev's table ranks elements by order of weight in rows from left to right. He groups those with similar properties into columns and shows there is a periodic cycle. Most importantly, he leaves gaps in the middle of the table for elements that have not been discovered yet. When the missing elements that he predicted are subsequently found, the table is fully validated. The fundamental building blocks of all matter have been discovered. It is shown that they are organised in a rational way. There is one flaw. There is no theory as to why they are organised like this. It is not until the discovery of sub atomic particles in the early twentieth century that the reason is found.

At this moment of reductionist triumph, there are disturbing discoveries in another branch of physics which, in time, will kill reductionism. Scientists have been investigating the properties of the latest high tech wonder: the steam engine. While trying to make steam engines more efficient, Lord Kelvin postulates the Second Law of Thermodynamics. This states that entropy always increases. This is best illustrated by a bar of hot iron in a room. Gradually the iron bar cools and the room heats up until everything is the same temperature. This is the state of maximum entropy. The Second Law asserts that the natural state of everything is the lukewarm; greyness, mediocrity and a uniform blandness is where we are all headed. Applying the same argument at a much larger scale, everything in the universe will eventually end up the same temperature. This is the moment of heat death; when the universe has 'run down' to such an extent that it can no longer sustain motion or life.

These discoveries suggest that the natural state of the universe is not order and progress but degeneration and decay. Such gloomy musings by scientists turned Victorian concepts of progress on their head and were soon echoed in the horrific slaughter of World War I. Thermodynamics, by analysing the entropy of the system as a whole, was also striking the first blow against the reductionist approach. It is a science based on a view of the system not its component parts.

Worse, however, was still to come. Nils Bohr publishes his model of atomic structure in 1913. This explains how atoms are made up of electrons, protons and neutrons. It also finally explains the mechanisms behind Mendeleev's periodic table of elements. It is shown to be based on the atomic number: the number of protons in the nucleus. Much more importantly, it is the birth of quantum physics which destroys the scientific certainty of the previous two centuries. Quantum physics is the death knell of reductionism.

To understand why, we need to look at the Uncertainty Principle first articulated by Bohr's assistant, Werner Heisenberg, in 1927. This states that it is impossible to know both the position and velocity of an electron with certainty. The more you know about where it is, the less you know about how fast it is going. Conversely, if you know an electron's speed then you can't know where it is. This is because an electron exhibits wave-particle duality. Sometimes an electron expresses itself as a wave and can be diffracted when passing through crystals. Sometimes an electron exhibits the properties of an electrically charged particle. It is both a wave and a particle. This is of course impossible in classical physics. The only way of resolving the paradox is this: an electron is both a wave and a particle but can only be observed as one or the other. We can switch back and forth between the different views, but we can never see both at the same time.

This paradox is best illustrated by the thought experiment put forward by Erwin Schrodinger in 1935. He imagined a cat in a steel box. There is also a flask of poison in the box. A random quantum event can trigger a hammer that breaks the flask, releasing the poison and killing the cat. When we open the box we can see if the cat is alive or dead. But before we open the box, quantum theory states that the cat is both alive and dead at the same time. It is the act of looking in the box that resolves the quantum superposition. The cat then becomes either alive or dead. Schrodinger was trying to illustrate the bizarre nature of quantum physics and meant his cat parable to be a *reductio ad absurdum*.

Quantum physics brings reductionism to a full stop. It shows that at the smallest level the universe is fundamentally unpredictable and uncertain. The very act of observing an experiment will influence its outcome. The observer is not independent of the observed. There are not two separate realms of mind and matter. They are both interlinked. The line that Descartes drew to separate them has been erased.

At the same time, at the other end of the scale, Einstein has developed his general theory of relativity which shows that energy and mass are the same thing: $E = MC^2$. There is a strange parallel in the art world. Picasso and Braque are painting shocking new pictures in the Cubist style. Instead of showing objects from one viewpoint, these paintings present the subject from a multitude of viewpoints at the same time. The objects are broken up and reassembled in an abstracted form. Einstein and the Cubists are both saying the same thing, but in different languages. They are denying the integrity of mass.

So where we once had a single cohesive corpus of classical physics, we now have three levels: Quantum mechanics at the sub atomic level, Newtonian mechanics at the human scale and Einstein's relativity at the galactic scale. Einstein developed his Special Theory of Relativity into a general one that incorporated Newton's Laws of Gravity. So Newton is a subset of Einstein. But the phenomena that relativity describes, such as time dilation and gravitational lensing, are only observable when looking at things on a very large scale. It is very important for astronomers but not much practical use for anyone else. The laws at these three levels are all true scientifically, but only really pertinent at their appropriate scale. Applying Quantum physics at the Newtonian level leads to absurdities like Schrodinger's Cat. The effects of relativity are only significant when travelling at close to the speed of light. At that speed, travelling from the Earth to the moon would take about one second.

Applying rules at one level which belong at another level is catataxis. Schrodinger's Cat is an example of catataxis. We can generate another one by applying quantum mechanics to cosmology (which is governed by Relativity). Consider this. Quantum theory splits the world into two parts: the part under study and the part that contains the observer. The system hovers in a state of near existence until the observer makes a measurement at which time it becomes real. Since no observer can exist outside the universe, quantum cosmology can never make sense because then the universe could not be real. So, applying quantum theory at the wrong scale leads to ridiculous conclusions; another example of catataxis.

Since the 1920s, progress in physics seems to have slowed down. In the hundred years from 1830 to 1930 there are an impressive number of theoretical advances: magnetism, electricity, radio waves, relativity, radioactivity, X-rays, thermodynamics, cathode rays, quantum mechanics and big bang theory. These are all significant breakthroughs, many of which have had a major impact on our daily lives. Now look at the period since 1930; in terms of new discoveries there has been nothing much. It has mostly been extensions of previous theories. A lot of effort has gone into the search for a Grand Unification Theory which would tie together all the fundamental forces of the universe. Such a theory would reconcile Quantum Theory and Relativity, explaining how the discrete universe of one and the space time continuum of the other can both be true at the same time. Despite many attempts, such a theory has yet to be proved, even after eighty years of effort. Maybe the conclusion should be they can't be reconciled, and that different levels require different rules.

The night of the living dead

Reductionism in physics is dead, killed by the silver bullet of Quantum Theory in the 1920s. Physics changes direction and takes a more holistic approach: viewing the system as a whole rather than just the component parts. In contemplating the infinite and the beginnings of the universe it becomes more in tune with Asian philosophy. Its brash certainty is tempered by a mellow wonderment; arrogance transformed to contemplative maturity.

In other disciplines, reductionism takes a surprisingly long time to die. In mathematics the end comes quite quickly and tragically. Bertrand Russell and Alfred North Whitehead spend twenty years labouring over their magnum opus, *Principia Mathematica*, named in honour of Newton's earlier work. Maths is a deductive science. Everything is deduced from first principles, but these principals have never properly been defined. This is Russell and Whitehead's self-appointed task. They attempt to underpin the foundations of maths with a set of axioms in symbolic logic. To give you a flavour of the book, it takes 392 pages of manipulation of logical symbols to derive the proof that $1+1 = 2$.

The futility of this reductionist effort is brutally demonstrated by Kurt Gödel's *Incompleteness Theorem* in 1931. This states that there will always be mathematical statements that are true, but cannot be proved to be true. In other words, maths itself is incomplete. Another way of putting it is this: the *Principia Mathematica* can either be consistent or complete, but not both. This sounds similar to Heisenberg's Uncertainty Principle and has the same effect in mathematics as the latter does in physics. Russell, realising that his life's work has been a failure, abandons logic and devotes the rest of his time to pacifist causes.

Biologists have also had their 'Quantum' moment. Darwin's

Theory of Evolution in 1859 explains how natural selection accounts for the diversity of life on Earth. But the mechanism by which the adaptations were passed down the generations are still unclear. Just as Mendeleev's periodic table had to wait until Bohr's atomic theory for validation, the underlying mechanisms of evolution are only fully made clear with the discovery of DNA in 1953 by Crick and Watson. For a brief moment there is a perfect reductionist model. The DNA double helix is composed of four different types of base molecules that encode the genetic information. So the DNA is composed of strings of genes. The DNA is itself organised into long structures called chromosomes. Children inherit one set of chromosomes from each of their parents. Natural selection favours the fittest of the children. Hence, new species evolve. Just as atoms are the building blocks of matter, genes are the building blocks of life.

The mechanistic purity of this reductionist vision is soon lost. Molecular biologists probe deeper and discover a number of surprises. First, genes can jump around to different positions on the DNA strand. These 'transposons' can cut and paste themselves into a different sequence within the genome of a single cell. Second, genes are not only passed from parent to child (i.e., vertically) but can also be transferred horizontally. In other words, between organisms which are not offspring. It seems this is common in bacteria and single cell organisms. Then there comes another shock. When the techniques to read the human genome are finally developed, it turns out to be astonishingly similar to all other genomes. How can such a vast difference in the creatures in the living world be explained by such a small difference in DNA?

The way in which genes express themselves is much more complicated than first imagined. It is not just a simple one-to-one mapping between the presence of the gene and the effect on the individual. Groups of genes interact with each other. Genes can be selectively turned on or off by environmental stimulus, or even by other genes (Hox Genes). In fact, genes are not independent building blocks at all but more like nodes in an information processing network. You can only understand them by looking at the whole system. You need a holistic view.

Elsewhere, reductionism still staggers around like a zombie, particularly in the softer 'social' sciences. Social sciences are sometimes seen as poor relations of the natural sciences. They have had a much harder time gathering empirical evidence and are less fluent in the language of mathematics. Perhaps in their earnestness to be taken seriously, they trail rather than lead intellectual fashion. So the message that physical science has moved on takes some time to filter through.

In Psychology, the Behaviourists such as Pavlov and Skinner are still dominant until the late 1950s. Their experiments with dogs and bells, or rats in cages, attempt to show that all actions are conditioned responses or learnt behaviours. An individual is merely a sum of these underlying components. Actions can be explained in terms of responses to external stimuli. The 1960s usher in the 'cognitive' revolution. This puts the concept of the mind back at the centre of psychology. It recognises that the mind is a complex system composed of many interacting parts and capable of an infinite range of behaviours. It is a holistic view, not a reductionist one.

The Earth sciences (such as geology and ecology) have their holistic awakening in 1972 when James Lovelock published his Gaia hypothesis. This suggests that the whole earth should be viewed as a single complex interactive system; in fact as a single organism. It puts forward the theory that the biomass of the planet acts in a self-regulating way to make the physical environment of earth more hospitable to life. Despite significant changes in inputs (like energy from the sun) the environment on earth has remained remarkably stable. Gaia theory states this is a positive feedback effect created by life on Earth in order to sustain life on Earth.

Medicine has its Quantum moment with the discovery of the placebo effect. In the 1950s, researchers conducting clinical trials began to notice that patients showed measurable positive responses even if they were given harmless sugar pills instead of medicine. The key thing was the patient had to believe it was medicine. The results were also affected by whether or not the doctor believed it was medicine. Clearly the mind is not separate from the body. Descartes is wrong. The mind and body are linked together as a system. *Mens sana in corpore sano.*

The realisation of the power of the placebo effect means that double blind tests become routine, in order to eliminate it. In addition, the door is opened for a host of alternative therapies. Aromatherapy, acupuncture and homeopathy are extremely popular treatments today even though they are unproven in the conventional sense.

This is infuriating for mainstream doctors. On the other hand, recent research has demonstrated that there is little difference in effect between anti-depressant drugs and sugar pills. Sales of anti-depressants topped $11 billion last year. Who is the charlatan here?

Some disciplines are having their Quantum moment as we speak. Economics, the dismal science, is still reductionist. Mainstream economic theory is based on *Homo Economicus*. This hypothetical individual makes rational choices based on utility, price and need. He acts in his own self-interest and is rational, in the sense that he always chooses the option that delivers the most gain for the least cost. An army of these individuals drives the economy. They create demand, cause price fluctuations and induce supply. These higher-level market forces are an amalgam of self-interested decisions made by a nation of *Homo Economicii*.

In financial markets, these ideas are expressed in the prevailing doctrine of Modern Portfolio Theory. This attempts to maximise returns and minimise risk. It is based on the assumption that the investors in the markets are *Homo Economicii*: they are rational and markets are efficient. The second assumption is that risk is normally distributed. These assumptions were seriously challenged by a series of financial crises: the Asian Meltdown of 1998, the Dot Com bubble of 2000 and the global banking crisis of 2008. There is growing evidence that investors are not rational and that markets are not efficient. A lot of this evidence comes from game theory where experiments produce results that cannot be explained by conventional economics. The hot new field is now Behavioural Finance, which raids the holistic toolbox of the cognitive psychologists and applies it to financial markets.

Another area where reductionism is still dominant is food. This is a highly politicised arena. Food manufacturers are keen to avoid blame for the obesity epidemic. Just like tobacco companies and lung cancer, they spend heavily on political lobbyists. As a result, the debate is shifted from food to nutrition. Food is seen as being composed of types of nutrients: protein, carbohydrates, fats, vitamins and minerals. Lobbyists ensure the discussion is focused on these building blocks and not the food itself, which is one level higher. The slogan is 'There are no bad foods, just bad diets'. So rather than saying, 'don't eat butter,' the advice from the government is, 'avoid saturated fats.' Food manufacturers can then produce a butter-style spread that is 'low in saturated fats' and everyone is happy. Well, everyone apart from the newly obese consumers of all that processed food.

The focus on component nutrients rather than food seems to be more 'scientific': it is the last place where reductionism is chic. Food labelling with a statistical breakdown of the nutrients has been introduced by most Western governments. The focus on nutrients means that everything can be processed to make it 'better'. The science here is questionable because we don't really understand nutrition yet. There seems to be a link between processed food and obesity, although the lobbyists are keen for it not to be emphasised. It's bound to be more complicated than we currently think. Food is more than a delivery mechanism for a bunch of identified nutrients. It is more than the sum of its parts.

The holistic approach

As with almost everything, holism has its roots in Ancient Greece. It was Aristotle who coined the phrase, 'The whole is more than the sum of its parts'. It is also an underlying theme of most Eastern Philosophy. It is only in the twentieth century that a holistic view becomes important in Western scientific process. As explained above, holism starts in Quantum Physics and then gradually moves through all sciences.

The holistic approach is the driving force behind systems theory; a new branch of science that starts in the 1950s. This has a strong anti-reductionist stance and examines the emergent properties of a complex system; in other words – the things that cannot be understood by reducing something to its component parts. Complex systems are inherently unpredictable. It is the interconnection between the different parts and the feedback between them that makes the system very hard to model. So that things, which on the surface seem simple, when put together, create all sorts of unexpected results.

Systems theory has come in many flavours and each decade seems to change its name, though bizarrely they all seem to start with a 'C'. In the 1960s it was Cybernetics, in the 1970s it was Catastrophe Theory, in the 1980s Chaos theory and in the 1990s, Complexity. The latest buzzword is 'Consilience'. They all address a similar area: non-linearity. Non-linear systems are unpredictable and very dependent on the initial conditions.

Imagine a pea inside a teacup. If you knock it slightly, it will roll around a bit and then settle back at the bottom of the cup. That is a stable linear system. We can predict where the pea is going to end up. Now turn the teacup over and balance the pea on the top. This is an unstable non-linear system. If you knock the pea, it will roll down the side of the cup across the table and onto the floor. It is very hard to predict where it will end up. Small changes in where you place the pea to start with will make big changes in where it ends up. This is sometimes called the 'butterfly effect'. It was Edward Lorenz, a meteorologist, who first observed that his computer model for predicting the weather was extremely sensitive to the initial input. So much so, that a single flap of a butterfly's wings could eventually trigger a hurricane on the other side of the world.

The underlying problem is this: mathematicians can't solve non-linear differential equations. Linear systems are predictable and there is a well-developed set of mathematical tools to analyse them. But nature is inherently non-linear. The world is a chaotic place. If you want to use maths, then you have to ignore the chaotic parts and just analyse the linear stuff. You have to assume that the world is stable and linear in order for the maths to work. That is the reductionist approach.

What tools can you use if you want to take a holistic approach? That's the problem. There aren't many. You normally have to try to make a model of the system on a computer. So you can throw together a few fractal[7] algorithms and generate something that looks similar to the object of study, for example, a share price chart. You can then make a plausible claim that stock markets are chaotic and fractal in nature. Then what? Your model has descriptive power but no predictive power. It looks *like* a share price chart but it is not a *real* share price chart, so you can't actually use it for making predictions that will make you money. So what use is it? Are we really any closer to understanding by simulating? I can make something that looks like a chicken out of rubber. But what use is a rubber chicken, other than as an amusing comedy prop?

Classical science was reductionist and predictive. Modern science is probabilistic. There are no more Laws. There are just demonstrations of impossibility, like Gödel or tentative suggestions of

7 We will discuss fractals and maps in the next chapter.

possibility. We know we need to analyse the system and not the parts but we don't have the tools to do anything useful at the system level. Descartes drew the line to separate mind from body with his *cogito, ergo sum*. That started the mechanistic worldview and the impressive advances of reductionist science. Now, that line has been erased. Almost all branches of science realise that the world is holistic, not mechanistic; chaotic, not stable. So we have come back to the same place where we first started, the difference being that, at least, we know more than the first time around.

Just the same, but different

I love Chinatown. It's the easiest and quickest way to temporarily immerse yourself in a different culture. And the food is great, especially the dim sum. My favourite is a dish called Crispy Cheung Fun. It's a deep-fried stick of dough wrapped up in a thin sheet of steamed dough. It's got all the illicit 'Carb on Carb' action of a Chip Butty,[8] but the texture is better. The slimy glutinous outside contrasts perfectly with the crunchy interior. But its true elegance is that it is two different versions of the same thing. It's a confection of pure texture. If you were to liquidise it and send it to a laboratory they would tell you it's just flour. It's the two different treatments of the flour that makes it special. It's the same stuff but with different structures.

It is possible to draw a dividing line not between two different things, but between two similar things with different structures. Chemists are familiar with this distinction. Atoms within molecules can have different spatial arrangements. That means there can be a right-handed version of a molecule and a left-handed version. These are called chiral molecules and the study of them is known as stereochemistry. Chiral molecules have identical chemical formulas and exactly the same number and type of atoms, but they can have very different effects. The most tragic case concerning a chiral molecule was the thalidomide disaster. One version of the drug thalidomide was completely safe. Its chiral twin caused deformity

---

8 A chip butty is the depraved acme of British Cuisine. Deep-fried potato chips between two slices of bread. It's a French fry sandwich. South East Asians have their durian. Japanese have natto. Brits have the chip butty as the test of a true anglophile.

in unborn children. The confusion between the two forms caused a rash of birth defects in the early 1960s. They were chemically the same, but different in that one important way.

For a long time the deep ocean was believed to be a uniform lifeless void. No light could penetrate deeper than 1,000 meters, so clearly nothing could live down there. Cold, dark and motionless, it did not seem a promising area for study. Now it is recognized as an exciting new frontier. Whole new ecosystems are being discovered. Strange new life forms are causing the Tree of Life to be redrawn. There are also rivers that have been discovered down there in the middle of the deep ocean. A river in an ocean? At first, it sounds impossible. Surely rivers need banks and land? In fact, these powerful currents may hold the clues to understanding the earth's climate. The point is this. The deep ocean has structure. It is all water, just organised in different ways. Same substance, different organisation.

Let's restate the problem. Reductionism ignores the system, but has predictive tools. Holistic analysis recognises the system but has few predictive tools. Reductionism is too small scale. Holism is too large scale. The solution is very practical: stratification. It's an engineering solution. Divide up the system you are looking at into hierarchical levels. Not the difference between this and that, but the difference between this and more of this: scaled divisions of the same thing. That means that you can examine the granular structure of a particular level in a reductionist way. At the same time, you are still recognising that it is part of an overall bigger system. So it is both a reductionist and holistic approach. Just make sure you use the right tool at the right level. If you don't, that is catataxis.

The PC paradigm shift

In the early 1970s, the nickname for the US computer industry is 'Snow White and the Seven Dwarfs'. IBM is by far the largest company, so Big Blue is Snow White. The seven other smaller companies are the dwarfs. In mid-decade, GE sells its computer business to Honeywell and RCA sells it's to Univac. The seven therefore become five. They are given the new acronym 'The BUNCH' (Burroughs, Univac, NCR, Control Data and Honeywell). So at the dawn of the 1980s, the computer industry is dominated by six companies: IBM and the BUNCH. They do not just dominate it, they *are* it.

At that time, the computer industry is vertically integrated. Each company makes everything itself. Computers are a business tool. You are a manufacturing company and need to manage the spare parts in your warehouse better. You explain the problem to Burroughs. They come and install a mainframe computer in a special room. The machine is built by Burroughs. The microchips in the machine are designed and made by Burroughs. The software that runs on the machine is written for you by Burroughs. Even the printers, the tape drives, the computer paper and the typewriter ribbons are Burroughs products. And the guy in the white coat who lives in that special room, nursing and maintaining the machine? He works for Burroughs.

As a customer, it is quite convenient. Everything is bundled into one price, your problem is taken care of and, best of all, you know who to blame if something goes wrong. If you ask your Burroughs salesman how much the software package costs, he looks blank and scratches his head. He can't sell it like that. Besides, it only runs on Burroughs hardware, so it's useless on its own.

The customers are happy, but for the computer companies things are getting difficult. Technology is advancing so fast. Everything is getting so complex. It costs a lot of money to keep developing the next generation of microchips. Clients' needs are getting more and more diverse, and it takes a lot of work to write all those different programmes. The upfront investment is getting greater and, therefore, so are the economies of scale. You need a bigger customer base over which to spread the development cost. That is what is driving the industry consolidation. That's why it's now the BUNCH and not the Seven Dwarfs. They all look enviously at IBM and wish they were as big. They dream of having economies of scale like that.

The truth is this: it is tough for IBM too. Down at the bottom end of the market, people are talking about something called a 'personal' computer. It's a bit of a joke. Something for the nerds and home hobbyists. Everyone knows the real money is in business computing. IBM does not want to get distracted from its important markets, and so, for the first time, subcontracts out the development work for this toy for geeks. They want to get to market quickly. They chose an Intel 8088 chip. It's far less powerful than their own IBM 801 processor, but it is cheap. They can't be bothered to write an operating system especially for it. They subcontract that out also, to a small company called Microsoft. Within fifteen years, Microsoft is the biggest computer company in the world, and IBM is almost bankrupt. The operating system which had previously been seen as unpriceable and unsaleable ends up being the most commercial thing of all. In a few short years, the industry snaps from being vertically integrated to a set of specialist layers. Manufacturers use the same 'off the shelf' components in all their gear and companies become dominant in their horizontal strata.

Today, it is hard to imagine the computer industry being organised in any other way. Intel makes chips, Dell makes PCs, Microsoft makes software, Amazon sells you products online and Google helps you find them. It is a rising hierarchy from hardware to software to services, each dependant on the layer beneath. It is a horizontal stratification, not vertical integration. Each company is the expert at its own level.[9] It seems so logical it is obvious. That's how the information hierarchy works and that is how the industry is now organised.

For you as the user it's still an integrated system – the software with no hardware is useless. You rely on that nested hierarchy in order to do your job. The words you type on the screen end up being stored as a set of electrochemical differences in a memory chip. The one is made of the other. But it is impossibly hard to edit your document by manipulating things at the microchip level. It's not just because the chip is so tiny. Imagine a miniature version of yourself wandering through a maze of corridors. Every wall is covered with little electrical switches. Which ones do you flip to correct your spelling mistake? It's Mission Impossible because the information has been encoded three levels down. There is no 'one-to-one' map between a switch and a letter. In order to make those changes, you need to use the right tool at the right level – in this case, a word processor at the software level. To try and do it any other way would be a catataxic blunder.

Newton, the Rosicrucian, believed in the motto 'As above, so below'. In 1687, his laws of motion demonstrated the mechanism

---

9 Apple has recently overtaken Microsoft to be the biggest computer company in the world by market cap. Its model is still a vertical one. It makes PCs, writes its own software and sells things through its iTunes store. Maybe the pendulum will swing back towards the old model.

that worked the heavens above. But it took some time for the 'universe as a clock' metaphor to catch on. This is not because no one believed him. It is because not that many people had a clock. Time-keeping was originally done with candles, sundials or measured water flow. Christiaan Huygens invented the mechanical pendulum clock in 1656 which enabled accurate counting of the hours for the first time. In 1759, Thomas Mudge invented the lever escapement and made the first pocket watch. It was so accurate it had a minute hand too! It was only when people started to walk around with this mechanistic marvel on their person that the phrase 'like clockwork' had any meaning. Personal familiarity with the machine births the metaphor.

As with the 'personal clock', so with the personal computer. Now that the PC is part of all our daily lives, the idea of a hierarchical stack of discrete levels can become the new paradigm for understanding the world. So it is no longer smart or particularly resonant to describe things as working 'like clockwork'. The new metaphors are based on hardware/software analogies. Business jargon is now littered with computing terms which imply nested levels: 'reboot', 'drill down', 'scalable', 'content delivery', 'bandwidth', 'onboarding' and 'interoperable'.

The wave particle duality of quantum physics can be viewed as a hardware/software split. The wave is the software and the particle the hardware. Corporate balance sheets have a similar split between tangible and intangible assets. It was only in the 1980s that intangible assets like brands were perceived to have a financial value. Likewise, DNA can be seen as a coded molecule. Life stems from the interaction between these nucleic acids (software) and proteins (hardware). So the best analogy for the post reductionist age is the PC. The world is not a clock but an ascending hierarchy of information layers. We cannot find the answers by digging deeper because the whole is more than the sum of its mechanical parts. We can step back and meditate on the holistic glory of the system but this does not get us very far. We need to recognise the stratification and treat each layer appropriately. Right tool: right level.

If stratification is the answer, how do we recognise these levels? It involves either dividing things or combining things. That's the subject of the next chapter.

CHAPTER 3

Making Levels: Combining and Dividing

Division: The Liminal Zone

The expression on his face is so peaceful it seems he is asleep. In fact, he has been dead for 2,500 years. Every detail on his face has been perfectly preserved by the peat bog he has been buried in. You can see the stubble on his chin, the crow's feet around his eyes and the wrinkles on his forehead. He wears a pointed woollen cap. Around his neck is something more sinister: a rawhide garrotte. He has been sacrificed, ritually strangled and then pushed beneath the dark water of the bog. The acid in the peat has pickled him like vinegar. He is preserved forever; the soft parts that is. The bones have been dissolved away. He is an anti-skeleton. Dark pickled flesh, not bleached white bones. By passing through the mirror of the water he has become an opposite.

There have been hundreds of Iron Age bog people found across Northern Europe. No one knows why they were sacrificed. They seem to be high status individuals, with a healthy diet and manicured hands. They have been ritually killed: stabbed, strangled or pinned down with stakes and drowned. One interpretation is that they are offerings to the gods. They have been put in a sacred pool which is a doorway to another world.

Pools or wells were sacred in Celtic culture. An echo of this still exists in the Clootie wells in Scotland, Ireland and Cornwall. If you visit one today, you will see people dipping strips of cloth in the water and then praying, while tying it to a nearby tree. These days it is normally a prayer to a saint but it was originally a pagan ritual. The mirror-like surface of the water seems like a gateway to the other side. The pool is a liminal zone. A threshold. A place of transformation from one state to another.

This chapter is all about dividing things and combining things. These are the two mechanisms involved in creating different levels. So before we apply our catataxic analysis to the fields of politics, business, media and the rest, I want to spend some time looking at the intriguing problems of creating levels. On the way, I will be going through some basic maths and science. (Feel free to skip to the next chapter if you already know this stuff or if it bores you.) But you may be surprised to find that dividing things into groups is more complicated than you may think. Drawing a dividing line is not so simple. When you group things together, you may gain information, or lose information or get something completely unexpected, as we shall see.

The surface of the water was a sacred dividing line for the Celts. The other common type of sacred threshold is the gate. Shinto temples in Japan have a Torii gateway in front of them to mark the transition from the profane to the sacred. They can be made from stone or, sometimes, just two posts with a connecting rope high up. The most common form is two vertical posts topped by two horizontal ones with the whole thing painted bright red. Sometimes there is a whole series of Torii on the processional path to the temple. There are similar structures outside temples in China, known as Pailou, and India, called Torana. The purpose of all of them is the same: to make the act of crossing the dividing line special.

Dividing lines are always special. Tourists seem to love them. You can stand at the Royal Observatory in Greenwich and straddle the prime meridian. You have one foot in the Eastern hemisphere and one in the West. You can have your photo taken under a sign in Nanyuki, Kenya, with your body split by the equator. In the USA, you can actually be in four places at the same time. If you contort yourself at the Four Corners monument, you can have one limb in each of Utah, Colorado, Arizona and New Mexico. The challenge is, when the photo is taken, can you still keep your dignity?

Sometimes a dividing line is more than just a marker. It can serve many purposes. Hadrian's Wall in the north of England is a timber and stone fortification that marks the edge of the Roman Empire in antiquity. It has a series of forts along its length and is manned by soldiers. But it is a mistake to think of it purely as a defensive structure. It is not a barrier to keep the barbarians out. It's more a mechanism for projecting power and keeping the peace. It puts a stop to cattle raiding. Gates in the wall control the flow of people and goods, and allow taxes to be levied. The Great Wall of China serves a similar purpose.

The threshold of logic

Dividing lines are breeders of logical problems. The best known is Zeno's paradox. This states that Achilles can never catch the tortoise in a race. Achilles starts the race 100 metres behind the tortoise. He runs to catch up with him and gets to the place where the tortoise started. But in that time, the tortoise has moved 5 metres further on. Achilles runs those 5 metres, but the tortoise has moved on again. Every time he gets to the place the tortoise has been, the tortoise has moved on a bit. So the tortoise will always be in the lead. The similar paradox can demonstrate why it is impossible to cross a line. In effect, you will always get to the halfway point before you get to the finishing line. There are an infinite number of halfway points. That means that you can never cross the line.

These paradoxes all have the same root: dividing something into infinitesimally small units while approaching a limit. This held the key to a major mathematical breakthrough: calculus. Newton used the 'calculus of infinitesimals' to discover the laws of planetary motion. By breaking things down into infinitely small parts and performing a 'differentiation', or an 'integration', you have a mathematical language that can describe velocity and acceleration. Actually, this *is* rocket science but it's not that hard. Everyone is taught it as a teenager in their maths classes. Maybe you weren't listening at the back?

Crossing the dividing line creates another paradox in the digital world. In this world, only one and zero can exist. In the analogue world, change is smooth and continuous. You move from peak to trough in a gentle undulation like a sine wave. But the digital world has only two states: on and off. There is only black and white and no grey. Something changing in the digital world looks like a square wave, not a sine wave. Now think about what happens when a one becomes a zero. It happens instantaneously, but in that instant it is both one and zero. Before the event, it is a one. After the event, it is a zero. But, what about at the precise time of the event? Then it must be both. But it can't be both because in the digital world it has to be either one or the other: Hence the paradox. By trying to draw a dividing line, you allow the possibility of something being on the line that belongs to both categories. If something can belong to both, then it is not a dividing line.

What about if you draw the line so carefully that there is nothing on it to start off with? Everything falls on one side or the other. That's fine in a static system in which nothing changes. But as soon as you allow the possibility of change, then you are back to the paradox again. By moving from one side to the other, it must cross the line. At the instant of crossing the line it belongs to both categories. Computer scientists get around this problem by using the concept of 'signed zero'. In arithmetic, you have positive numbers and negative numbers. But, what about zero? Is it a positive number or a negative number? Computer scientists say there are two zeros: positive zero $(+0)$ and negative zero (-0). All floating-point calculations on computers use this signed zero concept.

The edge of chaos

Given the logical problems of the dividing line, it is sometimes better to think of it not as a line but a zone: a liminal zone. This zone belongs neither to one side nor the other. It is where the transformation takes place. Next time you are standing in the queue at passport control at the airport, turn to your neighbour and tell him you are both in the liminal zone. You are physically in the country but not legally, since your passport has not been stamped yet. You can then happily chatter on about bog mummies and calculus and see if his eyes glaze over. Queues at the airport are a very boring liminal zone, but normally they are the most interesting place to be. Liminal zones are where it all happens. This is known as the 'edge of chaos' proposal.

The phrase 'edge of chaos' was first used by Christopher Langton when researching Artificial Life. This involves studying cellular automata: computer models that consist of a large grid of cells with different rules for switching cells on and off. If a cell is *on*, it is coloured black and if it is *off*, then it's white. A rule might be something like this: If you have three black neighbouring cells, then turn on (i.e., black). As you run the model, on each turn, the pattern of the grid changes following some simple rules that have been set up. Some sets of rules are boringly stable. After fifty turns or so, the grid locks in to a fixed pattern and does not change any more. Other sets of rules are completely chaotic. You just get a random pattern of noise. But some sets of rules show complicated repetitive patterns that move across the screen as though they were alive. They replicate themselves; they eat others; they exploit gaps in their environment. This is Artificial Life.

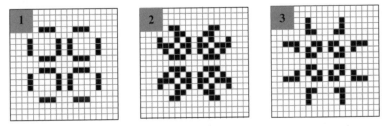

Artificial Life: three steps in a cellular automata program

The 'interesting' rule sets that exhibit Artificial Life exist on the edge of chaos. Not stable and dull, not totally random, but in a liminal zone between the two. Maybe this is a fundamental property of life: that it exists on the edge of chaos. That is the place of greatest adaptability; the most flexible zone. So creatures that exist there will be favoured in the Darwinian struggle for evolution. Anything that lives on the edge of chaos has evolved to evolve. This is a message that is enthusiastically embraced by the wider community of non-scientists. Christopher Langton uses the phrase 'edge of chaos' in a specific way to describe the lambda variable in his experiments. Before long, it becomes a much more general concept.[10] Management consultants use it to urge CEOs to make their companies more responsive to the marketplace. Politicians

---

10 This is maybe another example of catataxis - the misapplication of a rule from one area elsewhere.

use it to justify panicky short term decisions at times of crisis. Traders in bank dealing rooms use it to explain away their losses. Here are my two favourite takes on why the liminal zone is so special. The first is to do with the evolution of Homo Sapiens, the second with the warrior elite.

The Aquatic Ape

The Aquatic Ape Hypothesis was first proposed by Max Westenhofer in 1942. Its best-known champion is Elaine Morgan, who has published six books on the subject. The story goes like this: man did not just move from an ape-like existence in the trees to bipedalism on the savannah, in one step. There was a water dwelling period in between the two. Apes can walk on two feet for short distances but are much faster on all fours. Walking upright also causes a lot of strain on the lower back. So why would a creature adopt bipedalism if it was slower and mechanically cumbersome? It only makes sense if you are wading or paddling in water. You stand up to keep your head out of the water, and the water supports some of your body weight. There are several other reasons to suppose there was an aquatic phase in human development: Humans are hairless, with sweat glands and subcutaneous fat, unlike apes but just like dolphins and whales. Human babies have a waxy coating at birth and show the mammalian diving reflex. A diet rich in fish may have been a causative factor for our larger brains.

The aquatic ape hypothesis is controversial and not accepted by mainstream scientists. But it is a seductive idea. Humanity was born in the liminal zone, between the land and sea. The seashore provides abundant food. When threatened by land predators you can retreat into the water. When sharks attack, you can return to the land. It is the flexibility in being able to exploit both environments that sparks the crucial adaption from ape to man. So next time you are relaxing and sunning yourself on a beach you can be doubly happy. Yes, it truly is where you belong.

The Shepherds of War

The second step in the human story concerns the change from nomadic hunter to settled farmer. The invention of agriculture is the first and most glorious of our technological revolutions. Its birthplace is the Fertile Crescent (modern day Jordan, Turkey and

Iraq) around 9000 BC. The big surprise is that despite having a steady supply of food, life expectancy actually goes down. Studies of Neolithic skeletons show that average height declined by four inches and people died earlier. This is because dense populations, supported by regular harvests, were breeding grounds for disease. Around this time smallpox, influenza and measles mutate from being animal diseases to human ones. So like all technological revolutions, it brings positives and negatives. In this case, agriculture is good for the group but not for the individual: more people, but with shorter lives.

Let's take one step backwards. Our focus is not on the settled farmers nor the nomadic hunters but a third group: the pastoralists. This is the group in the liminal zone. Farmers have a regular supply of food and, in our analogy, represent order and stability. In contrast, hunter-gatherer tribes are foraging for food in the wild. They roam widely in search of their next meal. They represent disorder and chaos. In between the two are the pastoralists. They are herdsmen, following flocks of animals. They are nomadic, but they have a regular food supply from the animals that they follow. So, living on the edge of chaos, they have the best of both worlds: plenty to eat and fewer infectious diseases. They still exist today in groups like the Sami in Lapland, following the reindeer, or the Maasai, with their cattle in Kenya.

In antiquity, pastoralists at the edge of chaos invent three world-changing technologies: the wheeled chariot, the re-curved bow and the stirrup. If you want to protect fast-moving herds from attacks by predators, you need an equally fast-moving platform from which to fire missiles. The chariot, with light spoked wheels, was probably invented to fulfil this need. Likewise, a bow which was short enough to handle from the back of a chariot, but still powerful, was required. The re-curved bow, made from laminated wood and horn bent back upon itself, was invented around 2000 BC by the tribes on the Asian steppes. These two together made a formidable military force. Chariot archers had the speed and accuracy to kill a running wolf and the knowledge of how to work a herd. When these troops met conventional foot soldiers, they were able to inflict crippling casualties with impunity. By constantly circling their chariots and firing from a distance, it was almost impossible for foot soldiers to retaliate.

In 1700 BC, a tribe of skilled charioteers, known as the Hyksos, sweep into Egypt from Syria. Easily slaughtering the Egyptian troops, they establish the 15th Dynasty and rule as Pharaohs in Lower Egypt for 100 years.[11] The Hyksos are the first, but there are many later waves of conquering herdsmen. The Hittites invent a new lighter chariot with a wheel in the middle that can carry three warriors. They conquer most of the Fertile Crescent in 1300 BC. Selective breeding of horses eventually produces steeds with backs that are strong enough to bear a rider. These new beasts and the invention of the stirrup on the Central Asian steppes around AD 200 mean the chariot can be dispensed with. But the tactics remained the same. The swift moving horse archers of the Huns bring the Roman Empire to an end in AD 476. The Mongols, under Genghis Khan and his sons, created the largest empire in history in the thirteenth century with similar troops. The vigour of these hordes from the steppes comes from their pastoralist roots at the 'edge of chaos'. They are the conquering warriors from the liminal zone.

There are other topics to discuss concerning the liminal zone. A marketplace is a liminal zone. It is where a buyer meets a seller and prices are created. A marginal constituency is a liminal zone. That's where elections are decided. (We will return to these in later chapters.) It is now time to change focus from the line between categories to the categories themselves. We have discussed how difficult it is to divide things and why the dividing line and the liminal zone is so interesting. Now let's look at the groups that are created when combining things. No more division, it's time to contemplate addition.

Addition: combining things

This book is all about adding things up. It's about the difference between some and lots. By aggregating things together, you end up with something complicated enough to be more than the sum of its parts. This is the moment that it begins to show 'emergent' behaviour. This is the moment when you need to step back and change focus. You need to reach for a different toolbox to analyse the system at a meta level. Don't look at the trees, look at the wood.

---

11 Fans of historical adventure fiction should read Wilbur Smith's *River God* to get a feel for this period.

All sorts of interesting things happen when you achieve this change in perspective. But it all starts at a basic level, simply adding things together. Adding things up sounds very straightforward. In fact, it is not. There are plenty of wrinkles in the fabric and I want to spend some time exploring them.

The first problem, when combining things together, is picking a way of representing that group. One way to do this is to define the bucket in which they all sit. Then everything in that bucket can be called by the same name. In maths, this is known as 'set theory' which we will turn to later. The other way is to create some sort of representative average. This is the first step into the field of statistics: the science of getting one number to represent a bunch of other numbers. So it's really the numerical equivalent of a political election. It often has just as much skulduggery and underhand manoeuvring.

We are all familiar with taking the average of something. If my test results are above average then I am better than half the other people who took the test. It seems obvious but in fact it's not true. Read it again and see if you can spot the error. As so often in statistics, things are more complicated than they seem. Imagine a class of ten students taking a test with ten questions in it. Seven of them are fairly able but three are complete dunces. These three are so bad that they score zero in the test. I get seven questions right. Two of my fellow students get eight of them right. All of the remaining guys do really well and get nine of the questions right (but they were probably cheating). Now let's work out what the average is. If you add up all the scores and divide by ten you get a number just less than six:

3 people score 0
1 person scores 7 (that's me)
2 people score 8
4 people score 9
The average is $(3 \times 0 + 1 \times 7 + 2 \times 8 + 4 \times 9) \div 10 = 5.9$

So the average is just less than six, I scored seven. So I got more than the average, but was still in the bottom half of the group. The reason is that the dunces pulled the class average down so much that the sample was heavily distorted.

There are three types of average: mean, median and mode. We

have just calculated the arithmetical[12] average, otherwise known as the mean. The other types of average are equally good ways of trying to find a representative. The median is the one in the middle. If you rank all the scores in order, it's the one halfway down the list. In this case it is eight. So, for my starting sentence I should have written this: If my test results are above the median I am better than half the people who took the test. The last type is the mode. This is the score that most people got. In this case it is nine.

So we can summarise the test scores using three different types of representative averages: the mean is six, the median is eight and the mode is nine. Any of these three figures can be legitimately called 'the average', so you can see how tempting it is to just pick the average that supports your argument best.

Statistics: losing money, saving lives

The distribution of scores in my example is unusual, and there are data sets where the mean, median and mode are all the same number. A data set like this is called a 'normal' distribution and the pattern of results is defined by a bell curve. In 1809, Karl Friedrich Gauss first describes it and so it is sometimes called a Gaussian distribution, in his honour. This Gaussian bell curve is the most commonly found statistical pattern and the foundation stone of most statistical tools. So much so, statisticians often take the assumption of a normally distributed data set for granted. That was the error in the test results statement earlier. It would be correct to say: 'Assuming a normal distribution, if my test results are above average then I am better than half the other people who took the test'. The trouble is most people forget to put the caveat, 'assuming a normal distribution . . . ' at the front of their statements. It is quite understandable. It sounds pedantic. But that was the main reason for the banking crash of 2008 as we shall see.

The best example of a normally distributed data set is the heights of a group of people. If you pick a bunch of guys at random they are

---

12   There is also a geometric mean and a harmonic mean. The arithmetic mean is always the largest of the three and the harmonic mean the smallest. One of the easiest ways for a government to manipulate, say, inflation or unemployment figures is to change the way they calculate the average by using a different type of mean (for example, CPI *v*. RPI).

likely to be around 178 cm. (5ft 10in) tall. One of them might be as tall as 2m. (6ft 6in), or as short as 140 cm. (4ft 7in). But no one would be 5m. tall (16ft 4in). It is beyond the bounds of possibility. The bigger the group the closer it will approximate the idealised mathematical function: a smooth bell-shaped curve. If you take as the group all adult men in the USA, then the average (mean) height is 178 cm. (5ft 10in). Since this is a normal distribution, it is also true to say that most American men are 178 cm. tall (mode). The median is also 178 cm. so if you are taller than that you are in the top half of all American men.

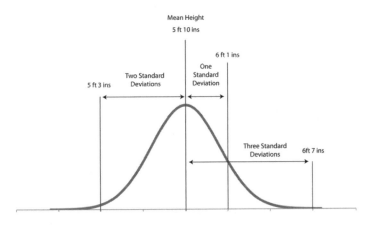

Bell curve showing average height of American Males.

We can also measure the bounds of possibility using the standard deviation. For a normal distribution, 99.7% of the sample population will lie within three standard deviations of the mean. The standard deviation for the height of American males is 8 cm. (3 in). It's very unlikely that you will meet someone either 24 cm. (9 in) taller or shorter than 178 cm. (5 ft 10 in). So if you meet someone taller than 202 cm. (6 ft 7 in), it is quite correct to call them a freak. This would, of course, be very rude and since he is bigger than you, not very advisable.

I'm sure this all seems simple and obvious, but we are only a short step from the long grass. Let's look at another population measure: age at death, or life expectancy. In medieval Britain, life expectancy was only thirty years. Most people are shocked when they hear that statistic. They imagine young men cut down in their prime, maybe as a result of all the wars. Others picture serfs toiling in their master's fields and prematurely ageing through overwork. In truth, it is a statistical mirage caused by a non-normal distribution. In medieval Britain, most people were dying either very young or relatively old. Even in the early eighteenth century, 75% of children born in London died before their fifth birthday. So age at death is not a bell curve-shaped distribution, it looks more like a dumbbell. There is a big group that die before five, then another group that die after sixty, and only a small scattering in between the two. Average these out and you get thirty years' life expectancy. If through better hygiene and medicine you improve infant mortality you can have a dramatic jump in life expectancy. You are removing one end of the dumbbell. It does not really mean that suddenly 'everyone is living longer'. It just means that fewer babies are dying. This happened in Britain during the industrial revolution, in Asia in the last century and is still happening in Africa today.

Life expectancy data is an example of a positive surprise when discovering that your sample data is not normally distributed. More often, this discovery gives you a negative surprise, as is the case in the Global Banking crisis of 2008. The crisis was triggered by the realisation that the risks associated with certain financial products had been dramatically understated. Collateralised debt obligations (CDOs) are a structured financial product created by repackaging mortgage repayment streams. The riskier mortgages are mixed up with safer ones, just as good wine is mixed with bad, to make a blended product that is of acceptable quality. How do you measure that quality? Well, the credit agencies do it with their spreadsheets full of statistical models. However, the maths behind the process relies on the efficient market hypothesis which assumes that risk is normally distributed. In other words: that financial markets fit the bell curve. Unfortunately, the distribution of risk in financial markets turned out to be very different from a bell curve. The result was that two trillion dollars of CDOs were suddenly recognised as being worthless and many banks went bankrupt.

So the misuse of the bell curve almost destroyed the global financial system. But the bell curve has also saved lives. The field of clinical trials illustrates this point well. A large number of clinical trials don't come to any firm conclusion. There may be a slight indication that the drug is beneficial, but it is not a strong enough association to be conclusive. But if you do a meta-analysis of a bunch of inconclusive trials, a stronger picture can emerge. In effect, you are doing a study of existing studies; sifting through the trials data that is already out there. This is the mission of the Cochrane Collaboration, a non profit organisation based in Oxford. For any particular procedure or drug, they pool together the results of a large number of trials from all around the world. By running a statistical analysis at this 'meta' level, trends can emerge that would be missed in a single fragmentary study. Lots of small trials can be synthesised together to make one big review which can give conclusive results.

Here is a good example. In the period from 1972 to 1991, there are fourteen different small scale clinical trials examining the effects of steroids on the survival of premature babies. Though promising, they are all inconclusive. But when you combine the data from all of them together a different conclusion emerges: steroids can reduce the odds of death by thirty per cent. This picture only emerges at the larger scale. The success of this type of meta-study means the Cochrane organisation now has 27,000 volunteers in ninety countries. It has published over 4,000 reviews and, as a result, has saved countless lives. In terms of impact, it's probably one of the most significant medical breakthroughs of the last thirty years. It's not new science. It is a statistical aggregation: moving up one hierarchical level and seeing the wood from the trees.

Support or Illumination?

So lumping things together can be either disastrous, as in the banking crisis, or life saving, as in the clinical trials. More often than not, the results are somewhere in between the two and open to various politicised interpretations, as our next example shows. Andrew Lang (1844–1912) was a Scottish Man of Letters and an avid collector of fairytales. A perfect blend of two northerly adjectives: Caledonian and Grimm. But he is probably more famous for this rebuke to an unscrupulous colleague: 'He uses statistics as a drunk man uses lamp posts – for support rather than illumination.' In other words – picking the statistics to support the argument, rather than the other way around.

The Climategate scandal is a good example of how politicised a statistical average can become; an attempt to portray Global Warming as a fairy tale. In 2009, e-mails are stolen from the University of East Anglia's Climatic Research Unit. These purport to show how the calculation of average temperatures is being deliberately skewed by omitting outliers. In other words, data that supports the case is included and that which doesn't is excluded. It is alleged that the statistics are being manipulated to support a pre-established conclusion: that Global Warming is caused by human activity. This scandal breaks a month before the Copenhagen Global Climate Summit which hopes to come up with a successor to the Kyoto Protocol on CO_2 but ends in shambolic chaos. So now conspiracy theorists on both sides can accuse the other. One side holds that Global Warming is a fairy tale and that scientific truth is being suppressed. The other believes sinister forces timed the scandal to wreck the talks.

So is this a case of support rather than illumination? It comes down to a question of judgment. The scientists at the university are trying to create an average global temperature series for the last 2000 years. This has to be pieced together from a patchwork of data sources. In recent times, there are direct measurements with thermometers. In ancient times, temperature can be inferred from examining the pattern of tree rings, known as dendroclimatology. In both cases there are distorting factors which means that the data sets are quite noisy. Extracting a signal from a noisy background is notoriously tricky, as we will see. For now, here are some illustrations of this particular problem. Temperatures measured in or around big cities are likely to be a few degrees higher than those in the open countryside. So this is a factor that must be adjusted for in the data. Another distorting factor is that most of the recorded temperatures are land-based and in the Northern hemisphere. What about the Ocean or the Southern Hemisphere? How should we adjust for that? Similarly, tree rings can be affected by more than just temperature. Rainfall, leaf eating predators and CO_2 levels can also have a big impact and so need to be adjusted for. More troubling is the divergence problem. Sometime around 1950, the thermometer records and the tree ring records diverge from each other. The thermometers show rising temperatures and the tree rings don't. The temptation is to use the thermometer data because it is a direct measurement and so presumably more accurate. But if you switch from using one to the other a distortion will be introduced.

That's a lot of extraneous factors that need to be adjusted for. If you start with a firmly held conviction, then is it not inevitable that you will bias the adjustments in favour of your beliefs? Despite U2's song to the contrary, you *will* always find what you are looking for. Quantum Physics teaches us that you cannot separate the observer from the experiment. Corporate financiers put it more cynically: if you torture the data enough, it will always confess in the end. But this is science and not finance. This is the domain of ethics, evidence and sound judgment. An international panel is asked to review the work of the climate scientists at UEA to decide if they have deliberately distorted the data. Their conclusion is no they have not, but they do criticise the statistical naivety of their methods. The panel was surprised ' . . . that research in an area that depends so heavily on statistical methods has not been carried out in close collaboration with professional statisticians.' Who would have thought that calculating the average would be so complicated?

Set theory: Grouping things together

One way of representing a group is to take the average, but this only works if you are dealing with numbers. How do you represent a group of objects if they are not numerical? You need to define a conceptual container inside which they all will fit.[13] You can't take the average of a chair and table and a footstool – but you can put them in a group called furniture. In fact, you can probably put them in a sub-group called four-legged furniture. Mathematicians call groups like this 'sets' and the science of grouping things is known as set theory. You might remember it from school – all those interlocking circles and Venn diagrams. Again, like statistics, it starts off very simply and then gets very complicated.

Set theory is founded by Georg Cantor in 1874. Before this, the notion of sets is seen as being trivial. Something is either part of a group or not. Sometimes things are part of more than one group. That's about it. It does not seem like there is much to explore there, does it? It is all very simple when you are dealing with finite sets. Cantor's paper introduces the notion of infinite sets. That's when it becomes a whole different ball game. Previously, people thought that 'the infinite' was an unknowable realm for philosophers and priests to debate. Cantor shows it is part of the

---

13 Actually set theory works with all objects – numerical and non-numerical. Cantor's ground-breaking work was about numerical sets.

mathematical universe because there are different classes of infinity. His paper demonstrates that the set of real numbers is bigger than the set of natural numbers.

The series of natural numbers such as one, two and three is infinite; you can keep on counting forever. Real numbers are all the natural numbers plus all the other numbers in between, like 4.67 and pi. The series of real numbers is also infinite. Both things are infinitely big, but one is bigger than the other. So there must be more than one class of infinity. In fact, Cantor later demonstrates that there are an infinity of infinities. After this brainwave, he spends the last twenty years of his life in a mental asylum. Others pick up the ball and begin discovering some difficult paradoxes in set theory. One example is David Hilbert's Grand Hotel, put forward in 1900. This posits a hotel with an infinite number of rooms. Even when the hotel is full and every room has a guest staying in it, Hilbert shows the hotel can still accommodate an infinite number of new guests.

More troubling is Bertrand Russell's paradox concerning the set of sets that do not contain themselves. It is often put like this: Imagine a village where men who don't shave themselves are shaved by the local barber. The paradox is this. Who shaves the barber? The answer is that if he does, then he doesn't, and if he doesn't, then he does. In other words, a complete logical tangle caused by a self-referential feedback loop. Russell wants to purge maths of all these paradoxes. He begins his masterwork, *Principia Mathematica*, which attempts to insert a firm logical foundation beneath the baroque edifice of mathematics: an axiomatic set theory. As we noted in the previous chapter, these effort are demolished by Kurt Gödel with his Incompleteness Theorem in 1931. This uses set theory to demonstrate 'there are things that are true, that cannot be proved to be true'. This is an obvious conclusion to anyone who has religious faith, but it is a devastating bombshell to the mathematical community. So set theory, which begins so simply, as just a question of which category to put something in, ends with a big bang because of the problems of infinite sets.

The power of the name

Deciding how to classify something is a puissant delight. The most powerful weapon in a bureaucrat's armoury is the ability to decide which group something belongs to. That junior clerk behind the counter looking at your application form and deciding which pile to put it in has, for a moment, authority over you. And he knows it. It harks back to an ancient belief: once you know the true name of something you have power over it.

In many religions the true name of God is a secret, because man cannot have power over God. The Jewish tetragrammaton YHWH is used as a substitute for the name of God which cannot be pronounced. For Muslims, Allah has ninety-nine names plus a secret one known only to him. In the *Book of Genesis*, it is God who creates all the living creatures, but it is man who names them. This demonstrates man's dominion over the animal kingdom. On a more mundane level, for children an unusual middle name is a curse. Once the other kids at school find out what that middle initial stands for they will use it to humiliate you. They know your secret name and so have power over you.

The power of names and the love that those in authority have for them is beautifully ridiculed in Henry Reed's World War II poem, *The Naming of Parts*:

> Today we have naming of parts. Yesterday,
> We had daily cleaning. And tomorrow morning,
> We shall have what to do after firing. But today,
> Today we have naming of parts. Japonica
> Glistens like coral in all of the neighbouring gardens
>   And today we have naming of parts.
>
> This is the lower sling swivel. And this
> Is the upper sling swivel, whose use you will see,
> When you are given your slings. And this is the piling swivel,
>   Which in your case you have not got . . .

It is such an evocative poem. We have all daydreamed in a drill session when an instructor drones out a litany of names. The point is this: he believes the names have a power even if you do not. There is another man whose whole life is names. If names have power, then he is a veritable superman. Meet the taxonomist.

Taxonomy is the science of classification. Librarians do it with the Dewey Decimal System to organise books on shelves. Computer scientists do it with database designs and network structures. But the area of concern for most taxonomists is biology. The job of a biological taxonomist is to identify species or to resolve conflicts over existing nomenclature. Correctly naming a species may seem a dry and theoretical concern, but it can be a matter of life and death, as anyone who likes eating wild mushrooms knows. In London, taxonomists do this with reference to the vast plant and animal collections in Kew Gardens, or the Natural History Museum. Most laymen believe that everything has a unique Latin name, but this is not the case. Taxonomists spend a lot of time sorting out problems of synonymy: a species that has been named twice by two different scientists.

There is no central global database for biological taxonomy.[14] As a result, there are an estimated 350,000 plant species on earth but one million names. In other words, each plant has been named on average three times. Lag times between discovery and publication and incomplete knowledge mean it is quite common for a botanist to name a species that he believes is new to science when it is not. It's the taxonomists who have to sort out the mess.

Science is taught in schools with didactic authority. Teacher instructs: you take notes. It comes as quite a shock to realise that the whole body of knowledge is much more fragile than you suppose. And taxonomy is the nervous system of that body – so, if you've got problems in getting the names right, then you really have got serious problems. It's not just that the names are changing in the tree of life. The tree itself is changing. It has been fundamentally redrawn six times in the last hundred years. I learnt at school that living things are divided into two kingdoms: animals and plants. The latest re-categorisation in 2004 has six kingdoms: Bacteria, Protozoa, Chromista, Fungi, Plants and Animals. Every time a new technology comes along, it prompts a reshuffle of the classified species. In 1735, Linnaeus starts grouping things by the way that they look. Then new technology, in the form of powerful microscopes, allows far more detail to be seen, which prompts some major reclassifications. The next technology revolution is biochemical analysis, which triggers more changes. Most recently, the ability to read DNA upsets the

---

14 The Internet has made a huge difference. The online Catalogue of Life project is attempting to integrate 66 different taxonomic databases from around the world into one central global standard.

applecart again. This has introduced the concept of a cryptic species: two species that look identical, but are genetically different.

Taxonomy has always been a matter of judgment by experts, particularly when drawing the dividing line between species. Taxonomists are often ideologically divided into two camps: 'lumpers' and 'splitters'. Lumpers tend to put things into existing categories and splitters love to make new species. The latest trend is to try to take some of the subjectivity out of the process by using a cladistic approach. This uses DNA analysis to follow the genetic line of descent. It's less about what things look like now and more about where they have come from. The tree of life is being redrawn again as a cladogram; a family tree. Current species are the leaves on the tree, the forks in the twigs and branches are the common ancestors. In this redrawn tree, categories such as 'reptiles' no longer exist, because their common ancestor gave rise (at different times) to both birds and mammals. So the old category of reptiles consists of parts of several different branches and a bit of the trunk too.

Harmony: separate but together

We have been examining the ways of combining things together – either by averaging them out or putting them in the same group. But genetics brings another interesting possibility: combining things while keeping them separate. When Charles Darwin first publishes *On the Origin of Species* in 1859 it prompts much scientific debate. A negative review is written by Fleeming Jenkin, a professor of Engineering at Edinburgh University. He points out what he believes to be a fundamental flaw in Darwin's theory: natural selection cannot work because of blended inheritance. His argument runs like this. If a tall person and a short person have a child, then that child is likely to be of average height. It will be a blend of the two parental extremes. The natural trend of sexual interaction is to eliminate the outliers and revert to the norm. So Darwin's theory of 'natural selection' does not have anything to select on. It is continually presented with a middle of the road average. Every generation is a blend of the two before it. There is no underlying trend towards diversification and new species. Instead, there is a trend to grey mediocrity.

Darwin believes that sexual interaction produces a mixture, but not a full fusion of two individuals but he does not really know how such a mechanism works. He makes an attempt at a theory called pangenesis which suggests that cells shed gemmules which collect in the reproductive organs. But this theory is deeply flawed and not supported by evidence. At exactly the same time, an Austrian monk called Gregor Mendel, is experimenting with cross breeding pea plants. He publishes *Experiments in Plant Hybridisation* in 1866. In it, he puts forward the theory of particulate inheritance. When crossing a white flowered pea plant with a purple one, you might expect some sort of pink result. In fact, the result is not a blended colour but the original shade of purple. Mendel theorised that the offspring inherits two factors, one from each of its parents. One factor is dominant (in this case purple), the other recessive. The white coloured trait is still present in the purple flower. It is just not expressed. So the two factors have been mixed together, but not blended. They are combined, but still separate. Mendel's theory is correct, but it is ignored. It is sometimes claimed that a copy of Mendel's paper was in Darwin's library, but with its pages still uncut, proving that he never got around to reading it. What a sweet irony if true, but this story is probably apocryphal. It is not until the twentieth century that scientists rediscover Mendel's work and rename his 'factors' as genes. Mendel is now recognised as the father of genetics.

So, genetics is one mechanism of combining things, while keeping them separate. Harmony in music is another. When two people are talking at the same time, it's hard to understand what either is saying. When they are singing in harmony, you can comprehend both parts at the same time. Spoken voices tend to cancel each other out. The result is cacophonous noise. Sung voices in harmony enhance each other. They combine together but are still identifiably separate. It can work with more than two voices. It is a great way for a composer to show his technical skill. Verdi is a master of this. His quartets, in operas such as *Rigoletto*, mark important nexus points in the story. He blends four voices, while keeping each individual viewpoint separate. Mozart had gone even further with sextets in *The Marriage of Figaro* and *Don Giovanni*.

Maybe the whole purpose of music is to be a vehicle for group expression. The grammar of music is the grammar of the group, not the individual. When a small group is playing music to a larger audience, the audience is immediately drawn in. It is almost impossible to avoid tapping your toe or, maybe, singing along. The purpose of music is to turn a bunch of individuals into a group. Work songs and sea shanties promote teamwork in manual labour. The rhythm of the song coordinates the group activity. Some anthropologists see the origins of music and humans as being closely intertwined: we are the musical apes.[15] What ants do with pheromones and bees do with their waggle dance, we do with music. Group rites, religious ceremonies and military parades are all associated with music. Music is how a tribe expresses itself. It is a transformative vector from one level to another.

Encoding: less than its parts

Genetics and music have the ability to combine things while still keeping them separate. Sometimes, when you combine things together, you lose something in the process. Consider the problem of turning a mass of diverse facts into a story. Some facts you keep, some you discard because they don't add anything. Eloquence is verbal economy. To get your message across effectively, you need to trim the fat. The act of honing your message is one of selection. So in combining facts together to make your story, you are deliberately losing some in the process. The sound bite is not the same as the interview; the headline is not the same as the story. These summaries exist at a higher level and can often be distorting. We can distil this in a Zen-like koan: The act of classification involves throwing away information. Just don't tell the taxonomists. They believe they are labouring to build the great wall of knowledge, but an alternate view is that their decisions are increasing the sum total of ignorance.

Cartography is another discipline that encapsulates this conundrum. A map is a conceptual representation of the things that matter. It also illustrates the relationship between them. Making a map is a selection process. It says, 'this thing is linked to that other thing like this. The rest is irrelevant detail'. A map is a drawing of a

15 Steven Brown, a clinical neuroscientist from the Karolinska Institute in Sweden champions a theory: musilanguage. Music and language share a common ancestor. Before either evolved to be a separate entity, our distant ancestors communicated their emotions by singing grunts to each other. Tonal languages like Chinese are a modern day echo of this.

concept. It's a subjective argument in graphic form. It is not reality. It is the cartographer's representation of reality. A meta-reality.

Every map is a distortion of the truth. Some distortions are deliberate. In the Cold War, Soviet cartographers would mis-locate whole towns to confuse their enemies. Lobbyists re-categorise census data to score political points. Some nations use maps as propaganda where borders are disputed. But at a more fundamental level, all maps are distortions because they have to be. Why? It is because of three issues: projection, symbols and scale.

Let's take the problem of projection. The earth is a sphere and a map is flat. In order to transform a 3D curve into a 2D plane, a mathematical projection system must be used. There are two main types: equivalent projections that conserve area and conformal projections that conserve shape. So Mercator's projection, the most common schoolroom map, has the shapes of the continents right, but the areas are all wrong. In this conformal projection, Greenland is eight times bigger than it should be. By contrast, on most equal area projections, continents at the edges, like Australia, end up the right size, but the shape is squished and distorted.

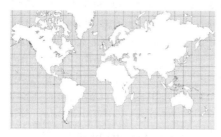   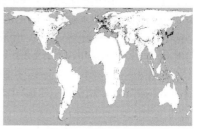

Mercator's Projection   Gall-Peters Projection

The choice of projection can be highly political. Right wing anti-communists love Mercator's map since it portrays a massive, threatening Russia looming at the top of the map. The Russians, on the other hand, prefer an oblique azimuthal equidistant projection centred on Moscow. This shows Russia surrounded on all sides by enemies (USA, China and Europe) and can therefore justify their defensive paranoia. In the 1970s, Arno Peters, a German historian, produces his 'politically correct' Gall-Peters projection. It is a cylindric equal area projection centred not on Greenwich but on Florence. Third world continents, such as Africa and Latin America, appear much enlarged when compared to Mercator. Peters, an adept self-publicist, claims he is correcting the evils of imperialism. So, right from the start in map-making, choosing a projection introduces distortion. Your view will always be controversial.

Next, let's look at symbols. This is also a source of bias. By selecting a set of symbols, the map maker decides what is relevant and what is not. A tourist map would have a particular set of symbols to show, for example, where public telephones, pubs, hospitals and tourist attractions are located. A military map of the same area would focus on terrain obstacles such as rivers, forests and hills. The symbols transform the physical landscape into an information landscape. The only things included are those that will be relevant to the intended audience. It's a deliberate simplification: A selectively incomplete view. An encoding, designed to lose information.

The endless coast

The most interesting problem is scale. Most maps are smaller than the things they represent. They print a scale on the map to tell us how much smaller. Put the other way around, the scale of the map tells us what factor to multiply a map distance by in order to get the real distance. Now let's consider the coastline problem: what is the distance around the coastline of Britain? At first this seems simple to solve. Just get a map, measure the distance around the coast and multiply up by the map scale factor. But what happens if you get a larger scale, more detailed map? The coastline will be a lot more crinkly. What was a relatively smooth line will be replaced by a jagged line with a lot more indentations. That means that your measurement of the distance around the coast will be much greater than before. In fact, each time you get a larger scale map your measured distance will be greater. Sooner or later, you will have to forget the map and measure the real distance with a tape measure. But what about that rocky outcrop? Do you stretch the tape over the top of it, or follow the contours of the rocks exactly? If you want to be accurate you must do the latter. And then it dawns on you. The coastline of Britain is of infinite size. The closer you look the bigger it gets.

So here is the conundrum. The coastline is of infinite size, but it is contained inside something of finite size. Think of an endless wiggly line on a map still contained within the four sides at the borders. How can something be bigger than the box that contains it? The answer lies in moving up a dimension, but not a whole dimension. A map is a two-dimensional object. The real world is three-dimensional. The coastline is somewhere between these two. It's a two-and-a-half-dimensional object. It's an object with a fractional dimension, otherwise known as a fractal. Benoit Mandelbrot first came up with this term in 1975. Many things beside coastlines are fractal in nature: snowflakes, rivers, broccoli and stock markets. Fractals have many interesting properties, such as recursiveness and self-similarity, which we will discuss later. For now, the conclusion is that maps are by their very nature an incomplete distortion of reality.[16] They summarise by removing information. Unlike music or genetics, it is a loss-making encoding process.

The act of map making introduces distortion. So does broad-casting on the radio. The aim for a broadcast engineer is to make the signal as clear as possible. In other words, not to lose the signal in the background noise. This is called 'a high signal to noise ratio'. When driving in your car, have you ever wondered why FM radio sounds so much clearer than AM? Frequency modulated (FM) broadcasting has a much higher signal to noise ratio than an amplitude modulated (AM) stations, because of the way the data is encoded. Noise affects the amplitude of a radio signal. If you are using changes in amplitude to deliver your message it will be badly affected by any background noise. FM transmission encodes the signal by changing the frequency. Any changes in amplitude are ignored, so the background noise is easily filtered out. Digital radio gives an even clearer signal. The data in a digital channel can only be 1 or 0. So if random background noise has degraded from a 1 to 0.95, it is fairly simple to correct this by rounding it back up again.

Efficient grunting and four-letter words

While working for Bell Telephone Labs in 1948, Claude Shannon publishes his *Mathematical Theory of Communication*, one of the most influential papers of the twentieth century. Shannon's Law

---

16 Town planning is map making in reverse. Maps go from reality to an abstract diagram. A town planner goes from the abstract back to reality. So a town planner is an anti-cartographer. If cartography inevitably ends with a misshapen distortion of the truth, then pity the poor town planner. He has to do it all in reverse. No wonder post-war town planning is such a disaster . . .

defines the maximum transmission rate for a noise-free signal in digital communication. In other words, how fast can you send something without losing any of it? At its heart is the observation that information is negative entropy. As we said in the last chapter, entropy is a concept from thermodynamics. It is a measure of how mixed up or random a system is. The discovery that entropy always increases was a shock to the Victorian scientists because it turned the concept of progress upside down. The natural state of the universe is one of random chaos and we are slowly reverting to that. The cosmos is a clock that is running down. Pockets of difference gradually dissipate. Hot things cool down, to leave everything the same lukewarm temperature. The smell of that ripe brie will eventually percolate through the whole house. Next time you leave the bathroom in a chaotic mess, you can tell your spouse it is reverting to its natural disordered state. It is inevitable. Nothing can be done about it. You can't fight a universal law.

Shannon's insight is that information is the opposite of entropy. The more unpredictable something is, the more information it contains. We have to be very careful here because we are using layman's words in a scientific context. In normal English usage, the words 'unpredictable' and 'random' mean the same thing. But in communications theory they mean the opposite of each other. Random noise, or white noise, is the static hiss you hear when your radio is not tuned to any station. If you combine every visible colour in the rainbow together evenly you get white light. Similarly, if you combine every audible frequency together, you get white noise. It's a blank canvas: A static background crackle. It is random because the probability of any one frequency is evenly spread. It has high entropy. It is predictable because it's the natural state of affairs. It is the blank background that you expect. So white noise is predictably random. Your signal introduces the unpredictability to the channel. It stands out against the blank background. It contains information. It is unexpected, but not random.

Computer scientists classify information in a message into two types: semantic and syntactic. The syntactical part concerns the grammar and structure of the message. The semantic part is the content of the message. If you want to communicate efficiently you should have a lot of content and little structure; lots of semantic information and little syntax. Let's compare two languages: Chinese and Latin. In Chinese, word order is very important and contains the subject and object information. This is similar to English. Take these sentences, 'John hit James,' and 'James hit John'. By changing the word order, you change the meaning of the sentence. The subject comes first and the object comes last. By changing them around you change the person who is doing the 'hitting'. A language in which word order is important is known as an analytic language. Its opposite would be a synthetic or inflected language, such as Latin. Here the word order is less important because the subject and object are identified by affixing a different ending to each word. So if you are a poet, Latin is the language for you. You have much more flexibility in the ordering of the words and can focus on getting the rhythm right.

English has some flexibility like this. Changing the normal word order is called anastrophe. Shakespeare often uses it: 'It only stands our lives upon, to use our strongest hands . . . ' (*Antony & Cleopatra*). So does Wordsworth: 'Bliss was it in that dawn to be alive' (*The Prelude*). Songwriters also use it to fit lyrics to the rhythm of the song. Here is a clumsy example from *Daydream Believer* by the Monkees: 'Our good times start and end, without dollar one to spend'. But there is a well-loved movie character whose whole script is anastrophe: Yoda in *Star Wars*, 'Teach you I will, young Skywalker'.

To summarise, Chinese is very context dependant because it relies heavily on word order to convey meaning. Latin is the opposite, word order is not important so it has simple syntax. English is somewhere between the two. So according to Shannon's law, Latin is a more efficient language for communication than Chinese. If it is easy to guess what the next word in the sentence will be, then it is not a very efficient language. So the most efficient means of communication would be a random series of inflected grunts. Conversations between Japanese salarymen often sound like this. Japan is a high context culture. To understand the grunts you need to know the context. It is similar to the problems that face cryptographers. The more elaborate your code, the less likely it is that outsiders will understand it, but the more difficult it is to use on a day-to-day basis. So the transmission part is efficient, but the coding and decoding process is cumbersome.

It is surprising how much you can remove from a sentence in

English while still keeping it comprehensible. If you remove the vowels, a sentence is often still legible: *cn y stll rd ths sntnc?* This is because the vowels that follow consonants are fairly predictable. There is enough information in the pattern of the consonants for you to reconstruct the words. This is the case in languages such as Arabic and Hebrew where the vowels are not written but implied. From an information theory standpoint, they are more efficient. There is even a lot of redundancy in the form of the letters of the alphabet themselves. By seeing just a part letter you can reconstruct the whole. In English, it's normally the upper half of the letter that contains the information so it is still fairly easy to read a word, even though the bottom half of the letters are missing:

can you still read this

Shannon calculates that the English language had a redundancy ratio of about 75%. In other words, you could throw away three quarters of the volume of text without losing the meaning. Imagine that you limit the length of all words to just four letters. If you count the total possible number four-letter 'words' you will find there are about half a million combinations, from *aaaa* to *zzzz*. The complete *Oxford English Dictionary* has a third of a million real words, so our four-letter scheme can easily cover this. The next step is to map the four-letter combinations onto the real English words. So 'tqkw' could be the replacement code for a long word like 'antidisestablishmentarianism'. From a transmission standpoint that is clearly more efficient. Four random letters replace twenty-eight more predictable ones. The only trouble is it's much harder to understand. So what you gain in transmission efficiency, you lose in the effort required to encode and then decode the message. Writing systems that use logograms take this to the extreme. Words are replaced not by four letters but by a single symbol.

Mayan, Ancient Egyptian and Chinese are all languages that use a logographic system. The advantage is you don't need to understand the pronunciation to understand the hieroglyphs or characters. The concept can be transmitted in written form independent of dialect or language. The disadvantage is it takes a long time to learn the 3,000 characters required to be literate. After six years of education, most twelve-year-olds will still have learnt only 1,000 characters. Some observers believe the different writing systems explain the fundamental cultural differences between the Far East and the West. They argue that the six years of rote learning required before you can read, makes a big difference in attitudes towards study, respect for tradition, creativity and individualism. The case is probably overstated. The main conclusion is logograms require more effort to encode and decode, but are very efficient at transmitting a message.

Another example of this is the use of acronyms. This is similar to our imaginary four-letter code system and probably easier to use since the letters at least stand for something. Some four-letter acronyms are so common that people have almost forgotten what the original words are. Consider these: AIDS, NATO, RSVP.[17] But for real virtuosity with acronyms no one can beat the military. If you overhear a conversation between members of the armed forces, it's almost incomprehensible. It is so liberally scattered with acronyms that you don't understand. It is alphabet soup. There are two possible explanations for this. The charitable one is that the military strives for efficiency in all things and so they are just following Shannon's law. The uncharitable one is that they want to be incomprehensible, at least to an outsider. The acronyms are an argot that divides insiders from outsiders. A school-yard slang to reinforce your tribal loyalties. A veritable shibboleth.

Unfrying the egg

Acronyms are an attempt to communicate efficiently by losing detail. Sometimes detail is dropped deliberately to communicate inefficiently. Bureaucrats are the experts here. They are pressured by Freedom of Information rules to release data. At the same time, they know that information is power and no one wants to give that away freely. So the solution is to neuter the data. To transform it, by recategorising it. The result is reams of data that is content free. It's the statistical equivalent of a decaffeinated espresso. A product processed into pointlessness. My most frustrating experience in

---

17 I know you have not forgotten. I'm just putting them here for completeness: AIDS (acquired immune deficiency syndrome), NATO (North Atlantic Treaty Organisation), RSVP (repondez s'il vous plait).

this vein was when I was working as an analyst in Japan in the 1980s.

Japan is an information culture. Access to information is highly guarded. It is not freely given. It is bartered and traded for advantage. Bureaucrats worldwide are hesitant to divulge information. In a Japanese bureaucrat, you have data reticence squared. And if he works for MITI?[18] Well, MITI is the paragon of Japanese ministries. So if you have a meeting with a bureaucrat at MITI, you have arrived at the very sanctum sanctorum of skilful obfuscation. And this was in the 1980s when Japan's trade surplus with the USA was causing major political turmoil. I was trying to write a report about Japanese audio and video tape manufacturing. After several meetings with a MITI official, I was finally given a twenty-six page report full of magnetic tape production statistics. My delight turned to horror as I read it. I was expecting to find out how many C90 audio tapes, or 1 hour VHS tapes, had been made in the last year. What I received was total magnetic tape production by weight in kilograms. So, all the different types of tape, all lengths, widths and formats had been agglomerated into a single irrelevant figure: its weight. And I had that useless figure in incredible detail, month by month, for each one of Japan's forty-seven regional prefectures. It was a masterpiece of futile granularity. It was impossible to re-construct the detailed product information I needed from that data. The ministry had reformatted it to make it meaningless. It was irreversible. Like trying to unfry an egg.

A similar irreversible process operates when prices are formed in a stock market. People who analyse stocks can be divided into two camps: fundamental and technical. Fundamental analysts build models with spreadsheets to estimate a company's future profits. They then try to predict the company's share price based on how the market should value those future profits. Technical analysts, on the other hand, ignore what the company does and focus only on the pattern of the share price. They draw trend lines and use geometric ratios. They believe patterns repeat. So the stock's trading history will tell you how it will perform in the future. Each camp derides the other. Fundamental analysts believe in the efficient market hypothesis. They believe only future information

18 Another 4 letter acronym – MITI – Ministry of Trade and Industry.

can affect future prices, and so history is irrelevant. Technical analysts say prices are formed by buyers and sellers: real people with biases and expectations. The price they bought at in the past will influence the price they sell at in the future. So, history does matter. And history repeats itself. The one thing they both agree on is this: today's share price is an agglomeration of all current expectations. What MITI does with tape statistics, the market does in real time for all information. Collapsed into that one figure of the share price are every participant's hope, greed, expectation and fear. They are just arguing about whether it is possible to unfry the egg.

Mathematicians call unfrying an egg, 'reversing a one-way function'. As its name suggests, a one-way function is a mathematical operation that is easy to calculate but impossibly difficult to reverse. They are at the heart of the biggest revolution of the last few decades: e-commerce on the internet. If you are writing in logograms your reader needs a dictionary (or a good memory) to decipher them. So a dictionary is a straightforward decryption device, available to everyone. If you want to communicate in secret, then there are three basic principles. First, your message must be encoded into cipher text. Second, both sides must know the key to that cipher. Third, that key must be secret. This is fine if you are running a spy ring. You give your spies the secret key beforehand. But here is the problem: how do you communicate in secret with someone you have never met? How do you smuggle the dictionary to them? How do you send them the secret key without eavesdroppers listening in?

The answer is public key cryptography. This was devised by Martin Hellman and Whitfield Diffie in 1975, and it breaks the third rule. The key is not secret, it is publicly available. How can it be secret if everyone knows the key? It is based on a one-way function involving prime numbers. It is easy to multiply two prime numbers together. It is very hard to factor a large number back into two primes. The public key is the product of the two prime numbers. This ingenious system solves two problems: authenticating the sender and secret transmission. It enables you both to send the money and to sign the cheque over the ether. It was this break-through that made e-commerce possible. Just you imagine how cumbersome internet shopping would be if you had to pre-arrange all your purchases with both the vendor, and the bank, before hand.

Public key cryptography works its magic by losing detail when combining things together. The message is encrypted and cannot be deciphered. We started this section discussing map making and journalism. I want to return to that topic at the close. Selecting facts and details, when making a map or writing a story, introduces distortion by the very act of selection. But storytelling is also about encoded messages. These messages are intended to be deciphered, if only subconsciously. Consider three of the most popular authors of the twentieth century: C. S. Lewis with his *Narnia* books, J. R. R. Tolkien with his *Middle Earth* stories and Hergé with his *Tintin* series. That was pretty much my reading diet as a child. What did they have in common? All three were fervent Catholics, and their books had a strong moral message, disguised with varying success beneath their fantasy settings.

At its root, the storytelling impulse is the desire to establish order on chaos. To filter out the signal from the noise. A map maker creates order by selectively representing the real world in his cartogram. A journalist does the same with the facts in his story. A novelist does so by having a moral to his tale. Fictional characters have motivations, their actions have consequences. At the end of the story, all the loose ends are neatly tied together in a moral conclusion.

This ordered conclusion seems to fulfil a fundamental human need. Soap operas are compulsive viewing because we long for this resolution, even though we know in our rational minds that we will never get one. Most popular television series end in disappointment because the viewers' expectations are so high, they cannot be satisfied. Sometimes the process happens in reverse. We get a conclusion and we have to back-fill the story. Sport is a good example of this. Sport is the art form with no author. Listen to the pundits after a game. There is no end of opinions about why what happened, happened. This is post-hoc storytelling of the highest degree: a heroic attempt to impose order on chaos. (We will pick up this theme in the chapter on Spin.) For now, I want to focus on another aspect of sport: teamwork. We have been reviewing how combining things together often involves loss. Sometimes combining things together creates something magical. Something greater than the sum of its parts . . .

Emergent behaviour: more than the sum of its parts

I am watching the World Cup.[19] It's a boring game. Nothing much seems to be happening. Just some desultory back passing. And then suddenly the magic happens. A midfielder beats his man. A long pass out to the wing. The strikers are running into the box for the cross. A beautiful header. Goal! In those thirty seconds the players became more than just individuals; they were a team. Four inter-linking passes of the ball, and the correct anticipation of what your team mates will do, brings a triumphal result.

Football is the world's most popular game because everyone can understand it. It transcends language and culture. Anyone watching the game for a few minutes can tell which side is playing better – even my daughter, and she knows nothing about football. It is part of being human. We can all recognise that moment when people start to work together as a team.

Complexity theorists call that moment 'emergent behaviour'. If a system is complicated enough, sooner or later some higher-level activity will emerge. The collective exerts itself over the individual. Something surprising happens that could not have been predicted by a reductionist analysis of its components. It becomes more than the sum of its parts. The key question is this: how complicated does it need to be before emergent behaviour arises? I think the reason why football causes so much passionate debate is that it is poised right at the edge. It is in the liminal zone of complexity.

If it was just about teamwork, then there are plenty of other sports that require it. Think of a doubles match in tennis. You have to anticipate what your partner will do. The two of you have to work as one. That's teamwork. But for the spectators, it's not as exciting as a singles match if you judge by the prize money on offer. Singles' prizes are bigger. Maybe two people are not enough. There is not enough complexity. Let's go to the other extreme. There are fifteen players on a rugby team. Rugby is all teamwork. You can't pass the ball forward. You can only advance by running or passing the ball backwards to a team mate. That means you are completely dependent on your other team members. Also fifteen is probably

19 For American readers – The World Cup is a soccer tournament. When I say 'football', I mean 'soccer'.

the maximum number of individuals that can be coordinated into a single interacting unit. Rugby has many passionate fans but the football audience is ten times bigger. So why is rugby not more popular? Maybe, because it is too much of a team game. Football with only eleven players is right on the edge. There are long, boring spells but when team play emerges, it truly becomes the 'beautiful game'.

We discussed earlier the group nature of music. How a work song can bind a group of labourers together by providing a rhythm for their exertions. There are other examples of music's 'emergent' properties. In the top professional orchestras, it is common practice for the best musicians to send their understudies to rehearsal. So when a famous guest conductor spends a few weeks in rehearsals with the orchestra, he is actually spending most of his time conducting the understudies. But on opening night, the lead musicians are there and a perfectly nuanced performance is given.

The human body replaces all its cells every seven years. That means that the fleshy part of you is no more than seven years old. But despite the fact that every cell in your body has been replaced several times, you are still you. You are clearly more than the sum of your parts, since the parts have changed, but you have not (other than getting a bit more wrinkly). The same is true of the orchestra. The players on opening night are different from those in rehearsal, but the performance is the same.[20] The performance is more than the sum of its parts too.

Emergent behaviour is a function of complexity. Complexity is a function of scale. For something to be complex, there needs to be more than the critical number of parts. What is this critical number? It depends on the system. In the human body there are over 200 different types of cells and over 100 trillion cells in total. That's pretty complex. So it's not that surprising that this vast collection of different cells produces emergent behaviour; namely, you. But emergent behaviour can arise from a much smaller number of parts. A symphony orchestra has a hundred players. A football

---

20 Cynics might conclude that this says more about the role of the conductor. He may be a famous name, but the orchestra will play what it is going to play anyway. He is just counting out time. Even if you do subscribe to this uncharitable view, you must still concede that the orchestra has a 'group' mind.

team has eleven. Of course, it's not just the number of players that matters. You also must consider the way they combine through the rules. So it's eleven players, plus the rules, that generate the complexity.

A combination of cells produces the emergent behaviour that we recognise as the organism. A combination of organisms produces a society. Social animals, when combined together, exhibit behaviour that is greater than the sum of its parts. The optimal number of individuals to create this society depends on the species. Research by Robin Dunbar at the University of Liverpool, published in 1992, demonstrates a link between the size of social groups and the size of the animal's brain. The bigger the social group, the more complex the social interactions and therefore the larger the brain required. The link is so strong that it enables reasonably accurate predictions of the group size of a species just from looking at the brain size. So, for example, the average size of a group of vervet monkeys in the wild is twenty-four animals, but for baboons it would be thirty-six. Their brain sizes are 60 cc. and 140 cc. respectively. Dunbar then applies his model to humans, where the average brain size is 1200 cc. This results in a predicted social group size of 150.

Is the optimal size for human society 150 people? Agriculture evolved 10,000 years ago. *Homo sapiens* evolved 200,000 years ago. So humans have spent 95% of their time on the planet in hunter gatherer groups. What can that tell us about the ideal group size for society? Anthropologists who study hunter gatherer groups observe two critical numbers. A hunting band can support a group of ten to thirty people before it needs to break into smaller groups. At particular times of the year, when food is abundant, the bands coalesce into a larger social group of around 150 people. Rituals and ceremonies are performed to reinforce group culture and exchange marriage partners. After this, the larger group dissolves back into its smaller bands again. So to give a crude analogy, a football team can provide food for itself and its dependants on a day-to-day basis. A larger group is required to provide cultural nourishment at certain times of the year. So Dunbar's research fits reasonably well with the anthropological evidence. The magic number for society is around 150 people. This is the average size of an English Village at the time of the Doomsday Book in 1086. It is also the size of a company of soldiers in an army, the average number of Christmas cards we sent out to acquaintances, and the typical number of friends on Facebook.

What happens when society gets bigger than this? That is when the problems start, when the disorders of magnitude begin to emerge. When a company grows beyond 150 employees it stops being a small company and starts to be a big one. Suddenly, all sorts of organisational changes have to happen. In the main, a lot more administrators suddenly appear. (We will pick this up in Chapter 8 when we discuss bureaucracy.) What happens to a community when it grows beyond 150 people? Trust begins to break down. Formal legal structures need to emerge to dispense justice. Representatives need to chosen. (This will be covered in Chapter 6 on democracy and the rule of law.) How many friends can be part of your social network? Statistics from Facebook also suggests around 150. So, in a community that is bigger than this, you will not know everyone personally. You will begin to rely on hearsay and gossip rather than your own direct knowledge. (We will discuss this in Chapter 9 on the media and spin.)

An individual and a group of individuals are just two rungs on a hierarchical ladder of living things. This ladder goes all the way down to the DNA level and all the way up to a whole ecosystem at the top. Each rung on the ladder is the emergent result of behaviour on the rung underneath. So this biological ladder is a good place to start if we want to look at emergent behaviour in more detail. When is it appropriate to take a step back and look at the forest as a whole and not the trees?

CHAPTER 4

Emergent Behaviour and the Ladder of Life

The beauty of teamwork

I am standing in a packing line. I have lost my sedentary office job and am now doing manual labour. I am wearing overalls and safety boots, packing products with five other workers. The different tasks are split up between us. One person is assembling gift boxes, others are labelling and putting the products inside. The last person on the line is packing the finished products into corrugated cardboard shipping cartons. The products gradually move down the line.

Everyone in the line is dependent on their neighbour. If one person is working slowly then all the components will build up around them. The people downstream will not have enough to do. When it is working well, everyone locks into the same rhythm and the products progress smoothly to their finished state. When one person is slacking it throws the whole thing out. There is a natural inclination to help out your neighbour if she is struggling. It keeps the whole line flowing.

This is teamwork in its purest and most eloquent form. The repetition is not boring but soothing. Your mind is free to wander as your hands execute their task with rhythmic precision. The primary link with your colleague is through physical activity, but you have a bond beyond that. It is akin to making music, or even making love. You are all linked together in a common task. Such a taut synchronicity of action and purpose that it leads to this question: is such sense of teamwork possible without the physical labour?

Here is an excerpt from a job advert for a bank: 'We have a long-standing commitment to excellence, innovation and teamwork. The successful candidate will have superior interpersonal communication skills and work well in a team.' It is such a cliché. All white collar workers are exhorted to be team players, but once the physical component is removed then there is no real team spirit. Teamwork depends on a feedback loop. You need to see what the others are doing and then adjust your input accordingly. On a production line, this is easy to do. You see it in the progression of the physical objects in front of you. You sense it instinctively in the actions of others. It is the same in team sports. White collar work is different. Your output is no longer measured in physical terms. You can't really see what the others are doing. An abstract performance measurement system must be constructed. Targets and quotas are set up. But as quantum physics teaches us, the act of measurement changes the outcome. In the end, everyone can claim a piece of the credit, or complain that their input is not being measured properly. The rewards will go to those who are the loudest or most persuasive in extolling their own merits. This is the opposite of teamwork.

Teamwork cannot be imposed from the top. It must arise spontaneously from below. It is an emergent behaviour, not something dictated from above. We have all attended corporate training courses at which we are told this: There is no 'I' in 'Team'. The only appropriate response is this: Yes, but there is an 'Us' in 'Bogus'. White collar teamwork is an oxymoron. Teamwork is a second floor phenomenon that can only be accessed by the stairs from the first floor; the physical floor. The misguided belief of an office manager that his staff, in their cubicles, can make 'a great team' is a catataxic delusion. It is a rich seam of hypocrisy mined by the TV show, *The Office*.

There is one possible exception. When a group of people from the same company go and pitch to a client. Each person does a different part of the presentation, but these parts are skilfully woven together. Questions from the client are answered seamlessly, each team mate complimenting the others' response. The team is united in a common goal: bag a new client. This looks like white collar work, but I would argue that this still falls under the category of physical labour, which is why they are working as a team. Even though everyone is in the office wearing suits, what they are doing is ancient and primal. It is wolf pack behaviour when the prey is in sight. The prey in this case being the client; she is sitting right there on the other side of the table.

Rules for the flock

Predators often hunt in packs. The prey shows flocking behaviour in response. You can observe it throughout the animal kingdom. Fish shoal, birds flock, insects swarm and wildebeest herd. This type of behaviour is easy to model mathematically. The computer generated effects in movies use algorithms like this all the time to create, say, a herd of stampeding dinosaurs. Here is how to do it: set up a group of agents with three simple rules to govern their behaviour. These rules are:

- go in the same direction as everyone else
- try and get in the middle of the group
- avoid bumping into others

From these three simple rules you see quite complex behaviour emerging from the group which looks startlingly like a real herd of animals.

Flocking behaviour confers a number of advantages on the prey. First, there are more eyes in a group to spot predators and give the alarm. Second, is the safety in numbers principle. You can hide inside a group. The swirling mass of bodies is a complicated target and makes it hard for a predator to single out a particular individual. This is particularly true of zebras, where their stripes add to the visual confusion.

Permit me a small digression on the subject of zebras. In 2008, Dr Peter Thompson, a psychologist at York University publishes some controversial research. It refutes one of the cardinal rules of fashion: horizontal stripes make you look fat and vertical ones are slimming. Dr Thompson demonstrates that the reverse is true. Vertical stripes make you look fat. He cites the Helmholtz optical illusion to support his case. This has two equal-sized squares with stripes in different orientations. The one with horizontal stripes looks taller and thinner.

I can confirm this to be true. I was wandering around a Damian Hirst exhibition in an art gallery several years ago. One piece, titled *The Incredible Journey*, was a zebra in a tank of formaldehyde. A zebra has vertical stripes on its belly but horizontal stripes on its rump. So a lion chasing from behind will see horizontal stripes which makes the beast look skinnier and, therefore, a less tempting meal. I tried looking at Hirst's zebra from the back and then from

Taller?   Fatter?

the side. It seemed to work. Then I noticed the potential buyers circling the exhibit. Wealthy banking types with vertical pinstripes on their elegant suits. They did look fat.

There is a third reason why grouping together is safer. It's not just the principle of safety in numbers or hiding in the group. There is a subtler point that benefits the group as a whole. It is best illustrated by considering the battle between Atlantic convoys and U-boats. Most people will immediately think of World War II, but in fact, Atlantic merchant ships were first organised into a convoy system in World War I by May 1917. The concept of convoys is as old as naval warfare itself, having been used by the Romans, the Spaniards and the Royal Navy in the Napoleonic wars. The new factor in 1917 is the U-boat. There is a long and acrimonious debate about whether combining merchant ships into convoys is a good idea or not. Those against it point out that by presenting one big target it makes it easier for U-boats to hit their targets. But they misunderstand one key fact – hitting the target for a U-boat is not the problem. It is finding the target that's difficult. U-boats travel slowly and the ocean is huge. To give some idea of the scale and speeds involved, imagine travelling around the whole of Western Europe on a bicycle, looking for a convoy of twenty lorries.

If merchant ships sail on regular routes with regular frequencies, then if a U-boat misses one it can always hang around (in the best attacking position) for the next one to come sailing by. But by reducing the number of targets from a large number of sequential ones to a single large one, there is a greater chance of a U-boat not spotting the target at all.

Also, since the convoys are escorted by warships, the relative power of the Royal Navy's counter-attack is increased. The convoys mean that the U-boats are drawn to the merchant ships rather than the other way around. So the Navy's warships don't have to roam around searching for submarines. They can sit with the convoy and wait for them to show up. It's not an attack strategy, but a counter attack one.

For all these reasons, it is safer to travel in packs. So it is not surprising that flocking and herding is so common in the animal kingdom. The point I want to make is that, unlike marine convoys, there is no overall commander organising the animals into a flock.[21] The flock is an emergent phenomenon that arises spontaneously from the group behaviour. It arises from the bottom upwards and is not planned top down, bringing the benefits of safety. But sometimes grouping together has negative effects. A traffic jam is a good example of the negative effect of clumping together.

Controlling traffic Jams

I am standing on a pedestrian bridge over the M25. The man in front of me takes out a small metal box about the size of a packet of cigarettes with a black knob fixed on the top of it. 'Watch this,' he says, with a smile, as he turns the knob. Gradually, the motorway traffic that is zooming underneath us seems to slow down and then, incredibly, it comes to a complete standstill. It's now a static traffic jam – a big car park really.

'How did you do that?' I ask. He grins broadly and then turns the knob the other way. The traffic starts moving again. 'Really . . . how are you controlling them? What is in that box?' I ask again. 'It's classified,' he replies, 'I can't tell you. Let's just call it magic . . . '

The science of traffic flow is developing fast. Professor Dirk Helbing from Dresden is one of the leaders in this field and has developed a traffic model that treats cars as though they were particles of fluid. This 'traffic fluid' manifests several phase transitions similar to the solid, liquid and gas stages of a real fluid. Drivers will recognise these three stages. Free flowing traffic with clear roads is analogous to a gas phase. There is no one on the road, so you don't have to think about anyone else. You can just focus on the pleasure of driving your car. Then there is a time when things get a bit more crowded. You begin noticing other cars and lorries moving out to overtake them. Then the road gets really crowded.

---

21 The exception to this is when a single male is overseeing his harem of females in a herd of deer.

There is not much overtaking or lane changing because there is little space to do it in. Everyone is moving at pretty much the same speed in the same direction. This is the synchronised flow stage. We have changed from gas to liquid. Every little change in speed that one car makes, impacts everyone else. If one brakes, all brake. Then, suddenly, everything comes to a standstill and no one is moving at all. We have reached the third phase; it's solid.

These three phases represent the different levels of a hierarchy. The gas-like state of free-flowing traffic is the level of the individual. A driver is free to move as he likes and the actions of others have little influence on him. This is not true at the liquid and solid levels, where the actions of others have a big impact. So we can summarise in a table like this:

- Level 1   Gas   Clear Roads
- Level 2   Liquid   Crowded Roads
- Level 3   Solid   Traffic Jam

A traffic jam is an emergent phenomenon. It is a disorder of magnitude. The different levels have different rules. At level one, the fastest way to get to your destination is to stamp on the accelerator. At level two, you will get there quicker by going slower. That's the reason behind the traffic calming measures (temporary speed limits) on busy motorways.

To see why this is, we need to think about the most efficient way to use a road. The capacity of a road depends on two things: traffic flow (cars per second) and traffic density (cars per kilometre). Combining these two gives you speed (kilometres per second). So sometimes cars can slow down, but the increase in density as they get packed closer together can mean that the overall flow is still increasing. You are slowing the group down to get there faster. If the density gets too high, the cars come to a standstill in a traffic jam. The flow is zero and the density is at a maximum. It takes careful management by a higher authority than the individual to keep the density just right and optimise road efficiency. This is similar to the role of a central bank: to take away the drinks just as the party is getting good.[22]

22 Right-wingers who believe in the primacy of the individual and market forces rather than big government will refute this. They contend that it is

I have a confession to make. The story of the little metal box is made up. But it is not too far-fetched. Professor Helbing's fluid model of traffic flow has been used to accurately predict gridlocks on German autobahns. Rider Haggard's tales hinge on predicting the eclipse to astonished natives. Any advanced technology is indistinguishable from magic.

Emergent behaviour

The key variable in the traffic flow example is density. The interaction between tightly packed elements is what triggers the change in phase or level. The emergent behaviour is caused not just by having lots of things, but also the linkages between them. The latter is increasingly important as you scale things up. Consider this mathematical example. If you have two objects, there is only one way to connect them: one line between two nodes. If you have three nodes, you can connect them with three lines in a triangle. But when you have four nodes, you have to draw six lines to connect each node with every other one. When you have ten nodes, you have forty-five different connections. You can see that the number of nodes is growing arithmetically, but the number of connections is growing exponentially. By the time you have 100 nodes, there are 4,950 ways to connect them.

We can view the connection between two nodes as a mechanism for influence. So each connection is a potential feedback loop. Adding one more node to a network increases the number of feedback loops exponentially. In a feedback loop, the output affects the input, causing instability, non-linearity and chaotic behaviour. So with 100 nodes or objects, you already have a fairly complex system. In fact, the maths involved in analysing just three objects – say the earth, sun and moon – is so hard that the problem has its own name: the three-body problem. It was not solved until 1912. A system with 100 objects is effectively beyond mathematical analysis. It is certainly complicated enough to begin to exhibit emergent behaviour.

When a new pattern is generated by the self-organising activity of a complex system, it is said to be 'emergent'. The complicated

---

not possible to regulate in practice. 100 years of central banking have not eliminated boom and bust. There are still traffic jams, since no one pays attention to those temporary speed limits anyway . . .

hexagonal patterns of snowflakes are an emergent property of ice crystals. There are 10^{18} water molecules in an average snowflake. There are so many different ways to stack those molecules that no two snowflakes are the same. Ripple patterns on a beach are an emergent property of sand. They are not planned out by a master designer. They emerge from the interaction of the sand grains and the waves. They are not predictable, but they do have a pattern. The pattern arises spontaneously from the enormous number of grains of sand on the beach. Another example is a hurricane. This is an emergent weather phenomenon. When atmospheric pressure, humidity and temperature differentials are just right they emerge spontaneously over the ocean and meander towards land to wreak destruction. These examples all involve inanimate objects. Animate objects add a whole new level of complexity.

Biology is full of complex systems exhibiting emergent behaviour. A termite mound is an emergent phenomenon. These tall towers can house over a million termites and can last for thousands of years. Despite these impressive capabilities, they are not designed by some external architect but arise spontaneously from the actions of individuals. The flocking and herding that we discussed earlier is emergent behaviour. There is no leader drilling them. It's a manifestation of instinctive animal behaviour. One level lower down, an animal itself can be seen as an emergent expression of its genetic code. One level higher up, an ecosystem is an emergent expression of the plants and animals inside it. Likewise, the biosphere is an emergent phenomenon, created by all the different ecosystems on earth. The Gaia hypothesis, made popular by James Lovelock, views this biosphere as a single organism.

Our society is an emergent phenomenon created by the interaction of individuals. Any coherent society needs answers to some basic organisational questions: Who is in charge? What are the rules? How shall the tasks be divided up? The answers to these questions are political, legal and economic structures which reflect the general will of the people.[23] So the government, the corpus of law and the economy are all emergent constructs. They are patterns generated

---

23 You may argue that a totalitarian society does not reflect the will of the people. We will explore this in the chapter on democracy. The point I am making is that Stalin was human and not an alien being.

by the self-organising activity of a large group of individuals. They are not imposed from above by some superhuman designer.

On a more philosophical level, solidity can be said to be an emergent property of sub-atomic particles. Imagine a sphere eleven miles in radius, containing only two objects: a football in the centre and a single grain of sand at the edge. That's a scale model of a hydrogen atom. It's also a hell of a lot of empty space. Even worse, wave particle duality means that the football and the grain of sand are themselves not really solid objects and can be expressed as waveforms. So we perceive a table to be a solid object, but it's made of atoms that are anything but solid. The solidity is an emergent phenomenon. It only becomes apparent when there are lots of atoms. So if you want to demonstrate that more of the same is different, rap your knuckles sharply on the table.

Some physicists believe the only way to reconcile relativity with quantum theory is to reclassify time as an emergent property of the universe. The best way to explain this is to think of a barter system. Before the invention of money, you can exchange three sheep for two goats, and then two goats for a cow. They have a value that is implicit. The invention of money makes that value explicit. The money is a common reference point for all transactions: a token of exchange. But at a more fundamental level it is possible to have an economy without money. So in that sense, money is an emergent property of the economic system; it is an explicit valuation system. It's the same for time. It is possible to define the universe in purely spatial terms. A tuning fork at concert A oscillates at 440 times a second. A heart beats eighty times a minute. So we can calculate that 587 fluctuations in the tuning fork are equivalent to one heart beat. In this way, it is theoretically possible to define change without needing the concept of time. Both time and money are emergent phenomena. I just wish they would both emerge my way a bit more.

Biological hierarchies

Biology offers useful lessons about hierarchical structures. The contrast we drew between the individual and society is just part of a much larger hierarchy. This has DNA and cells at the bottom and the whole biosphere at the very top. Individual organisms, like humans, are somewhere in the middle. Perched on our rung, we can look both upwards and downwards and ponder which way power and control flows. Looking downwards, we can ask the following questions: do our cells control us or do we control them? Can you heal yourself by positive thinking? Looking upwards, do we drive the economy or is the economy driving us? Do we control the biosphere? Can individuals do anything about global warming? These are all catataxic questions. In order to answer them, we need to spend some time looking at the biological hierarchy in detail.

The biological hierarchy is fractal, like the coastline of Britain. At whatever level you examine it, you will see a complex substructure with similar patterns to the level above. The Gaia hypothesis sees the whole world as a self-regulating biosphere. The same could be said about a human body, or even an individual cell. The closer you look, the more you are surprised by the complexity.

Mighty microbes

Let's start with the human body. Some ninety per cent of the cells in our bodies are not ours, but microbes. Of course the microbes are much smaller, so by weight you are mainly human tissue. But if you go by cell count, then you are mostly an alien colony. The majority of these microbes are bacteria, but they also include yeasts, archaeons,[24] parasites and viruses. It is an extraordinary diverse menagerie with each microbe exploiting a different niche, both inside the gut and outside on the skin. Some are famous celebrities, like E. coli; the most studied bacterium of all time. Others were only identified yesterday. There are corynebacteria in your navel, propionibacteria behind your ears, micrococci between your toes and staphylocci in your armpit. Let's face it, you are a filthy beast.

The microbes inside the human gut are vital for digestion. It is a symbiotic relationship and we could not live without them. Bacteria in the intestines convert indigestible starches into short chain fatty acids through a process of fermentation. Bacteria also produce vitamin K and stimulate the growth of cells. In addition, helpful bacteria help to train the immune system and repress harmful

24 Archaeons are a newly discovered class of living things. They are single celled organisms with no nucleus or other organelles and can live in extremely harsh environments like toxic waste and volcanic hot springs. As their name suggests, they are believed to be one of the earliest life forms on earth.

microorganisms, like C. difficile. This has been a difficult area to study since ninety-nine per cent of these microbes cannot be cultured in a Petri dish. The Human Microbiome Project hopes to shed light here by launching a coordinated five-year study to identify the flora in the human gut. It's a project of similar size and importance to the Human Genome Project, which successfully mapped our DNA.

There seems to be a close association between microbes and allergies: the more bacteria you are exposed to, the less likely you are to get allergic reactions. This is known as the 'hygiene hypothesis' and may explain the startling rise in allergies in the last fifty years. Broad spectrum antibiotics, fewer childhood diseases and cleaner living environments mean that we are less exposed to bacteria. The antibacterial hand gels that have become so popular recently may, in fact, be bad for you.

The beneficial properties of microbes have only just begun to be fully realised. Probiotic drinks, like Yakult or Actimel, fill your stomach with 'good' bacteria to help digestion. These drinks have a more extreme cousin in a hospital environment. [Sensitive readers should skip the rest of this paragraph.] Some doctors view the mass of microbes in the human gut almost as an organ in its own right, and are experimenting with transplants of them as a possible cure for illnesses like diabetes, Parkinson's disease and obesity. The polite way of describing such a procedure is a Human Probiotic Infusion (HPI). Another name for it is fecal bacteriotherapy. In Anglo Saxon, that means having someone else's shit pumped up your bottom. That's if you are lucky. Some doctors favour administering it with a nasal drip . . .

One famous experiment went wrong because of a miscalculation about microbes. Biosphere 2 was an attempt to create a sealed ecological environment of a type that could be used for colonising other planets someday. A huge glass dome was built covering three acres of land, divided into different zones such as rainforest, savannah and mangrove swamp. In 1991, eight people entered this enormous greenhouse and it was sealed off from the outside world. Unfortunately, despite all the careful calculations, the systems engineering and a huge number of trees, oxygen levels began to steadily fall. The terms of the experiment had to be broken by injecting oxygen into the system every few months. The scientists had forgotten to include the microbes in the soil in their calculations. These were happily converting oxygen into carbon dioxide. This proves that you ignore the level beneath you at your own peril.

Level 1: DNA

Microbes may be one level below us, but they are not the lowest level. It is DNA that is the bottom rung of the biology ladder and arguably the top rung of the chemistry ladder. All living things have DNA, even microbes. In fact, since microbes outnumber the cells in our bodies by a huge margin, most of the genetic material inside you is not human. The human genome has 20,000 genes, but the microbes inside us collectively have 3.3 million genes. So in that sense, right down at the genetic level, you are not really you at all.

As we noted in Chapter 2, the way in which the genetic information in a DNA molecule expresses itself is complex. The Human Genome Project had high expectations. The hope was that once our DNA had been decoded, the Book of Life itself would be open for everyone to read. What they found in that book was a big surprise. The number of genes in the genome has little bearing on the complexity of the organism. Flies have 20,000 genes, which is a similar number to humans. A rice plant has 46,000. Also, only two percent of the human genome seems to be fulfilling any useful function. There does not seem to be a one-to-one mapping between a gene and a particular characteristic. Rather, genes can be viewed as nodes in a complex network being switched on or off by the environment or other genes. The inheritable genetic information is known as the genotype. The expression of that information in the physical world is called the phenotype. In a PC analogy, the genotype is the software and the phenotype is the hardware.

You can build a whole world view based on genes. Since they are the fundamental unit of biology, everything above them in the ladder can be seen as an emergent expression of genetic information. The story of evolution can be written as a tale of competing genes rather than competing individuals. This is the ultra reductionist viewpoint. Notice also that the influence of genes can go way beyond the individual, out into the wider world. This is the 'extended phenotype' concept, as espoused by Richard Dawkins. This argues that genes express themselves not only in the physical form of the animal but also in its behaviour. So a beaver's dam is a form of genetic expression in the outside world. The beaver is driven by its genes to build the dam. The dam causes the river to flood. So the influence of the beaver's genes has been extended way beyond the beaver's tissues and flesh. The flood is an emergent consequence of beaver DNA. The beaver's dam is a catataxic construction.

Level 2: the cell

Genes are coded in the DNA molecule, which is contained in the nucleus of a cell. Genes are a complex network. One level up, viewing things from the perspective of a cell, one sees an equally complicated landscape. Many cellular biologists think that the importance of DNA and the cell nucleus is overrated and put the cellular membrane at the centre of things. Their argument runs like this: Life begins with two divisions. First is the membrane that separates the inside from the outside; the second, when it is time to reproduce – the division of one cell into two. Single-celled organisms can survive without a nucleus. In fact, there is a whole domain of single cell organisms with no nucleus, called Prokaryotes, which includes bacteria and archaeons. These are some of the earliest life forms on earth. To cell biologists, this is proof of the fundamental primacy of the membrane. DNA replicates when cells divide, but before the cell division comes the cell, and the cell is defined by the membrane.

Cell membranes are semi-permeable. Under certain chemical conditions they allow molecules through to the inside, but most of the time they act as a barrier. This semi-permeability is similar to the semi-conducting transistors in a microchip. Semiconductors sometimes allow electric current to pass; membranes sometimes allow biochemical molecules to pass. So the membrane can be seen as an information processor operating in a complex biochemical environment of enzymes and proteins. To extend this PC metaphor further, we can draw some parallels like this:

Computer	Human Body	Cell
Microprocessor	Brain	Membrane
Hard Drive	Gonads	Nucleus
Power supply	Lungs	Mitochondria

In this analogy, the cell membrane is the brain or microprocessor unit. The nucleus which stores the genetic information is the hard drive, or, in a human body, the sex organs. The energy in a cell is supplied by mitochondria, which function similarly to the power supply of a computer or the lungs of a human. Mitochondria add an extra level of complexity because they are essentially a cell within a cell. Mitochondria have their own membrane and DNA [25] which is distinct from the host cell. One hypothesis suggests that mitochondria were an ancestral bacteria swallowed by another cell to make a symbiotic relationship which benefited them both. There are other organelles besides the nucleus and mitochondria inside a cell. There are vesicles which provide a transport network, ribosomes to translate RNA into proteins, the Golgi body, which sorts and packs those proteins and vacuoles to dispose of waste. It is a whole mini-ecosystem. With so many different parts performing specialist functions, a cell can be seen as an organism in its own right.

Human cells can live quite happily outside the body. Cell lines in laboratories can keep cells alive almost indefinitely. All they need is a cell culture plate, the right temperature and a mix of nutrients and gasses. So immortality is possible both at a genetic level (by passing genes to offspring) and at a cellular level in a laboratory. The HeLa cell line is used extensively in medical research. Some 300 scientific papers a month are published on research using those cells. They were originally grown from a tissue sample taken from Henrietta Lacks in Baltimore in 1951. The patient died soon after the sample was taken, but the family attempted to sue twenty years later when they learned that their grandmother was technically still alive as a tissue culture in a laboratory test tube. This was a catataxic argument: to what extent are the cells the same as the person?

This 'cell as organism' viewpoint should not come as a surprise. For the first two and a half billion years, life on earth consisted of just single cell organisms. Multicellular creatures are a relatively recent development. Some organisms fall in between the two. Slime

---

25 Mitochondrial DNA is inherited from the mother only. So unlike nuclear DNA, it does not change from parent to offspring. This makes it a very useful tool in tracing ancestry through the maternal line. This goes all the way back to Mitochondrial Eve, the mother of us all, who lived in East Africa 200,000 years ago.

moulds spend most of their lives as single cell creatures, but when triggered by a particular chemical signal, they coalesce into a multicellular organism. Sponges are multicellular, but only just. They have no nervous, digestive or circulatory systems and little cell differentiation. They are not far removed from a permanent colony of single celled organisms. All multicellular animals, from a certain perspective, can be seen as an emergent outcome from the complex interaction between a large group of cells. In the case of a human body, that group is quite large: around 50 trillion cells.

Level 3: the immune system

The bottom two rungs of the biological hierarchy are DNA and the cell. Both are complicated enough to prompt catataxic issues. The next level up from these two is the immune system. When organs are transplanted, it is the immune system that 'decides' whether to accept or reject the organ. In other words, this is the system responsible for identifying what is *you* and what is *not you* or foreign. It has its roots both in the genetics and the workings of the cell membrane. A region of genes on chromosome 6 encode proteins that embed themselves on the surface of the cell membrane. These proteins are known as human leukocyte antigens (HLAs). The closer the match between my HLAs and your HLAs the better an organ donor I will be for you. If my HLAs were identical to yours, then from an immune system perspective I would *be* you.

A famous experiment that demonstrated that an individual is more than just a collection of cells was conducted by H. V. Wilson on hydra in 1907. These simple, tiny, tube-like creatures are found in most freshwater pools. Wilson took one and liquidised it. He then passed it through a fine mesh sieve and put the resulting gloop into a beaker of water. He was astonished to see it reassemble itself back into a single creature. When he repeated the experiment with two hydra, he was disappointed that he did not end up with a hybrid. Some system was clearly at work that identified cells as belonging to a particular individual. There is a sense of identity at a level above the cell. In hydra, it enables the animal to regenerate itself. In humans, it is the immune system.

The immune system can sometimes be too weak or too strong. This leads to two different types of disease. If it is too weak, immunodeficiency diseases occur. The best known example is acquired immune deficiency syndrome otherwise known as AIDS. In contrast, auto-immune diseases such as Lupus result from an overactive immune system. In these cases, the body starts to attack itself mistaking healthy tissue for foreign organisms. Metaphorically speaking, auto-immune diseases demonstrate that the immune system has 'a mind of its own'. It certainly has a memory; the principle of vaccination relies upon it. Vaccines are weak forms of viruses that are injected into the body to train the immune system. When exposed to the strong form of the virus at a later time, the immune system 'remembers' how to fight it.

Recent research[26] also suggests that your immune system may be influencing your political views. Studies show that there is a strong correlation between the presence of infectious parasites in an environment and how individualistic or collective the local populace are. Communities are more xenophobic if there is a high risk that interacting with a stranger will give you an infectious disease. Right wingers are likely to have weaker immune systems according to this recent research, which may explain why they are anti-immigration and pro-traditional values. It is worth noting that the post-war permissive society coincided with major health advances due to antibiotics, and that the neo-conservative backlash started at the same time as the AIDS pandemic. So just as the beaver's dam is an extended expression of its genes, your political views may be an extended expression of your immune system.

Level 5: the group

So looking below the level of the individual there are three sub layers: the gene, the cell and the immune system. Looking up there are three higher levels: the group, the ecosystem and the biosphere. Groups of individuals can often act as though they were a single entity in their own right. Flocking and herding is one example of this as we noted earlier. A herd of animals, or a convoy of ships, acting as a single entity have a number of advantages over an individual on their own.

A larger group than just a herd is the whole species. When Darwin

26 Fincher, Thornhill, Murray and Schaller, Royal Society, February 2008: 'Pathogen prevalence predicts human cross-cultural variability in individualism/collectivism'.

first presented his theory of evolution it was a 'species level' argument. He called his book *On the Origin of Species*. In other words, he was making an argument about how new species came to be. These days, biologists find the species concept tricky to nail down. This is partly to do with philosophical issues like the 'problem of the universals' (from Chapter 2): do species really exist outside of a human mind? But there are a host of more practical problems that vex today's taxonomists. There are at least twelve different proposals for the best way to define a species conceptually. Some are based on physical characteristics, some on interbreeding ability, others on ancestral lineage and others still on environmental niches. If you are a reductionist, you might subscribe to a genetic definition of species like this: a species boundary is an observable barrier to gene flow. If you prefer a holistic viewpoint, you might define a species as a set of organisms adapted to a particular set of resources in the environment. Though everyone knows instinctively what the word 'species' means, the battle over its formal definition is ongoing.

Let's leave that contentious debate for now and focus back on a group of interacting individuals. Animals demonstrate social organisation to differing degrees. Each degree has its own name. Subsocial animals interact with their young.[27] Presocial animals live collectively like dogs in packs. But the highest form of social organisation is seen in eusocial animals like ants, bees and termites. These eusocial insects divide labour up between distinct castes, have overlapping generations and care for their young co-operatively. Some animal species may show one or other of these features, but to be classified as eusocial they must exhibit all three.

Eusocial insects can be viewed as cells making up a larger organism: the hive. As we noted in the Introduction, an ant colony is to some degree an organism in its own right. It moves, it reproduces by splitting in two, and has a digestive system with specialised fungus tended by gardener ants. The colony is coordinated by chemical messaging using pheromones, which is analogous to the biochemical enzymes that control the cells in our bodies. These pheromones are used for identifying different castes, passing information such as where food is, or sending out alarms. Pheromones are mixed with

---

27 If your parents complain that you are being antisocial, you can tell them that they are subsocial in return.

food and passed mouth to mouth which means the colony has a form of collective stomach. So just as specialist cells make a multicellular creature, and specialist organs make a human, specialist ants make a superorganism: a group of eusocial insects that is an organism in its own right.

Recent research[28] shows cooperative behaviour amongst plants as well as animals. A study of Douglas fir trees reveals that the older trees transfer carbon and nitrogen to saplings of the same species via their mycorrhizal networks. Beneath the ground bacteria and fungi form a symbiotic relationship with the tree roots. These fungal threads physically link the roots of trees together into a single network. This mycorrhizal network can be used to share not just food but also information. When predators or parasites attack one tree, all the other trees begin producing defence chemicals. The network seems to spread some type of alarm signal. So a small copse can be viewed as a single organism, rather than a bunch of separate firs. This brings new poignancy to the phrase 'can't see the wood for the trees'.

Level 6: the ecosystem

One level above the group is the ecosystem. Here different populations of organisms are seen as an interlinked whole. An ecosystem is both the living things in a particular region and the physical environment. The linkage is created by the flow of energy and nutrients though this system. Typically, the inputs are sunlight, water and minerals. These are transformed into biomass through the food chain. Plants convert sunlight into starches through photosynthesis. Herbivores eat the plants. Carnivores eat the herbivores. At the top level is the apex predator, who preys on those beneath but upon whom no one preys. These food chains rarely have more than five or six levels. The reason for this is the low level of energy conversion when eating prey. Only ten per cent of the biomass is converted into tissue in the consumption process. In other words, a predator has to eat ten times its own body weight to survive. So a six level food chain needs 10^6, or one million times more mass at the lowest level, to support the apex predator. The food cycle is brought full circle by the action of bacteria and fungi. They

28 *ESA Ecology*, Vol. 90, Issue 10, October 2009

decompose any organisms that die back to their original nutrient parts. So the ecosystem as a whole can be seen as a complex set of interdependent cycles: a nested group of organisms interacting with the environment and each other.

Just as with a portfolio of stocks, the greater the diversity of an ecosystem the more stable it is. But so long as you observe on the right time-scale, ecosystems can be seen to move, grow and die as climatic conditions change. A rainforest is the most diverse eco-system on earth. The Amazon was once thought to be 60 million years old, but recent research suggests that the region was mainly dry scrub vegetation as little as 6,000 years ago. As the climate slowly changes, forest regions migrate. The influence of Homo Sapiens can shorten these time-scales dramatically. Humans have caused ecosystems to crash. England's native forests were obliterated in a few hundred years. North American prairies were converted to farmland in the space of two or three generations. Of course, humans are not immune from these changes. The stone statues of Easter Island and the abandoned cities of the Maya are mute testaments to this. In both cases, over-exploitation of the ecosystem caused a crash that brought down the civilisations that initiated it. Eloquent proof that we are *a part* of the ecosystem and not *apart* from it.

So humans can kill ecosystems. But we can also cause them to grow abnormally fast. The limiting factor for the growth of most ecosystems is not water or sunlight, which are generally quite abundant, but access to nitrogen. This has a dramatic impact on plant growth which is the base of the ecosystem pyramid and therefore influences everything higher up. In 1909, Fritz Haber develops a process to capture nitrogen from the atmosphere and turn it into fertilizer. Before this, only microorganisms in the soil or legumes (peas and beans) were able to perform this feat. The Haber[29] process kicks off the modern era of synthetic fertilisers which brings dramatic increases in agricultural productivity. Today

---

29 The Haber process makes nitrates which is used for both life giving fertilizers and death dealing explosives. Had BASF not commercialised the Haber process in 1913, it is unlikely that Germany could have fought World War I. The only other commercial source for nitrates was Chile, whose mines were controlled by British industrialists and the imports were protected by the Royal Navy.

a billion tons of synthetic fertiliser are used each year, which sustains a third of the world's population. Of course, this artificial fertility has its downside. Since fertilisers promote the growth of everything, pesticides are needed to kill unwanted weeds. These poisonous pesticides then end up distributed through the food chain. Overuse of fertilisers depletes minerals in the soil, reducing its long term productivity. Rain washes excess fertiliser into rivers and oceans causing algal blooms which denude the water of oxygen. So the ironic result of using too much fertiliser is to create lakes and coastal zones that are biologically dead.

Can we view an ecosystem as an organism in its own right? It is certainly complex enough. An ecosystem metabolises energy through its complex food chain. It grows, moves and adapts in response to external pressures. Biologists observe the birth of ecosystems on newly created volcanic islands. They move through several adolescent stages known as *seres* before reaching their mature climax. As noted above ecosystems can die, often killed by the hands of humans. In some places, ecosystems even have human rights as championed by the growing 'Wild Law' movement. In 2006, the borough of Tamaqua, Pennsylvania passes an ordinance recognising the rights of the local ecosystem. Any resident can file a law suit on its behalf. Ecuador's new constitution in 2008 recognises the legally enforceable Rights of Nature. At first, you may be tempted to scoff at these 'tree huggers gone mad'. On reflection you might note that it is part of a longer term historical trend. Many things that were viewed as property in previous eras are now recognised as having rights. In the past women, children, slaves and animals have all been viewed as mere possessions. Thankfully, we have more enlightened views today. Maybe viewing an ecosystem as legal person with rights is the inevitable next step.

Level 7: the biosphere

One of the characteristics of an organism is homeostasis: the ability to regulate internal systems to produce a dynamic but stable environment. At the cell level, vacuoles perform this function. At the human level, we have homeostatic systems to keep our blood temperature constant like sweating and hot flushes. Insulin, which regulates blood sugar levels, is another example of a homeostasis. Ecosystems reach a homeostatic climax after passing through their adolescent seral stages. The number of species plateaus out as the feedback mechanisms in the food chain begin to interlock. If we look one level higher at the whole biosphere, what then? The Gaia[30] hypothesis puts forward the view that all life on earth is part of a single homeostatic system: the Earth itself is a single organism.

In the 1960s, James Lovelock develops his Gaia theory while working for NASA where he is studying the possibility of life on Mars. He notices that some features of the earth's environment are remarkably stable: surface temperature, the composition of atmospheric gasses and the ocean's salinity. Something is acting to regulate them to make conditions favourable to life. He proposes that the biomass of earth is that something. In other words, life itself creates a feedback loop to make its environment more favourable. In the strong version of the Gaia theory, the largest living creature on earth is the planet itself. Earth is like a single cell organism. It is regulating temperature, gas and salinity just as a cell does. It will soon reproduce by 'splitting' into two cells when humans travel in space to colonise another planet.

The Gaia theory attempts to link biology and geology into a single discipline. The environment affects living things, that's the basis of Darwinian selection. But animals also affect the environment; vegetation transforms atmospheric gasses. Likewise rocks, minerals and the morphology of the earth cannot be understood without taking living things into account; remember that oil and coal were once alive. So the separation into two different disciplines of life science and earth science is wrong. Animal, vegetable and mineral are all part of a single system: Gaia.

That completes our tour of the hierarchies in biology. The ladder stretches from DNA at the bottom to Gaia at the top. A case can be made for viewing each rung as an organism in its own right. The next question is which one is the correct perspective? Which way does the control flow? Is it bottom up or top down? Since humans are somewhere in the middle, either answer would be troubling. A bottom up argument would suggest that our cells rule us. A top down one implies that our actions are inevitable responses to environmental pressure from above. If you believe in 'free will' then you have to

---

30 The theory takes the name Gaia from the female earth goddess of the Ancient Greeks.

propose an awkward mechanism of control from the middle flowing both up and down. You also have to explain why our human rung and not any other one in the middle. None of these answers seem satisfactory. We need to examine the issue in a bit more detail.

Teleology and anthropomorphism

Many biologists think that Gaia theory is fanciful nonsense. It is an entertaining metaphor, they say, but not a scientific theory. Where are the actual mechanisms that regulate the environment? Where is the evidence of natural selection between planets? Worst of all, it is labelled with the filthiest profanity in the scientific lexicon: teleological. A teleology is an explanation that invokes a purpose or a final cause. Consider this question: Why is the water boiling? The scientific answer is, 'because it is at 100 degrees centigrade'. The teleological answer is, 'because I am making a cup of tea'. The first answer is addressing the 'how' with a mechanistic explanation. The second answer addresses the 'why' by invoking a purpose.

The most famous explanation of this type is the teleological argument for the existence of God. This states that nature is astonishingly complex. It cannot have just happened by accident. It must have been designed for a purpose. The name of the designer is God. The purpose of life is to discover what God intends for us.

The scientific answer is that there is no purpose. Invoking a designer does not explain anything because who designed the designer? Complexity does not imply design. Simple rules can generate very complex patterns, as demonstrated by fractals. Something that can be completely defined by a simple mathematical equation can still deliver unpredictable outcomes. Complex objects and behaviours are often self organising. They appear without the need for a central authority or top down planning. The simple mechanism of natural selection explains the wondrous diversity of life on earth.

Scientists view any explanation that invokes a teleological argument as no explanation at all. They have a similar distaste for anthropomorphism, sometimes known as the pathetic[31] fallacy.

---

31 Pathetic is used here in the sense of 'empathy' or similar feelings. But a 'pathetic fallacy' still sounds like a double insult: You are not just a failure but a pathetic one too.

This is the sin of ascribing human feelings to non-human objects. Aesop's fables are a harmless example of anthropomorphism. Animals such an ant and a grasshopper are given human characteristics in order to teach moral lessons. These metaphors can be powerful and can sum up a complex argument very neatly. Consider these aphorisms: 'Nature abhors a vacuum', 'Information wants to be free', or even 'The selfish gene'. They all express a deep concept in a short and easily understood anthropomorphic metaphor. The problem comes when the metaphor is interpreted factually. Of course, information, nature and genes don't actually have feelings. It's just a convenient shorthand for a weighty concept.

Descriptions of complex systems often stray into teleological or anthropomorphic territory. Traders of stocks and bonds view the market as a creature with a mind of its own. Like anxious flunkeys in a medieval court they are in endless debate about what 'The Market' thinks. It is their autocratic sovereign who can elevate them to fabulous wealth or destroy them at whim. Politicians are similarly nervous about the views of 'The General Public'. Even machinery can be anthropomorphised. Think of Scotty nursing the engines in the Star Ship Enterprise saying, 'She can't take much more of this, Captain'. As for jurisprudence, as Mr Bumble observes in *Oliver Twist*, 'the Law is an Ass'. Complicated things seem to have a mind and purposes of their own. Humans are prone to the pathetic fallacy.

Gaia theory is accused of being both teleological and anthropomorphic. Critics say it ascribes 'earth mother' characteristics to the planet and implies some sort of purposeful activity in the different life forms on earth. A weaker form of the Gaia hypothesis has stronger scientific support. There is no doubting that life has had an influence on the planet. The emergence of photosynthetic bacteria[32] had a major impact on the atmosphere. These early microbes converted sunlight, carbon dioxide and water into starches and oxygen. This oxygen, produced as a waste product,

---

32 Have you ever wondered why leaves are green? Why not black, which absorbs light much better? Photosynthesis evolved at a time when earth was dominated by purple brown halobacteria. Green was the only unused part of the light spectrum. So like a pirate radio station, early chloroplasts exploited the gap in the frequency spectrum.

was poisonous to all the anaerobic life on earth at that time. Only later did animals evolve to breath this oxygen and eat the starch in the photosynthesising plants. So the oxygen content of the atmosphere is heavily influenced by the evolution of life. There was no free oxygen 600 million years ago. It made up thirty per cent of the atmosphere 300 million years ago and has since settled down to a stable twenty per cent. Supporters of Gaia theory say this is evidence of a homeostatic regulating mechanism and therefore the planet is an organism in its own right. Detractors say it is only evidence of a symbiotic relationship: a co-evolution of life and the atmospheric environment.

The unit of selection

The fundamental mechanism of evolution is simple. It relies on two things. First, there needs to be something that generates variations. Second, there must be something that chooses which of those variations will survive. This selection mechanism could be a farmer choosing which cows to breed from. In the case of natural selection, it is not a farmer but the environment which is doing the selecting. We call the thing that is being selected the 'unit of selection'. The big question is *what* is being selected: is it the genes? The individual ? The species?

The unit of selection problem is still a matter of debate in biology. We have laid out the ladder of life from DNA to Gaia. There are many rungs but which perspective is the correct one? We can rephrase this question as 'where does the unit of selection lie?' Different biologists have championed different rungs on the ladder. In Darwin's original theory, the unit of selection is the individual organism; in other words, the middle rung of the ladder. In the 1960s, V. C. Wynne-Edwards moves it up a rung. He puts forward the group as the unit of selection. His evidence is the altruistic behaviour seen in social animals. Ants sometimes sacrifice themselves for the good of the colony. Humans do the same. The group benefits from this self sacrifice and so the group must be the unit of selection.

These arguments are vigorously rebutted in the 1970s by biologists who take a gene-centric view of the world. The most prominent is Richard Dawkins with his book, *The Selfish Gene*. He argues that altruistic behaviour is genetic in origin. A mother will try to save her baby from a burning building. If she dies, at least her genes will survive through her child. Supporting evidence for this view came from the unusual division of chromosomes in social insects. This is called the haplodiploid system, where males have only half the genetic material that females have. This has the mind-boggling result that a male ant has no father or sons, but does have a grand-father and can have grandsons. In humans, a maiden aunt will look after nieces and nephews because they are family. With no children of her own, that's her best shot at propagating her genes. With ants the maiden aunt is an uncle.

Perhaps the most persuasive case for the gene-centric view is the ratio of males and females in harem species. In a herd of deer, one dominant male fertilises all the females having beaten off the other males in the rut. Viewed from a group perspective, the unsuccessful males are a waste of resources. It would be much more efficient to have a lot of females and just a few males. In fact, the ratio of males to females in harem species is 50:50. This inefficiency is a puzzle when taking a top down view. It can only be explained by looking at things bottom up. From a gene's perspective, the average change of mating is the same whether you are male or female. Female deer are all equally likely to mate. As a male, you will either be spectacularly successful or get nothing at all. But when you average out the extremes of this 'all or nothing' strategy, you find the probability of mating still supports a 50:50 split of the sexes. Hence the gene must be the unit of selection because only the bottom up view makes sense.

So the gene viewpoint trumps the group viewpoint. What about the viewpoint of the individual organism? Gene enthusiasts dismiss that fairly easily too. They argue that if things were optimised for individuals then we would not grow old and die. Genes are immortal. The bodies of the individuals are just disposable sacks to contain them. They need replacing when they get a bit worn out. Again, genes must be the unit of selection.

So far it's a pretty compelling case for genes. But recently, the cell centric view is beginning to mount a challenge. Leo Buss is a leading proponent of this argument. The issue revolves around how a single fertilised egg becomes the vast collection of special-ised cells that make up an individual. As the single starting cell starts to divide and replicate, the copies are not all identical.

Differentiation begins to creep in. Liver cells, brain cells and skin cells are all different but they all started from the same original cell. So, to a certain extent, these different types of cell are competing with each other in the development race, skin cell *v.* liver cell, and so on.

Think back to a time when the only life forms on earth were single cell creatures. The rules for a single cell creature are simple: replicate as fast as you can. But for a multi cell creature you need specific amounts of the different cell types; enough liver cells to make a liver but no more. So at some time in the past, a 'cell level' control mechanism must have evolved when multi cell life forms first appeared.

If you look at a class of animals such as salamanders, you will see a very large variation in the shape of their limbs, and some even have no limbs at all. But this big difference in body shapes is not matched by a big difference in genetic material. The DNA seems very similar, the creatures look very different. So where does the difference come from? The answer is an epigenetic phenomenon, in other words something operating above the level of the genes. The expression of genes is regulated. They can be switched on and off. The fact that a gene is present does not mean it is active. So what is controlling the switching? A small number of genes in the genome make up a developmental genetic toolkit. The most important of these are the Hox genes which specify the main axis of the body and where structures like eyes and legs are placed.

If you go to a steel plant you will see machinery made of steel producing steel girders. The tools are made of the thing they produce. Likewise, the genetic toolkit consists of genes controlling genes. To a gene centric scientist that is the end of the mystery. To a scientist who believes in the primacy of the cell, it is no answer at all. They want to know who is operating the machinery. In their view, the cell controls the network of protein pathways that cause genes to be expressed. As evidence, they point to the non-specific nature of protein interactions.

The genetic determinist view goes like this: Genes encode for proteins. Each protein does a specific thing like a piece of a jigsaw puzzle. The pieces of the puzzle fit together to form the whole picture: the cell and beyond that, the body structure. Cell enthusiasts disagree. They hold that the action of a protein is not fixed like a piece of a jigsaw puzzle. The shape of the 'piece' can change depending on the environment. The environment is controlled by the cell. Cellular level processes control the protein networks. So they draw the arrow of causality the other way around. Cells control the expression of genes. Therefore, natural selection operates at the cellular level and not the genetic level. The cell is the unit of selection.

Even poor old Wynne-Edwards who got trashed for his views on altruism in the 1960s is seeing a mini revival. David Sloane Wilson, a professor of biology at New York University, has revisited the group level selection arguments and put forward a multi-level selection theory. This proposes that the unit of selection is not fixed but moves between the different levels. At a certain times genes may be critical, at others it is group level interaction that is most important.

What can we conclude from this debate? Maybe it is best to leave the experts to argue it out. We can draw the curtains and tiptoe quietly away with two thoughts. First, theories come in and out of fashion because debate is the lifeblood of science. Second, different levels have different rules. That is cataxis.

Supervenience and the p-zombie

Wherever there is a good argument, you know the philosophers will have something to say about it. In philosophy, there is a type of relationship between the rungs on the ladder which is called supervenience. This is a linkage between two domains where changes in one require changes in the other. Let's take physics and chemistry. We can say that chemical properties supervene on physical properties. If you change the atomic structure of something, you will also change its chemical properties. Add a sodium atom to a chlorine atom and you get table salt. The chemical properties have changed completely. A poisonous gas and a volatile metal combine to make an edible condiment. Notice that this is a one-way relationship. A change in chemical properties requires a change in physics but not the other way around. If I take a glass of water and move it to the other side of the table I have changed it physically but its chemical properties are the same. So supervenience is best summed up like this: change on the higher rung of the ladder requires change on the lower rung but not necessarily vice versa. In the biological ladder, we can say that cells supervene on genes, animals on cells and so on.

For philosophers, things get interesting when debating this question: does the mental world supervene on the physical world? This is a debate that goes back to Descartes and is still unresolved. Technology has recently supplied a new tool to help gather evidence. The MRI scanner allows neurologists to see pictures of the brain as it is thinking. Different areas of the cerebral cortex light up as the experimental patient performs mental tasks. Clearly, if you change your mind then something physical in your brain changes too. But supervenience is a one-way phenomenon. So there can be physical changes in the brain that don't result in a change of mental state. These issues are often explored by putting forward a hypothetical being which is exactly like a human but has no consciousness. This philosophical zombie, or p-zombie for short, would react when poked with a sharp stick but would not actually feel any pain. His responses to external stimuli would be exactly the same as yours but he would have no feelings. A neurological p-zombie would display the same pattern on an MRI scan of the brain as you, but he would not be thinking what you are thinking. In fact, he would not be thinking at all.

Behaviourists refute this. They think a p-zombie is not possible. In their view, the whole is explained by the intermeshing mechanics of the parts and there is no free will. Supervenience is a convenient argument for those who want to refute this bottom up determinist view. It runs like this. The mind supervenes the body. A change in mental state requires a change in physical state. But the physical change does not 'explain' the mental state. It is not a one-to-one mapping. Two different brains can have the same thoughts. A human and a dog can both feel pain even though their brains are different. Likewise, the p-zombie example proposes two physically similar brains but with different thoughts (one thinking and one not). So the conclusion is there is a link between the two levels but not a causal link. It is a 'have your cake and eat it' argument. Higher levels are composed of lower levels but not explained by them.

Mind over matter

Some people go much further in rejecting the determinist view. They take a top down approach rather than a bottom up one. In this view, primacy is given to the top rung of the ladder: the mind. Matter exists below the mind in a teleological universe. *The Gospel of John* starts with the words 'In the beginning was the Logos, and the Logos was with God, and the Logos was God'. Logos can be translated as 'word' or 'wisdom', or maybe, 'reason'. So the origin of everything is the mind of God. Matter is secondary. It represents the extrusion into our material universe of the thoughts of a higher being. This is not just a Christian view. It is a common theme in other religions and new age mysticism too. When you see crystals emerge from a solution of chemicals it is order emerging from chaos. A mystic may believe this is evidence of a mind in another dimension poking through into our universe. It is the same with mushrooms that spontaneously seem to appear overnight. Hence the view that mushrooms and crystals have magic powers. The spontaneous emergence of order is taken as proof of an organising principle behind everything: a universal mind.

It is easy to dismiss anyone who believes in the magical power of crystals as a crackpot. In a more serious vein, many eminent philosophers have endorsed the view that the mind has primacy over matter. Descartes' famous *Cogito ergo sum* effectively says this: I don't know if the material world exists or not but I do know that my mind exists because I am thinking. Kant, though he disagreed with Descartes, believed that the material world is constituted by our minds. We create the world: the world does not create us. Husserl, the founder of phenomenology, took a halfway stance. He observed that when you look at a solid object you see only the front. You infer that the back part is there even though you can't see it. So some part of the world is given to us and the other part is created by us. Clever optical illusions can demonstrate this to be true. The retina of the eye collects information but the brain interprets it to give it meaning. So we see what our brains believe to be there not what is actually there.

So the material world is partly constructed by our minds. What about the mental world? Do our thoughts come from within ourselves or originate from somewhere else? The ancients believed

Real or Imagined

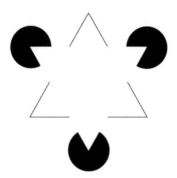

Our brains perceive a downward pointing white triangle
which is not really there.

that inspiration was a divine gift which came from gods or muses.
Some artists today still echo this. Authors sometimes describe the
act of writing a novel as 'channelling' their characters. It is as though
the fictional characters really exist in some other dimension and the
author is just describing what they are doing. Paul McCartney woke
up one morning with the song *Yesterday* fully formed in his head. He
just had to write it down, although the lyrics were about scrambled
eggs. Keith Richards describes the act of writing a song like being
an antenna picking up a message from elsewhere, almost like taking
dictation. It seems common for creative artists to believe that
inspiration comes from outside.

Scientists also have flashes of inspiration. Solutions to knotty
problems come in dreams or in the shower. James Watson's dream
of a spiral staircase helped him discover the structure of DNA. But
scientists tend to ascribe the flash of inspiration to a much more
prosaic source: the subconscious. This is the bottom up view again,
and the argument goes like this. The brain is a complex information
processing machine with many subroutines. Consciousness is an
emergent phenomenon. Our sense of self is a construct made from
parts of our subconscious. MRI scans now enable us to see the brain
at work. When we pick up a glass of water, our brain sends a message
to activate our arm muscles before we have consciously decided to
do the act. So our conscious brain is fooling itself into thinking it
'decided' to do something that our subconscious brain initiated.

(We will return to this topic in the chapter on the self). For now, we can just recognise it as evidence to support the bottom up view.

Genetic determinists have a bottom up explanation for art and culture too. They postulate a transmittable unit of culture called a meme. Just as a gene is the unit of biological selection, a meme is a unit of cultural selection. Pop songs, clothing fashions, gestures and rituals are memes that spread through the population through imitation. The selection process is based on how trendy they are; they are either copied or ignored. The copies are not always perfect. They can be refined, modified or combined with others. A song writer may feel he is channelling a higher power when he is composing. Maybe he is just performing a memetic mutation of some old blues riffs.

Corporate evolution

So culture can be explained either as a top down, an individualistic or a bottom up phenomenon. You can make a case for any of these three rungs on the ladder. The artist is either channelling something higher than herself, or making an intensely personal statement, or just a phenotypic expression of memes. What about the corporate world. Does a CEO make a difference? Just as with biology or culture we can identify a number of different levels in the corporate arena. Is the CEO just responding to higher level pressures from the global economy? Is he transforming things through his personal leadership style? Is she merely a symbolic figure head taking credit for the efforts of those underneath? You could argue any of those points depending on your views, but the answer is probably a bit of all three. As with the biological unit of selection, different rungs on the ladder are important at different times.

The unit of selection in the corporate world is hard to identify. Even though biological analogies are often used, the concept of 'corporate evolution' is more metaphor than fact. Companies come and go, and the concept of the survival of the fittest is strongly embraced in the business area. Managers exhort their commission-based salesman with macho epithets like 'it's a jungle out there; you eat what you kill.' Engineers strive to make products better, faster and cheaper to beat the competition. At first glance, the corporate world and the living world seem mirrors of each other; the marketplace, the urban twin of the Serengeti plains.

The problems come when you look closer. Evolution has two features as we said earlier: a unit of selection and a mechanism that does the selecting. It is hard to identify these in the corporate world. First, the selection mechanism; is it natural or artificial? You can argue either case. Artificial selection is what farmers do when they selectively breed cattle. You can view venture capitalists and shareholders as acting like farmers when they select which companies to invest in. Alternatively, you can make the case that the corporate jungle is creating the selection environment. The global economy stands in for 'nature' in this version of natural selection.

It is even more difficult to identify the unit of selection; the thing that causes companies to be different. You could argue that this is some sort of corporate strategy or business plan. The only problem is that evolution is supposed to be unplanned. That's the whole point. Maybe it is some form of corporate culture that exists at an instinctive level below planning; a proto-strategy, an attitude, an ur-plan. How would such a thing transmit itself or replicate? Until this corporate gene has been identified and its mechanisms laid bare then corporate evolution is, sadly, just a metaphor.

Different levels, different rules

Let's pull together the different strands of this chapter so far and summarise the different arguments. The biological ladder has the following rungs: DNA, cell, immune system, individual, group, ecosystem and biosphere. There is a debate about which level exerts control over the others.

The bottom up view is a reductionist one which can be called genetic determinism. Patterns that appear at the higher level are the result of activity on a lower level. It is an emergent hierarchy. The beaver's dam and the 50:50 split in harem species are higher level manifestations of genetics. By the same argument, CEOs take undeserved credit for the actions of others and artists are memetic replicators. The opposite view sees order and structure being imposed from above. This top down view invokes a teleological purpose to the way things are organised. Take this argument further and you must also conclude that an ecosystem has rights, that you can cure yourself through positive thinking, that artists channel a divine spirit and that companies are rudderless boats on a stormy economic ocean. Both approaches are too extreme. The right answer must surely be that selection is a multi-level phenomenon. Different things become important at different times and on different scales. Influence and control goes both up and down. The economy influences you and you also influence the economy. Genes affect the environment and the environment affects genes. There are complex symbiotic relationships between the levels. You need to recognise the integrity of each rung on the ladder. Each one has its own rules and it is a mistake to apply those rules outside of their hierarchical context. That is cataxis.

Kant in Iraq

One way of illustrating the balance between top down and bottom up is to look at the military. Your first impression is of a top down command structure. Generals tell Majors what to do. Majors instruct their subordinates. In the end, the grunt on the ground is told what to do and just follows his orders. It seems like the epitome of control from the top. On closer examination, it is not like that at all. The reason is best expressed in this maxim: no plan ever survives first contact with the enemy. War is full of uncertainty, chance and misinformation. So if you follow a rigid plan imposed from above, you will not be responding to the situation on the ground as it unfolds and therefore likely to mess up in a big way. Your plan is obsolete from the moment the battle begins. So the best thing to do is to set your overall objectives and allow the people underneath to take the initiative when trying to fulfil them. Your success depends on expressing a clear strategic intent and allowing tactical decisions to be taken lower down. The morale, ingenuity and fighting spirit of soldiers on the ground is the key factor in winning. These are all individual bottom up attributes. So in fact, your war may be planned top down, but it will be won bottom up.

Those who question the value of top down control point to Afghanistan to support their argument. The Afghan guerrilla fighters don't have much top down planning. Their fighting style is pure tactics with little strategy. It's a bottom up approach: emergent warfare. It has also been remarkably effective. They have defeated every invading Imperial Power; Britain, Russia and the USA. The jury is still out on the last one since as I write the war continues into its tenth year. But a deal with the Taliban and a US/

NATO withdrawal seems the most likely outcome. If so, then in a military context bottom up will have defeated top down.

US soldiers are now taught ethics with a course on Kant. The lectures illuminate the finer points of moral philosophy: Is it justified to kill one to save five? Is there a difference between actively killing and deliberately allowing someone's death to happen through inaction? US troops patrolling city streets in Iraq and Afghanistan are required to make moral judgements all the time. They are not just following orders. They are trying to stabilise and pacify a dangerous district. They need to win the support of the local community. This can only be done from the bottom up. Soldiers making the right individual judgements many times a day. There is a top down command structure but power resides in a subtle interplay between all the hierarchical levels. The top level exists to create the discipline and environment in which an individual on the ground is free to make the right choice. Choice and free will is the subject for our next chapter.

CHAPTER 5

The Subconscious, the Market and the Supermarket

Western democracies cherish freedom, particularly the freedom to choose. It is the illuminating light of a just society. It has also been a central debating point for philosophers down the ages. There are many subtle shades of argument as to whether humans have free will or not. A top down view can posit an omnipotent God. If God controls everything, then clearly humans do not have free will. On the other hand, a bottom up view put forward by a scientist can be equally restrictive. In this view, the past, present and future are all linked in a chain of causes and effects. This chain is governed by the laws of Physics which dictates the outcomes of any of these events. Free will has no place in this universe, because it would be an effect with no cause. If it had a cause, it would not be free will. Therefore free will is a logical impossibility. If you do believe in free will you are sitting on the middle rung of the ladder. You are rejecting both the notion of top down theocratic control and bottom up scientific determinism.

It would take a whole book to explain the various different arguments about free will in more detail. Instead, I want to focus on some of the catataxic angles to the issue. The first of these is the question 'Who in you chooses?' Our sense of self is a construct of many substructures. Imagine someone faced with a difficult choice. He may be saying, 'My head says this, my heart says that, but in the end I will go with my gut instinct'. There is a kaleidoscope of different thoughts and feelings swirling around at the subconscious level which go into making a final choice. The second issue is how the different choices of many people are combined together to express a general group view. In politics, this involves counting the votes that have been cast. In finance, it is the sum of all the consumers spending their money that sculpts the economy. In effect, each penny spent is an economic vote cast. In law, trial by jury requires twelve jurors to agree on a verdict. It is a group decision that delivers justice. In addition, the body of common law is an accretive residue of legal decisions over the centuries. A corpus of many judgments that determines what is right and wrong.

These two issues form two rungs in a ladder about free will and choice. The first examines the different parts of the psyche and how they combine to make a conscious choice. The second moves up one level to look at how different views combine to form the general will of the people, as expressed in law, politics and economics. They are both about collective decision making: the first at the level below the individual and the second at the level above.

The many parts of you

The idea that the self can be divided into many parts is not new. Plato is the first to put forward a three-part scheme. He calls these three parts the appetitive, the spirited and the rational. The appetitive part produces the base emotions such as hunger, lust and rage. The spirited part is where higher notions such as love and honour spring from. The rational part, as the name suggests, is the seat of reason that tries to reconcile the other two. Plato uses the metaphor of a chariot. The two unruly horses pulling the chariot are the appetitive and the spirited. The rational is the charioteer, trying to control them. Plato also sees this tripartite division as the foundation of a just society. In other words, he believes there is a similar structure on both the first and second rungs of the ladder. The composition of the individual mirrors the ideal structure of society one level up. At the societal level, the appetitive is represented by workers and manual labourers. The spirited is the military class of soldiers and other enforcers. The rational corresponds to philosophers and kings.

At the beginning of the twentieth century, Sigmund Freud proposes a similar tripartite scheme. In Freud's model the three parts are called the id, the ego and the super-ego. The id is a selfish pleasure seeker. It is disorganised, instinctive and responsible for our basic drives for sex and food. The super-ego is organised and responsible for spiritual goals and the conscience. It controls our sense of right and wrong. It is the seat of morality and engenders the sense of guilt. The ego is responsible for interaction with the outside world. It tries to mediate between the desires of the id and the guilt of the superego. However, it is often not able to do this and as a result generates feelings of anxiety.

You can see that the schemes of both Plato and Freud are quite similar. They both describe a balancing act between higher and baser desires. But there is one big difference. Plato's rational part is the strongest of the three. In contrast, Freud makes the ego the weakest of the three. Plato's charioteer is like a ruling king while Freud's ego is more like a negotiator. In essence, Plato sees man as inherently logical while Freud sees man as an irrational creature. Both agree, however, that the self is a construct that emerges as a result of competing forces at a lower level.

These three-part models are fairly simplistic. Maybe the best illustration of the true complexity is the large variety of terms used to describe the many parts of you. Consider the following: self, soul, consciousness, mind, spirit, character, animus, personality and psyche. Each has a subtly different meaning, but there is also a large degree of overlap between them. For example, personality and character seem very similar terms. Personality describes the type of person you are. You could be friendly, confident, outgoing and curious. Or maybe you are the opposite. Character is slightly different. It is more of a comment on your morals and integrity. Are you courageous, loyal and honest? How do you respond when faced with adversity? Similarly, we can draw distinctions between some of the other terms. When someone is suffering from Alzheimer's disease their personality is gradually eroded but they still retain consciousness. A brain dead patient on a life-support machine has no personality or consciousness but still has a soul. The p-zombie we discussed in the previous chapter has no soul but still has a functioning brain.

All of these different terms have hotly debated theories associated with them. Most of that debate is highly theoretical since it is difficult to get tangible evidence about how the mind works. Until recently, that is. Cognitive scientists now have a new tool. As we noted in the previous chapter, MRI scanners have radically transformed research in this area. They enable researchers to see images of the brain as it is actually thinking. Experiments of this type on decision making have revealed a startling fact: our brain acts *before* we consciously decide to do something. Our sensation of 'making a conscious choice' is an effect, not a cause.

In 1983, Benjamin Libet is the first neuroscientist to demonstrate this phenomenon. He places electrodes on the scalps of his experimental subjects and asks them to push a button. He records a gap of 200 milliseconds between the decision to act and the pushing of the button. No surprise there. It takes a brief time for your body to act after you have made a decision. The surprise comes when he sees the brain activity before the decision to act. Neurons start firing 300 milliseconds before the subject has even decided to push the button. Recent research with the latest MRI machines has pushed this gap out to as much as seven seconds. So some sort of trigger occurs in our subconscious. Up to seven seconds later, our conscious mind scrambles to claim this 'decision' as its own. It is a post hoc rationalisation. Just like a CEO claiming credit for great financial results, or a politician boasting about turning the economy around.

Those who oppose the concept of free will have welcomed the results of these experiments. By watching the brain on an MRI scanner, you can accurately predict whether a subject will use his left or right hand for a task. You can do this *before* he has even decided which one he is going to use. Is this proof that free will does not exist? To some, maybe. To others, the subject is still making a choice, just not with the higher conscious part of his brain. Most scientists now view the brain as a collection of sub units each with different specialisations. One sub unit deals with visual information. Another processes short term memory. Just as a PC is an assemblage of different sub processors so is the brain. Your higher conscious functions sit above the sub processors tying everything together. The choice about which hand to use is taken at the sub processor level. So, free will still exists but one level lower down. We make decisions with our subconscious.

The creature below

Stephen Spielberg is in terrible trouble. It is 1974 and he is an unknown director on the set of *Jaws* in Massachusetts. This is his big break. He was only the third choice of the producers to turn the best-selling novel into a movie. Shooting on the water is proving much more difficult than expected. Everything keeps going wrong and the crew have nicknamed the movie 'Flaws'. Worst of all, none of the three mechanical sharks work properly. They are always breaking down and look no more scary than a fake plastic log bobbing in the water. The movie is already way over budget, both in time and money. Spielberg worries that he will never work again as a director. How can you make a movie about a shark if you don't have a shark?

Necessity is the mother of invention. Spielberg has a flash of inspiration. He will shoot the movie in such a way that you can't see the shark, but you *imagine* it to be there. He shoots close-ups of people swimming with a hand-held camera. He keeps the eye line down at water level. As a viewer, you feel like you are in the water too and you can't see the shark. Now that *is* scary. There is one more thing he needs to pull it off. Something that will let you know there is a shark nearby, even though you can't see it. The solution is music. He needs a great musical score to complete the effect.

Spielberg explains his problem to John Williams who has just won an Oscar for the score of *Fiddler on the Roof*. A few weeks later, John Williams comes back excitedly saying that he has cracked it. He sits down at the piano and starts plinking away with two fingers on the same two notes. Spielberg thinks this is a joke. It sounds like he is trying to tune the piano or something. He asks Williams when he is going to start playing the theme tune. 'This is the tune,' says Williams. 'It's just two repeated notes.'

John Williams won another Oscar for those two notes. On a piano, they sound ridiculous. With a full orchestra, they sound tense, menacing and instantly recognisable. Once you heard that tune you knew there was a shark in the water and something horrible was about to happen. That's the power of a movie soundtrack. Your eyes are focused on the screen so you don't really notice how much the music is affecting you. Your conscious brain is following the dialogue and the visual story. The music is speaking directly to your sub-conscious and profoundly influencing your emotions. The old cliché about violin strings is true. The next time you find yourself welling up while watching a movie, take a moment to notice the soundtrack. You will surely be hearing violins. Or try this other experiment. Pick out a DVD of a movie that always brings a lump to your throat. When you get to that all important scene, turn on the subtitles and turn off the sound. Not so emotional now, is it? [33]

---

33 This is a top tip for when you are flying somewhere and sitting next to your boss. When watching rom coms, put the sound down and subtitles up. If he sees you crying, he will think you are a wimp.

The *Jaws* theme tune is the metaphor for a shark in two ways. First, it's the aural cue for the creature that you cannot see on the screen. But the tune is itself a shark, in fact all soundtracks are, in that they attack you unexpectedly from beneath. The famous *Jaws* poster with a swimmer on the surface and an enormous shark coming up from below is a visual metaphor for how a soundtrack works. It catches you unaware beneath the surface of your conscious mind and tears you up. You are defenceless. Once you put yourself in that darkened cinema, you will inevitably become the sound-track's victim.

It is not just sound that speaks to the subconscious. Images can do that too. There is an interesting reversal of the cinema experience that also takes place in a darkened room. This time the sounds affect your conscious mind and the visuals the subconscious. It is a TV show called *Dating in the Dark*. Couples go on a blind date . . . literally. They meet for the first time in a completely dark room. They have to get to know each other by chatting without seeing what the other one looks like. As the week goes by they have further dates in the dark and can message each other by computer. At the end of the week, the contestants chose from the dates they have met the one they would like to see in the flesh. When the lights are switched on their reactions are pretty instantaneous. More often than not, they reject the partner on physical grounds despite having formed a good relationship mentally. It is an emotional decision based on looks which outweighs the rational decision based on mental compatibility. For those of a cynical nature, this confirms their view that *Beauty and the Beast* is just a fairytale. True Romantics can reply that the show has a selection bias. You have to be pretty shallow to go on Reality TV in the first place.

The underlying point is this. Aural and visual cues can be very influential as they speak directly to your subconscious. The same is true of smells, which may be the most powerful subconscious influencer of all the senses. Smell is the only sense that is hard wired directly to the brain through olfactory neurons. The other senses rely on indirect methods of communication. Chemical scents known as pheromones cause major behavioural changes in other animals. As we noted previously, they are the prime communication channel for ants. In humans, pheromones are thought to control the timing of menstrual cycles and sexual attraction. Smells can also be a strong trigger for memories, particularly the perfume or cologne of an ex-lover. They are used metaphorically to mean an inchoate and instinctive sense. For example, 'I did not accept the offer because something didn't smell right.' The unease emanating from your subconscious is best described in terms of the most basic and primitive of the senses: smell.

All three senses, hearing, sight and smell are manipulated when we go shopping in a supermarket. Colour, music, flooring, placement and odours are all arranged to influence you psychologically. The colours of the goods are altered by subtle lighting, making the meat redder and the salads greener. French or German piped music can influence you to buy French or German wine. When the flooring changes from hard tiles to soft carpet, shoppers slow down and spend more time looking at the goods. Some shops even alter the size of the tiles, putting smaller ones in expensive areas. Why? Because the *clickity-clack* of your trolley wheels speeds up and so you slow down to compensate. Supermarkets waft the smell of baking bread baking through the store. This is comforting, but also makes you slightly hungry prompting you to buy more food. Harrods is reputed to have a different specially chosen fragrance in every location to enhance sales. All these elements are speaking to your subconscious because that is where your decision is going to be made.

Research suggests that seventy per cent of buying decisions made in a supermarket are unplanned.[34] Some shoppers will be focusing on the price and making a logical comparison. Others may be scanning the list of ingredients with rational concerns about health. But in the majority of cases it ends up being an emotional decision. After the price and quality issues have narrowed the range of selection, you are still choosing the one you like best from amongst several different things. Your logical brain prepares the data, but your subconscious is the true decider.

This may be one reason why the online grocery market has not lived up to its early expectations. Market penetration is still low at only three per cent, compared with thirty per cent for books. In

---

34 Thrifty shoppers know the best way to save money is to make sure your shopping decisions are planned in advance. Make a list before going into the supermarket and then stick to it. Like Ulysses tied to the mast, you will then survive the siren voices of the branded goods.

other words, people are happy to buy books online but not food. Books are a cerebral commodity, whereas food is far more emotive. So when you are presented with a list of hierarchical menus to choose from on a food shopping website it feels uncomfortable. You are being forced to shop in a logical way for an emotional product: you are using the wrong part of your brain.

Branding is asymmetric warfare

If buying decisions are made at one level below the conscious, then branding can be called a cataxic weapon. A brand is a set of perceptions and feelings that a company owns in the mind of a consumer. When a company is trying to brand its products it is trying to establish a set of emotional responses that the target consumer will feel. It is cutting down through the levels and talking to the creature in your basement.

Brands have a value that can be measured. Interbrand – a marketing consultancy -publish an annual survey of global brand value. Top of the list in 2010 is Coca-Cola with a brand value of $70 bn. That is, around $10 for every person on the planet. That means somewhere in the basement of your brain, alongside your fears and your childhood memories, is a little bit that is worth $10 and owned by Coca-Cola. How does that feel? Did you ask them to put it there?

In some ways, branding can be seen as a type of inverse terrorism. A terrorist act is conducted against an innocent victim with the aim of creating terror in the general populace and influencing some change at the national level. For example, a bomb is exploded in a crowded shopping centre to pressure a change in government policy. The victims are not the real target, the nation is the target. Terrorism is an act conducted at the individual level (level 1) to create an emotional response and change at the national level (level 2). That is why it is sometimes called asymmetric warfare. There is a difference in scale between the terrorist and the nation; they belong on different levels.

Branding is inverse terrorism. It is action at a corporate level (level 2) to create an emotional response in an individual (level 1). Where terrorism is a strike targeted upwards, branding is a strike targeted downwards in the hierarchy. A second difference is time scale. Terrorists favour a single spectacular act but branding is more of a long term game. It has taken decades of patient advertising for Coca-Cola to accumulate that $10 part of your brain.

The purpose of advertising is to create demand for a product. A company pays an advertising agency to engender desire: to manipulate emotions in favour of a particular brand. The trick is to persuade the consumer that the product will satisfy an emotional need. If you own this handbag or coat you will feel better about yourself. Having bought it, your need is satisfied but only fleetingly. Then, as with drugs and alcohol, you need more. Advertising persuades you that something it would be nice to have is something that you *have* to have. It conflates wants with needs. The truth is that emotional problems can't be solved by physical things. So in linking your subconscious needs to a tangible product they have created a mercantilist nirvana: endless, unsatisfiable demand. The more you have, the more you want. This is the engine of the global consumer economy. Shakespeare summed it up best when Anthony says of Cleopatra: ' . . . she makes hungry, where most she satisfies.'

Voting with your wallet

The British Museum has a 6,000 year old jade axe head that was found near Canterbury. It is shaped like a teardrop and is highly polished. It is a ceremonial object rather than a practical hand tool. This beautiful and prestigious item was made in Italy. Archaeologists have found the very block of stone it was cut from in a Neolithic jade mine high in the Alps. It seems even in the Stone Age Britain was importing luxury goods from Italy. What force caused the axe to be transported 800 km to a country that had no jade of its own?

The motive force that propels these objects down the trade routes is consumer demand. In Chapter 2, we looked at the thermodynamic concept of entropy. Entropy always increases. This is the reason why a hot iron bar in a cold room will cool down until they are both lukewarm. A concentrated group of molecules will gradually disperse. For example, the smell of freshly ground coffee will gradually permeate the whole house. In a similar way, luxury goods disperse from the place that they are made and travel to where they are valued. The more rare something is, the more valuable it is. Since there are many of those goods in the place where they are made, they will inevitably disperse to places where they are rare. There they will be traded for some abundant goods travelling in the opposite direction. So economic trade is a version of entropy.

Capitalists look at those who oppose the dominance of market forces with bemused puzzlement. The laws of the marketplace are natural laws, just like the laws of physics. They view attempts to curb the marketplace as being as ridiculous as trying to repeal the law of gravity. Moreover, they argue capitalism is fundamentally fair. Transactions cannot take place unless both sides benefit. If I want to swap your hat for my coat, then I must like your hat more than my coat. If the trade takes place then you also must like my coat more than your hat. So at the end of the transaction both sides have got what they want. If either was unhappy then there would be no trade. The very fact that the trade took place means that both sides are happy. A capitalist economy is the summation of millions of free transactions. Everyone is trading, so everybody is happy. QED.

A socialist would reply that all this getting and spending misses the point. Mercantile transactions do not equate to happiness because they do not take account of the natural laws of society. These are eloquently described by Marcel Mauss in 1924 in his essay, *The Gift*. His three fundamental laws of society are these: we have an obligation to give, an obligation to receive and an obligation to reciprocate. So, for example, in a pub if someone buys you a drink you are obliged to accept it and then buy one in return. That's how relationships are forged between people in most societies. If you view it materialistically, at the end of this transaction nothing has changed. Something was given and something of equal value returned; they cancel each other out and the net result is nil. But one level above the economic transaction something has been achieved: a social relationship. A banker will see a transaction with zero sum gain because he does not recognise the deposit in the 'social bank account'. The socialist therefore argues that it is a big mistake to try to run the world by monitoring mercantile transactions, because you are missing out the social dimension. Global capitalism, which believes the marketplace is the solution to everything, must be wrong because it ignores level two, otherwise known as society. To a socialist, capitalism is a catataxic fallacy.

In fact, a banker does understand that a zero sum gain transaction on level one can create something else on level two. He just has a different name for it. Suppose you are saving money under your mattress. One month you take those savings and put them in a bank account. It's still your money but you have 'lent' it to the bank. This is a zero sum gain transaction. Your asset matches their liability. But one level higher up, you have just increased the money supply. The bank has lent your money to someone else expanding the pool of credit in the economy. So the banker's name for level two is 'the economy'. In other words, you can view the difference of opinion between socialists and capitalists as an argument about what to call level two: economy or society?

These two concepts are often seen as opposing forces. Consider a statement like this: 'the government is focused too much on the needs of the market rather than the needs of people.' It may strike a resonant chord of empathy with many, but there is a flaw lurking at its heart. The problem is this. The market is an expression of what people want. So the needs of the market *are* the needs of the people, although it may not be all they need. At this point, it may be worth discussing the workings of markets in a bit more detail.

Markets and Derivatives

We can start by observing that there are two different levels: the objects and the desire for the objects. This desire, hatched in the subconscious and fed by advertising, is measurable. It's called the price. Much as physical systems reach thermodynamic equilibrium, marketplaces reach economic equilibrium. The supply and demand for goods balances out and prices are formed. The price of an object is the measure of the cumulative desire for that object. The economic equivalent of taking someone's temperature.

Supply and demand are rarely fixed. In fact, they are constantly varying. As a result the price is also varying. When demand rises, prices rise. When supply rises to match demand, prices fall back again. If you are a farmer and the price of rice is high, you will plant more rice. But so will everyone else. So next harvest there is a lot more rice for sale. This increase in supply makes prices fall. So farmers plant less rice and prices rise again. We are back where we started and the whole cycle begins again. Of course everyone wants to sell their rice when the price is high. So the smart thing to do is to sell your rice *before* you have even harvested it. In effect, you are selling your future rice. This is known as a futures contract. The first futures contracts were traded on the Dojima Rice Exchange in Japan in 1730. They are now traded not just in rice but in almost every conceivable commodity around the world. Up until the 1970s, futures trading was focused on agricultural commodities like rice, wheat and pork bellies. This is now completely dwarfed by financial futures where the underlying assets are currencies, stocks, stock indexes or other financial instruments.

Futures are a type of financial derivative; a tradable instrument that is derived from the price of some underlying asset. Other common derivatives are options and swaps. Swaps are agreements to exchange a stream of cash flows. Options give you the right to buy something at a particular price for a period. We can illustrate how options work by looking at the movie industry. Imagine that I have just written a best-selling book.[35] You are an independent movie producer who wants to turn it into a film. You don't have the money to buy the rights just now. But if you put together a package with a great director and some A list actors you might be able to get a major Hollywood studio interested. So you option the book. This means you pay, let's say, ten per cent of the value of the rights and you will pay the rest when the movie gets the green light from the studio. You in effect have *the option* to buy the book at the agreed price sometime in the next year. If no studio decides to make the movie, your option expires and you lose your money. Alternatively, the movie gets the green light and you exercise your option and pay the rest of the money for the book. You sell the package on to the movie studio at a higher price and you have made money on the deal. There is a third possible outcome. Let's go back to when it's still in limbo. You have managed to create a buzz about the project. Industry insiders think it might be as big a hit as *Jaws*. Someone offers to buy your option from you. You agree and sell your option for a higher price than you paid for it. So you make some money, which rewards you for all the work you have done promoting it, even though the movie is not green-lit yet.

The point of the story is that the *option* to buy something is itself tradable. With financial market options, you don't even have a movie that you have to promote. You are just betting on whether

35 In my dreams, one day, and only with your help, dear reader.

the price of something goes up or not. The option is traded separate from the underlying asset. This gives us the third level on our catataxic ladder. We have the object on level one. The desire for the object (the price) is level two. The desire for the desire for the object, otherwise known as the derivative price, is level three. This opens the door to an infinite series of rungs on the ladder because you can then have derivatives *on* derivatives. Let me explain this. An index like the Dow Jones, FTSE or Nikkei is calculated from a basket of underlying stocks. It represents the movements of all the stocks listed on a particular stock exchange. It is an amalgamation of them all together in a single number. So it is one level up from a share price. If you want to speculate on how the market as a whole will move in the future, you might take out a futures contract on the Dow Jones index. This is now two levels removed from the underlying shares. Then you might put a bunch of stock index futures into a basket and trade that. You are now one more level removed. Pretty soon you are way up in the stratosphere and many levels removed from solid earth.

This may seem abstract in the extreme and therefore irrelevant, but complex derivatives such as this blew a big hole in the global financial system in 2008 and caused a global recession. The culprit was Collateralised Debt Obligations, otherwise known CDOs. This financial crisis was a catataxic crisis caused by these multilayered products. A CDO is a type of derivative that packages together mortgages and sells the future income streams in different slices based on relative risk. The process of chopping and repackaging was so complex and opaque that no one really understood what the risks were. There were two processes at work. The first was amalgamation and the second was structuring of derivatives.

The amalgamation step is normally seen as reducing risk. This is the principle of diversification: don't put all your eggs in one basket. Buying an index like the Dow Jones is less risky than buying an individual stock, because the risk is spread over all the stocks in the market. So if one stock goes horribly wrong, it's not the end of the world. But there is also a way in which blending things together can increase risk. Think of a hamburger. If you see the butcher put some fillet steak into the mincing machine you can be sure that what comes out at the end is going to be great. But if you see some cheap minced meat discounted on a supermarket shelf it is probably a mixture of good and bad quality meat. Some of it may be fresh. Some of it may be frozen and over a year old. Some of it may be contaminated. You just don't know. You have to trust the super-market and hope it won't make you ill.

The average hamburger patty in the USA has meat from over a thousand cows. This is because processing plants are getting bigger, so meat from many different cows is getting all mixed up together. In addition, profit margins are always under pressure. This means the temptation to blend some dodgy meat in with the good stuff is quite high. If only one of those cows is diseased, then the whole batch of processed meat is probably risky and best avoided. So here is an illustration of how amalgamating things together is actually increasing the risk. It all depends on the visibility of what goes in to the mincing machine, how long the supply chain is and how trust-worthy the different people in the chain are. In 2008 bankers discovered deficiencies in all three areas in the supply of 'financial hamburgers' (otherwise known as CDOs).

The second step in the process was the structuring of the derivative products. As a general rule, investing in derivatives is more risky than investing in the underlying assets because of the effect of gearing. Let's look at options again to explain this. A stock is trading at £20 in the market. You take out an option to buy it at £30 in one year's time. The option costs you £1. A year passes and the price rises to £28. There is no point in exercising your option: why buy something for £30 which is only worth £28? On the other hand, if after the year passes the price rises to £35 then you would exercise your option. You can buy something for £30 which is worth £35. You therefore make a profit of £5, less the £1 cost of the option in the first place. Let's compare these two trades. In the first example, if you owned the option you would have lost all your money because the option expired worthless. If you owned the stock, you would have been up forty per cent (from £20 to £28). In the second example, if you owned the option you would have made four times your money; your £1 option delivered £4 of profit. If you owned the stock, you would have been up seventy-five per cent (from £20 to £35).

You can see from this example that investing in options is much more risky than investing in stocks. With the stock, you are making quite good returns in both cases. With the options, you either lose everything or make a fabulous profit. This is known as gearing or leverage. Generally speaking, financial derivatives are highly leveraged investment vehicles and therefore have higher risk. This is fine in moderation. What's wrong with a touch of spicy condiment to liven up your bland investment portfolio? The problem is financial derivatives have become so popular that they now dwarf the size of the underlying assets. If you add up the savings of everyone on the planet and subtract the debts, you get a global household wealth estimate of US $125 trillion. This literally *is* all the money in the world. The total value of outstanding derivative contracts in June 2010 is $580 trillion according to the BIS. So the value of financial derivatives contracts has grown from nothing in the mid 1970s to almost five times bigger than all the money in the world. So derivatives are not a spicy alternative condiment. Rather, they are a teetering inverted pyramid of bets that threaten to crush the foundations they are based on. A level three catataxic crisis waiting to happen. One butterfly flaps its wings and *crash* . . .

That's nonsense, say fans of unrestricted market forces. Derivatives reduce risks; that's the whole point of them. Remember the hat and coat trade earlier? The reason why financial derivatives are so popular is that people are swapping things they *don't* want for things they *do* want. One bank may not want to hold the mortgage of a customer they think is dodgy. So they swap it through a financial derivative for something they would prefer to hold: something less risky for them. Risk is not generic. It is specific to each individual or situation. What you think is risky is different from what I think is risky. Luckily, the market allows us to transact and we both end up better off. We all end up holding what we are comfortable with so risk has been reduced.

You can see that there is a healthy debate about both types of risk. If you diversify, you reduce risk by spreading your bets but you also get the 'what's in my hamburger' problem. Derivatives increase leverage which is inherently risky but give the flexibility to hold what you are comfortable with. There are pluses and minuses for both approaches. But there is something that unites them both together. Underlying both is the common theme of transparency and counter-party risk. If I trust my suppliers then I don't have to worry what's in my hamburger. Likewise, if I have a derivative bet on with someone else, everything is fine as long as he honours his side of the bargain. My trade has not eliminated the risk. It has simply passed it from my account to his account. If he goes bankrupt then so will I.

So we can characterise the two types of risk like this: one is horizontal, the other vertical. Counterparty risk is horizontal; it is to do with the guy on the other side of the table. I need to trust that the other party will not go bankrupt and that the structured product that I own really *is* what the bank that made it says it is. I need reassurance and transparency of information about that. The other dimension of risk is vertical; the fact that prices go up and down and that there are derivatives stacked on top of that. This is the cataxic dimension. I want exposure to this risk because otherwise I would not be investing in the market. This is the risk that brings rewards. I just have to believe that I can pick the winners.[36] The market regulator can take care of the counterparty issues. If those elements are policed in a satisfactory way, then derivatives and structured investment products are probably a good thing because they increase the transparency of price information in the market. In that sense, derivatives are like a magical post office sending us messages from the future.

The eternal rolling poll

One of the most derided and resented inventions of the modern age is the focus group. When a company is bringing a new product to the market they gather together a representative group of people from the target audience to look at the prototype. Following on from these discussions, the product is reshaped and tweaked to make it more appealing to the people it will be targeted at. It is a time consuming and expensive process, but it has permeated throughout the modern economy because it tells you something extremely valuable: what do consumers think? No major product launch today would happen without one, whether the product is a breakfast cereal, a political policy, a car or a Hollywood movie. In the latter case, it breeds resentment amongst the creative types. No director really likes being forced to stick a happy ending onto his

---

36 This is a whole different argument. There is a lot of evidence that no one really knows how to do this and that overconfidence about abilities here is, in fact, the biggest risk. That is a topic for a different book.

artistic masterpiece so that it plays better to the popcorn munchers in the multiplex. Focus groups are resented by bruised elitists because they are seen as part of the dumbing down process. They pander to the lowest common denominator.

This type of market research activity is big business these days. Around US$25 billion was spent last year by companies and governments on opinions polls, focus groups and other surveys, all trying to find out what people really think. A lot of time, energy and painstaking effort are being invested here. So it may come as some surprise to find out there is already a mechanism for finding out what people think. What's more, it does not cost anything and is happening constantly. It can tell you exactly what people think right now, every second of the day. It's called the market.

As noted earlier, the price of an object is a measure of the desire for that object. The more people buying and selling it, the more accurate that measurement is. It's the same as having a bigger poll. The more people you survey, the more accurate your poll is likely to be. The bigger the derivatives market gets, the more opinions there are in the poll. So a heavily traded item with a well developed derivative market will be a fairly accurate summary. The derivatives enable investors to articulate their views more precisely. The price will more accurately reflect everything that is happening right now.

Let's take the dollar to euro exchange rate which is probably the most heavily traded financial instrument in the world. Its price is changing every second, 24 hours a day right around the world. There was an explosion in a copper mine in Chile this morning? That's in the price. Bad weather affecting the wheat harvest in Kazakhstan? That's in the price. Your mother twisted her ankle yesterday and did not go to the supermarket? That's also in the price. One way or another, every single thing that is happening is influencing financial transactions, which end up being reflected as a perturbation in the price.

In that sense, a stock market is an eternal rolling opinion poll. A summary of what the public thinks. An expression of the general will. A democratic process that takes place not once every four years but a million times, every second of every day. A perfect condensation of *the now* in a single number: the price. All that information collapsed to a single point brings it own particular problem. How do you get the information back out again? You know the result but you don't know how you got there. You know *what* it is but you don't know *why* it is. It's a destructive summarising process as we discussed in Chapter 3, when looking at MITI bureaucrats and public key cryptography. Price formation amalgamates everything together, but loses all the contextual information. It is an extremely efficient transformation but it only goes one way. It's tough to see the world in that particular grain of sand. Given that single number you can't really reconstruct information about your mother's health or the weather in Kazakhstan. You just know it's all in there somewhere. At least market research gives you some context and lets you understand why something is unpopular. The stock market is the post office of the future, but its Delphic missive is almost impossible to interpret. In the words of Bob Dylan, something is happening here but you don't know what it is, do you Mr Jones?

Fractal markets

In 1979, the IBM researcher Benoit Mandelbrot discovered an extraordinary mathematical object. It was neither two-dimensional or three-dimensional but somewhere between the two: a fractional dimension, or fractal. This object, now called the Mandelbrot Set, can be described with an equation so simple it is almost trivial but generates something of infinite complexity. The closer you look at it the bigger it gets. It repeats itself like an endless hall of mirrors at smaller and smaller scales. This is called 'self similarity'. Imagine this. You examine a tiny microbe on your skin under a magnifying glass and see a perfect replica of you staring back up at you. It may sound like a bad sci-fi movie but objects like this do exist. In fact, they are quite common. Look closely at a cauliflower and you see that each floret is itself a mini cauliflower. The same is true of snowflakes, coastlines, lungs, ferns and more importantly stock markets.

Look at a chart showing how the price of a stock changes over time. Now change the time scale so that you are looking at it on a monthly basis, not a daily basis. It still looks quite similar. In fact, if you remove the time-scale from the bottom it's impossible to tell if it is a yearly, monthly or daily chart. There is nothing in the pattern that gives a clue to the time period that is being represented. Technical analysts, sometimes known as chartists, exploit this fact to try and interpret the Delphic message of the market. Certain patterns seem to regularly re-occur regardless of time-scale. These patterns have names like 'head and shoulders' or 'falling pennant'. If you recognise one of these patterns forming then you may be able to predict which way the price will go in the future and make some money. The point is that these technical analysis tools can be applied to an intraday chart or a ten-year chart. The time horizon does not matter because the patterns re-occur on all time scales: share price charts are self similar.

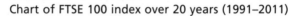

Chart of FTSE 100 index over 20 years (1991–2011)

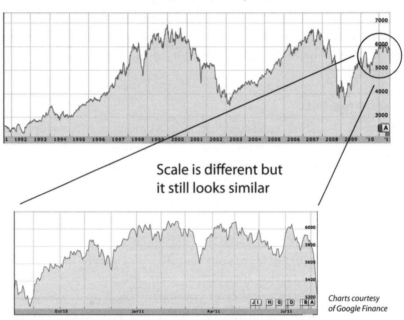

Scale is different but
it still looks similar

*Charts courtesy
of Google Finance*

Chart of FTSE index over one year

In Chapter 3 we discussed the rivalry between technical analysts and fundamental analysts. Fundamental analysts of the stock market reject the chartist techniques as mumbo-jumbo. They think technical analysis belongs in the same camp as reading tea leaves or studying chicken entrails. They think that changes in share prices are determined by changes in the fundamentals such as company profits and interest rates. So if you build a financial model in a spreadsheet to predict future profits, you can predict what the share price will be.

Who is right? Actually neither, or maybe, both. There have been numerous conflicting and controversial studies but the overall conclusion still seems to be this: you may as well toss a coin. Neither technical nor fundamental analysts can consistently demonstrate an ability to predict share price movements. I say 'maybe both' because I have never met an analyst of either persuasion who did not secretly listen to the 'other side' and allow it to influence his view. So both approaches may have some merit, but just not enough to consistently beat the market.

Into this fundamental *v.* technical debate steps the Mandelbrot set. It causes great excitement. The Mandelbrot Set is self similar, just like a share price chart. If something so complicated can be generated by a simple equation then maybe share price charts have a simple equation at their hearts too. We just have not discovered it yet. Needless to say, whoever discovers the equation first will become fabulously rich because they will be able to predict the market.[37] A new type of analysis is born, neither technical nor fundamental, but quantitative. Investment banks start hiring mathematicians and particle physicists to work as 'quants' using statistical techniques to analyse the market. They produce lots of equations by crunching historical data and observing statistical patterns.

Unfortunately, the fractal mathematics behind the Mandelbrot Set turns out to be descriptive rather than predictive. You can use an equation to generate a pattern that looks very much like a share price chart, but not exactly like this particular share price chart. It may look like a share price and act like a share price but it is still just a simulation. Likewise, the work done by the quants does not predict the future but it does reveal correlations in the historical record. It can't say 'this is going to happen,' but it can say 'last time this happened this also happened'. It is looking backwards and sideways rather than into the future. These patterns and correlations are used to build mathematical models for trading strategies and to hedge risk.

We now know that these mathematical models got it all wrong.

---

37 A moment's calm reflection reveals the quixotic nature of this quest. If there really was an equation that perfectly predicted the market, then there would be no need for a market. You could just type the numbers into the equation and find out what the correct price is. No debate, no argument, no market. In that sense, the definition of a market is 'the thing that exists because it cannot be predicted'

They dramatically underestimated the risks, as was clearly demonstr-ated in the global financial meltdown of 2008. The quantitative analysts turned out to be as ineffective as the fundamental and technical ones. Some have argued that this is because they did not understand the fractal nature of the market properly. As discussed in Chapter 2, most quantitative models were based on the normal Gaussian distribution: the bell curve. This predicts that extreme events are very unlikely. A fractal approach suggests that extreme events are much more common.

The fractal market hypothesis states that the market appears stable because it has no characteristic time scale. It is self similar: a ten-year chart and a five-minute chart look the same. The market is made up of people with many different time horizons. Short term day traders are looking to snatch a quick profit. Pension fund managers are investing for the long term and are taking a ten-year view. That's why they trade with each other. What looks expensive to the day trader looks cheap to the pension fund manager. Different time horizons mean different views. That makes a stable and healthy trading environment. Market meltdowns are caused by everyone suddenly becoming short term. The diversity of views disappears and everyone becomes a day trader. The market becomes unstable and can no longer absorb shocks. Everyone tries to do the same thing at once and dramatic lurches in prices result. So the stability of the market is the emergent result of a lot of disagreement one level below. It is a cataxic triumph. If the disagreement stops, the stability is obliterated.

Let's go back to the argument about whether derivatives are a good or bad thing. In the end, derivatives are just an advanced grammar for more precisely expressing your views. They contribute to the noisy debate and normally act as a big flywheel to smooth out irregular beats in the market. This is not how they are viewed by the press. You often see headlines like this: 'Speculators cause fuel price to skyrocket' or 'Hedge funds push Greece to the brink'. Far from being evil bullies, they are just voicing aloud what everyone thinks. The price is moving dramatically because no one disagrees. It can be impolite to speak your mind in public, but it is rarely morally wrong.

The astonishing feature of the Mandelbrot set is that something so complex can come from such a simple equation. At first, the hope was that a complex share price could have a simple equation at its heart. But this is looking at it the wrong way around. In fact, the share price is the simple thing generated by the complexity of all the different views and information out there. It is the one drop condensate of all that noisy chaos. The Mandelbrot Set converts simplicity to chaos. The stock market converts chaos to simplicity.

Tyranny of the teenager

From the stock market to the supermarket. You are wheeling your trolley up the aisle. So many branded goods stacked high on the long shelves. It looks like they are bulging out at you. Is it an optical illusion? Maybe behind those racks of product the pressure of modern consumerism really *is* bearing down on you. Big and brutal. If you put your ear to it, you might hear its breath. Worst of all, they all look the same. Two aisles full of breakfast cereal. So much apparent variety, but no choice. Fifty-seven expressions of the same idea.

So far in this chapter we have discussed two issues. First, how your 'choice' is actually the net result of a lot of subconscious activity heavily influenced by branding. Second, how a market creates prices by amalgamating many different views. Your mind and the market are actually performing the same type of summarising function, just at different levels. Your brain summarises a lot of activity on the level beneath and produces a simple result: a choice. The market summarises a lot of activity on the level beneath and produces a simple result: a price. So when you wheel your trolley down the supermarket aisle you are bringing those two summarising organs together: your brain *v*. the market, choice *v*. price.

The supermarket converts complexity to simplicity. It is an engine streamlined to find the lowest common denominator. Only popular products are stocked on the shelves, things that are in demand by the general public. You don't get what you want – you get what other people want. Hopefully, there is some overlap between the two. The more your tastes are in line with the average, the happier you will be. The result is plenty of variety but no choice. There are lots of different versions of the same thing but nothing that is odd, quirky or individualistic. Your choice is constrained by the will of other people as determined by the supermarket buyer. He is the one who decides what goes on the shelf. He has a counterpart in the world of TV who decides what gets shown on the box. She is the one who is responsible for the modern TV paradox: ninety-nine channels but nothing on.

What do I mean by variety but no choice? It means things that are superficially different but practically identical. Endless tiny variations around the same theme. For a simple example, consider men's shoes. There are essentially only three styles – formal leather ones to wear with a suit, protective work boots and casual trainers or sneakers. Three types to cover all eventualities: working in an office, working with your hands or playtime. Women get a much better deal. They have appropriated all the male styles but in addition they have a glorious array of pumps, stilettos, straps, sling backs, mules, kitten heels, flats and wedges.[38] But for men it's just three types. If you want something to wear with your suit they will be dark coloured and made of leather. There will be subtle variations in the shape of the toe, from pointy to blunt. There will be a muted colour spectrum from black through ox-blood to brown. And then each colour and style will be available in ten different sizes. All in all, there could be 2,000 different pairs of shoes in the shop. Tremendous variety, but no real choice because they are all dark leather sensible shoes. What's that? You are looking for a pair of yellow suede pixie boots? Sorry, Sir. Don't stock them. There's no demand . . .

Warhol's silkscreen prints of 32 Campbell's soup cans made this point far more eloquently. In that wall of near identical soup cans, each is a different 'variety' but they are all essentially the same. Choosing one of them is no real choice at all. That static image, made in 1962, was a portentous warning of the future. But misses one key feature: things are not static but dynamic. Let's return to the three flocking rules from Chapter 4:

- go in the same direction as everyone else
- try to be in the middle
- don't bump into other people.

Those are also the rules for the supermarket buyer or TV executive.

---

38 Differences in male and female footwear is the theme of the movie *Kinky Boots*. The plot revolves around a traditional shoemaker who discovers a lucrative niche market making shoes for male transvestites

We can take them one by one. First, you have to follow the current trend. You have to respond to what is popular or you will have no customers. Second, you have to be in the middle. Your job is to get as many customers as possible and by definition, they are clustered around the middle. Third, don't bump into other people. Your product needs to be slightly different or you will get sued for copyright infringement.

These three rules when taken together create flocking behaviour. So a better metaphor for consumerism than Warhol's soup cans is a flock of starlings on a winter evening. As the birds group together in the darkening sky, the patterns they make coalesce and fragment unexpectedly. Three simple rules make something complex and startlingly beautiful. It is jittery, unstable, individually free, but bounded by the group and impossible to predict. This is the modern consumer economy: an evening murmuration of starlings

The instability comes from the balance of two opposing forces. There is the push of trying to be different and the pull of trying to belong. This is classic teenage angst. It's no coincidence that advertising gurus peg the aspirational age at seventeen. This is the age that everyone in the modern consumer economy would like to be. It is the nexus of cool. Those younger than seventeen want to be just like those older kids. They aspire to the maturity and freedom of a seventeen year-old. Those older look to recapture their youth. So if you pitch your product at seventeen year olds you will hit a much broader market. That's where trends are born. It's the centre of gravity for the starling flock.

Most movies these days are aimed at a teenage audience. In fact, the movie that triggered this change was our old friend *Jaws*. It was the first true summer blockbuster and opened the eyes of movie executives to just how much money could be made from a teen-friendly 'event' movie. Cinema multiplexes are the supermarkets of the visual arts. You now get a large number of screens showing a small number of movies. It's variety with no choice again. In fact, there is not even that much variety. Most multiplexes show the same movie on multiple screens. But complaining that 'they don't make movies like they used to' is a catataxic fallacy. You think it's about entertaining you. This is the individual perspective or level 1. The studio thinks it's about extracting revenue from an audience. They are operating at level 2. It's true they don't make movies like they used to. The target audience is different these days. Now get over it, and try and enjoy yourself.

Of the two opposing forces, the push to be different is getting stronger than the pull of belonging. The key emotion behind it is this: I want to stand out from the crowd but in a good way. This aspiration is fuelled by advertising which says buying this product will make you different. Against a general background of corporate blandness, companies are trying to make their products more quirky and offbeat. This leads us to a pert oxymoron: individualism is the new trend. But this is not true individualism, it's a branded corporate construct. In the 1960s, worn, torn and faded jeans were symbolic of the hippie counter culture. It was a potent and rebellious statement that said: 'I may look scruffy but at least I am real'. This anti-establishment theme followed through to Punk Rock and the Ramones in all their torn jean glory. Now, a pair of artfully dis-tressed jeans from a designer boutique are far more expensive than a normal pair. It's 'authenticity' that you can buy in a shop, which of course is no authenticity at all. Rock and roll these days is rebellious pose in a neat corporate package. It used to be about teen idols. It's now about idolising teens.

All this stands in stark contrast to traditional societies, where the veneration of the elderly is the norm. In Bali, this has been taken to extremes in an unusual way. Balinese surnames are the opposite of patronymic. In the West, if Donald has a son called John then his name will be John Donaldson, or John McDonald or maybe, John O'Donnell. The surname is the name of the father. In Bali, it is the other way around. The father's surname is the name of his son. In our example, the father would change his name to Donald Johnfather. Later, when his grandchild Tom arrives, he becomes Donald Tomgrandad. At first glance, this seems like veneration of the child because everyone is forced to change name in his favour at his birth. In fact, it is the opposite. As the adult goes through life his identity is gradually eroded. Finally, at the moment of death he has no name. He becomes one with the nameless ancestors. But, crucially, the nameless ancestors that are the venerated ones. They are the gods. In the West, you cease to be at death. In Bali, you start ceasing to be at birth. The more you lose your identity, the more divine you become.

Despite the patronymic surnames, the western world is obsessed with youth. That's why the aspirational age is seventeen. It is also demonstrable in the 'Kidult' phenomenon; middle-aged people, normally men, who still act like teenagers. These forty somethings play computer games, read graphic novels (otherwise known as comics), party hard with a younger crowd, dress down and avoid growing up at all costs. What causes this behaviour? There are many possible explanations. It could be fear of death. Unlike the Balinese, modern western society struggles to accommodate its inevitability. It could be fear of responsibility. It's a difficult, fast moving and uncertain world, so making any sort of commitment is a challenge. But it may just be selfishness: The desire to make sure that, whatever happens, you have as good a time as possible. This trait is something that today's consumerism encourages. Advertising transmutes your wants into your needs and the vast engine of the global economy is geared up to service them.

The modern consumer is a spoilt child. He wants to belong, but at the same time he wants to be different. Multinationals fawn upon his whim. He is petulant, selfish and prone to tantrums. He gets what he wants whenever he wants it. I have a friend who runs a struggling organic vegetable box business. Customers pay an annual fee to have a weekly box of vegetables delivered. The exact contents of the box are unspecified, other than the fact that it is local, seasonal organic produce. He despairs when customers ring up in January complaining that there are no tomatoes. He has to patiently explain that they are not in season. Tomatoes are a summer vegetable. But the customer wants tomatoes in January. There they are in the supermarket, and what she wants she shall have. My friend wonders this: when will someone say 'no' to that spoilt child. Where is nanny?

This is how my organic vegetable friend would like things organised. Instead of the free market system, consumer choice should be overseen by a trusted intermediary who would only offer up the right things. The 'right things' in this case are those that do not harm the environment and therefore are better for all. That way consumption becomes ethical and sustainable. The selfish child becomes a responsible adult. You will notice that in my friend's system, the trusted intermediary is . . . himself! I point out to him that there are no trusted intermediaries left any more. Consider the roll call of the fallen: Estate Agents, Lawyers, Journalists,

Stockbrokers and Politicians. These once trusted intermediaries are now mistrusted charlatans. Trusted intermediaries live in the silken tent of Neverland alongside the benevolent dictators, some unicorns and a friendly giant called Progress.

We know what you want before you do

Back to the murmuration of the starlings. The overall shape of the flock of birds emerges from the independent actions of hundreds of individuals. You end up with a complicated object. A pattern that is jittery, ephemeral and restless. It flips between fragmentation and coherence but is not random. All that complexity arises from three simple rules. Complexity from simplicity? Sounds like the Mandelbrot set, and indeed they are cousins. The murmuration of the starlings is like a 3D share price chart. The finance industry hires quants to crunch the data to try and predict the future. The retail industry does the same thing. Retailers have a vast amount of data; every transaction is recorded. They know the time, cost and description of every item that has been purchased from their numerous stores. They then use statistical techniques to mine this data in order to reveal patterns and correlations. This sometimes throws up unexpected linkages. Urban legend has it that data mining in one city revealed beer and diapers are often bought together. This prompts a store to put these items next to each other on the shelf. Sales boomed. You can put your own interpretation on why someone would buy both at the same time. Explanations range from the charitable to the depraved. Let's not go there because the point is this: it doesn't matter. Data mining, like chart analysis, does not tell you *why*, it just tells you that a pattern exists.

Once you see a pattern, you can use that information to minimise risk or optimise returns. If you put diapers on special offer you might sell more beer. Putting both on special offer probably won't attract any extra people to the store. For retailers this data is extremely valuable. That is why they are so keen for you to get a loyalty card. It helps them to link your personal details to the contents of your shopping trolley. This adds demographic details to their database and gives a fuller picture of your buying choices. In other words, they don't just know the exact position of every starling in the flock but also their age, wealth, relationship status and so on. This is a tremendous help when trying to forecast demand.

Here is an example. The weather forecast says this Sunday will be the first hot sunny day this spring. People are likely to want to fire up the barbecue. Supermarket managers will stock up the store in advance not just with charcoal but also all the other related items that your data mining has correlated: kebabs, burgers, hats, sunscreen, beer and yes, maybe, diapers. The point is they know what you want before you do. You walk into the supermarket to make your 'spontaneous' choice, but they have already anticipated that. Maybe your choice was not very spontaneous after all. Are you really exercising your free will?

The level below (the subconscious) and the level above (supermarket) seem to be running things. You think you are choosing but the levels above and below you get there before you do. You are just a way point between your desires and the market. Does that make free will just a catataxic dream? I think not. You are free just as the starlings are free, but the patterns that the larger group makes are bounded and not completely random. In Chapter 2 we discussed how statistical aggregations, such as those done by the Cochrane Collaboration, can reveal patterns at the macro level that are not visible at the micro level. Taking the average of something is a level changing mechanism. This is sometimes called the Law of Large Numbers: the more data in your sample the more you can be confident that the average is accurate. The Cochrane Collaboration uses this to save lives. The supermarket uses it to predict what you will want to buy this weekend.

This effect is best illustrated by considering gasses. You may remember Brownian Motion from school. Robert Brown, a botanist, first describes it in 1827 when examining pollen grains suspended in water under a microscope. He notices that the pollen particles have a strange jittery motion. He speculates that they are being bombarded by other tiny particles too small to see. In classrooms today, the experiment is repeated with smoke particles in a test tube. The jittering 'Brownian' motion observed is proof that atoms and molecules exist. The smoke particles are being knocked about by random collisions with invisible gas molecules.

At the micro level, you have individual gas molecules moving randomly about. At the macro level, the behaviour of the gas is predictable. Its pressure, temperature and volume are all interlinked in the ideal gas law. If you keep the temperature constant and change the volume you know exactly what the pressure will be. That pressure is caused by random collisions of gas molecules with the sides of the container, but is still predictable with the laws of physics. It's random at the small scale (level one) but predictable at the large scale (level two). That's the power of statistics and the law of large numbers. The randomness cancels itself out and a larger scale pattern emerges. So it is possible to have both free will *and* predictable behaviour. It sounds incompatible until you realise that there are two different levels. As we know different levels have different rules. That is catataxis.

Slaves to the general will

The shelves of the supermarket are stacked with what's popular; what everybody else wants. But what if that is not what you want? You have variety but no choice. Have you become a slave to the general will? Not really. In this retailing example, you do have other options. The main one is to shop somewhere else. You can rebel against the supermarket buyer by shopping in farmers' markets for groceries or in second-hand stores for vintage items. Both have become increasingly fashionable in recent times. Buying vegetables from the man who grew them cuts out the supermarket buyer, as does wearing second-hand clothes. Both are also kinder to the planet; one reduces food miles, the other is a form of recycling. This anti-consumerist rebellion has been given a big boost by the internet: eBay transforms the market for second-hand goods. YouTube lets you escape the TV controller, allowing you to choose what you watch and when you watch it.

So when it comes to shopping there are plenty of options for rebelling against the general will. The shelves of supermarkets express majority rule but you don't have to shop there, you can go somewhere else. Failing that, go on the internet, where lower retailing costs mean less popular items can still be profitably offered. There is no 'Ministry of Shopping',[39] determining appropriate items for sale, despite the wishes of my organic vegetable friend. Retailing is organised on a bottom up basis to cater for the spoilt

---

39 Sometimes the government does regulate what can be sold, for example banning harmful substances and pirated goods. But this is for exceptional items on the fringes of the grand bazaar.

child of the modern consumer. He gets what he wants. The global economy is now organised such that her desires are paramount. It's a vast transmission mechanism for individual selfishness.

In the past, there were mechanisms to control this spoilt child. High transport costs, tariff barriers, royal charters, protectionist laws, licences and guilds stifled free trade. This forced communities and nations to be far more self-sufficient. These barriers meant that the bulk of what was consumed was produced locally, and later nationally. In essence, the will of the community was stronger than the desires of the individual. In many cases, these barriers were so strong they had to be broken down by military force. The Imperial wars of the eighteenth and nineteenth century had trade issues, at least partially, as ultimate causes. International and then global trade effectively raised the desires of the individual above those of the community. To pick up on the theme from earlier in this chapter, economy became more important than society. In some communities, for example the Amish or North Korea, barriers either religious or political remain. For the rest, the desires of the individual are triumphant.

As a general rule, hardship reinforces community values, while a time of plenty promotes individualism. Hardship means sharing and a focus on what you can give. Plenty means a focus on what can you get. So as international trade boosts economies creating a time of plenty, the selfishness of the consumer is amplified, creating a feedback loop. The genie is out of the bottle and cannot be put back again. Economic growth in recent times has been astonishing. The global economy was similar in AD 1600 to the size it was in 800 BC, at around US$140 per capita.[40] On average, no one got any richer for 2,500 years. In the next 200 years (1600–1800) global GDP per capita doubled to $300. In the following 200 years (1800–2000), it went up more than 20 fold to $6,500. Did the economic growth cause individualism or was it the other way around? It's a chicken and egg debate, but few would deny that the two go hand in hand.

Just at the beginning of this period, as economic growth begins to kick off, the rights of the individual *v.* society becomes a major

---

40 These figures are estimates by Professor DeLong at Berkeley University. Per capita GDP is used to eliminate the increase in GDP caused by population growth.

topic of public discussion. It is framed in terms of moral or political philosophy since the discipline of economics had yet to be born. There are four key voices in this debate: Hobbes, Locke, Rousseau and Smith. All express their viewpoints between 1650 and 1770 and they form the four posts of a boxing ring that still sees active use today.

Hobbes is first with his *Leviathan* in 1651. Strongly influenced by the English Civil War, he argues that for society to function there needs to be a benign dictator. Individuals acting in their own self interest can only create anarchy and their lives will be, in his most memorable phrase, 'solitary, poor, nasty, brutish and short'. In order to avoid this, people must come together and cede authority to a single absolute ruler. They surrender some of their individual rights to a sovereign in return for a just and harmonious society.

Locke disagrees. In his *Treatise of Government* in 1689, he argues that having to do what someone else tells you to do is wrong. That is tyranny. But if the majority decide upon a just law, then the individual should be governed by that law. Laws become legitimate not because they are the will of a monarch but because they are the will of the people. He draws the distinction between liberty and license. Liberty does not mean being free to do whatever you want. Liberty means freedom from oppression. It is liberty *under law* where the law is majority rule.

Rousseau is next. In his *Social Contract* in 1762, he refutes Hobbes' notion that Man's natural state is one of wickedness and puts forward the ideal of the noble savage. Man's natural state is moral and incorrupt. As society develops, property laws emerge. These do not bring justice, rather they create social injustice: inequality between rich and poor. Society enslaves man. Since it is impossible to go back to a pre-social era, Man can only be free by acting in the name of the general will. Unlike Locke, this is not the same as majority rule. Rousseau's concept of the general will aims to benefit everyone, not just the loudest and largest crowd. Rousseau believes that man 'must be forced to be free'. He must subjugate his individual will to the general will. It is liberty under law where the law is not the majority but the will of the people. Sadly, Rousseau does not describe the mechanism for discovering the will of the people. This opens the door for the worst excesses of the French Revolution and the Totalitarianism of the twentieth century.

Adam Smith in his *The Wealth of Nations* in 1776 does describe a mechanism for discerning the will of the people. He calls it the 'invisible hand' of the market. He explains how individuals may be selfish but they deliver a public good. Self interest leads to competitive behaviour, which increases efficiency, lowers prices and responds to public demand. It is an insight as powerful as Darwin's Theory of Evolution one hundred years later. Both theories extol the benefits of selfish competition and it is not until the twentieth century that the underlying mechanics of both can be fully demonstrated.

So there you have the four posts of the boxing ring:[41] Hobbes the Monarchist, Locke the Social Democrat, Rousseau the Totalitarian and Smith, the Free Market Capitalist. Four opposed views expressed at the dawn of the explosion of economic growth but still debated today. Each attempts to define the relationship between the individual and society, or in catataxic terms, between levels one and two. Three of the four arguments require subjugation of the individual in the form of a social contract. In other words, level two rules over level one. Adam Smith is different. His name for level two is not 'Society' but 'Economy' and his mechanism is bottom up rather than top down.

In the two hundred years since the publication of the *Wealth of Nations*, global GDP per capita has increased by 4,000 per cent. It is only now that the subjugating element of the fourth argument is becoming apparent. The early days of free trade increased choice dramatically. It became possible to buy all sorts of goods that had never been available before. But over time, the winnowing efficiency of the global marketplace has driven things to the opposite extreme. Variety now expresses itself not in different types of goods but in different variations of the same goods. It used to be more variety, more choice. It's now more variety, less choice. So, in the end, even Adam Smith's argument requires a subjugation to the will of the people. Your choice is constrained by what everybody else wants. The quirky, the unusual and the off-beat are outcompeted by the populist power of the lowest common denominator.

41 This is a crude characterisation of four profound thinkers. I have exaggerated their differences to delineate the boundaries of the debate. These one sentence sound bites do not do them full justice.

The supermarket is there to serve the general populace and you can always opt out. Rare and unusual things are still available, just hard to find and very expensive. It's a free market after all and the defining vector is bottom up. The next chapter is about democracy, which is there to serve the people too. Its defining vector is also bottom up, in theory anyway. The difference is you can't opt out. Imagine writing this to the Inland Revenue: 'Thanks for your letter last month explaining your income tax scheme. After much consideration, I have decided not to take up your offer . . . ' It's not optional, it's compulsory. Also, you make dozens of shopping choices every day, but you chose a government in a democracy only once every four years or so.

CHAPTER 6

The Flaws of Democracy

Auntie's ghastly Christmas present

Shopping is a selfish pleasure. Even if you are shopping at Christmas time, you will probably notice this. While you are looking for presents for other people, you can't help noticing things that you would like yourself. That presents a new challenge. Can you hint to your partner subtly enough? Then, if they buy it for you, it can still be a partial surprise. Maybe it's easier to just buy it for yourself anyway. It is one of life's most fundamental pleasures to spend your own money on yourself. That way you get exactly what you want. What is more, you are probably buying it at the right price. If you buy a present for someone else then the price is also right, but it may not be exactly what they want. The opposite of this is for someone to use your money to buy themselves a present. Suppose you lent them your credit card and sent them out shopping. They would get exactly what they want but you would probably be unhappy with the bill. Not a good outcome, but not the worst. The worst situation would be using other people's money to buy things for someone else. Then you can be pretty sure that it will be the wrong thing *and* the wrong price. Sounds like a bad idea? That's exactly what a government does.

Fans of small government use this argument to make their point. You get the best results when you spend your own money on yourself. You get the worst results when the government takes your money through taxes and then decides how to spend it. It will end up spending far too much on something no one wants. So government budgets and taxes should be as small as possible. You can't trust them with your money.

The argument only works because it draws a dividing line between you and the government, creating a 'them and us' mentality. If you oppose this argument you can exploit that. In theory, a democratic government is not separate from you. It exists to serve you. It reflects your wishes. It *is* you, so long as the 'you' is being used in a plural sense. This counter argument replaces 'them and us' with a single entity: justice because just 'us' (if you will forgive the pun). So a democratic government is not spending other people's money on things for someone else, it's spending our money on us. If you disagree then you are a mean-spirited loner with no sense of community.

You can see that the whole issue hinges on how representative the democratic government really is. Is it 'them' or 'us'? This is a cataxic issue. One argument asserts the boundary line between two levels, the other negates it. In this chapter, I want to look at this issue in more detail and examine the different forms of representative government. Along the way I want to discuss questions like this: Is populist politics bad? Can there be democracy without suffrage? Does the press represent the public interest better than politicians? How representative is democracy really?

The will of the people

The concept of democracy is easily grasped. The word comes from two Greek words: *demos* meaning people and *kratos* meaning power. So it literally means 'people power', more eloquently phrased by Abraham Lincoln in his Gettysburg Address as 'government of the people, by the people, for the people'. But while the concept is easy, the execution is quite hard. There are over forty different types democracy; some direct, some indirect and some a blend of the two. Democracy can be liberal or illiberal depending on whether the citizens have the rights of assembly and free speech. It can be parliamentary or presidential, depending on whether the head of state is elected or not and the degree of separation between the executive and the legislative. In some democratic systems candidates put themselves forward for election. In others, they are chosen at random through the drawing of lots, otherwise known as 'sortition'. Democracy can be multi party or non partisan depending on whether voters align themselves into party blocs. Some argue that a single party system can still fit under the democratic label. Others have put forward the concept of 'Totalitarian Democracy' as a legitimate concept, even though it seems like a contradiction in terms.

This large array of different variations and flavours of democracy demonstrates two things. First, transforming 'you singular' into 'you plural' is not as straightforward as it seems. There is cataxic friction between level one (the individual) and level two (the general public). There seems to be plenty of debate about the correct way to determine the 'will of the people'. What the market does effortlessly in the economic arena becomes a complex and strenuous task in the political arena. The second conclusion is that almost all governments in the modern world claim legitimacy in the name of the people. In earlier times, the concept of the Divine Right of Kings was prevalent: the ruler was appointed by God. Today, governments see their authority coming from below and not above. They represent the people's will, although the degree to which this is true is clearly debatable. The oxymoron of 'Totalitarian Democracy' effectively says the following: the state has the right to control everything and suppress dissent in the interest of the public good; citizens can vote but not participate in the decision-making process of government. Notice that the claim for legitimacy still derives from the general will.

The first democracy developed in Athens in 500BC. It was a direct democracy; citizens were able to vote and speak in the Assembly themselves, rather than through representatives. Officials were chosen at random from the populace through sortition. This works well in a small city state but has many practical problems in a large nation. The most common system in the West today is indirect or representative democracy. With this system, citizens elect others to represent them in the assembly or parliament rather than attending themselves. Direct democracy still exists in the cantons of Switzerland and in New England town meetings, and sortition is still used to select members for jury service. But for most people, 'democracy' now means representative democracy with candidates putting themselves forward for election. This has become so much the norm that many would view the other forms of democracy as peculiar fringe activities, or maybe not really democracy at all.

There has been a complacent certainty in the West that its form of representative democracy is the only true way to reflect the will of the people. This has become more shaky of late. The first troubling issue is voter apathy. The number of people eligible to vote and who actually bother to exercise this right has been steadily falling in most established democracies. Voter turnout in the UK has fallen from eighty per cent in 1960 to around sixty per cent today. In Japan, the numbers show a fall from seventy-five per cent to fifty per cent for the same period. In the US, voter turnout declined from sixty-three per cent in 1960, to fifty per cent in 2000, but have seen a uptick with the election of President Obama. On the other hand, elections in non-presidential years have seen voter turnouts fall right down to thirty-seven per cent. Low voter turnouts damage the legitimacy of representative democracy. It's hard to claim that you have a popular mandate from the people if only half of them bothered to show up. Some countries, such as Australia, Bolivia and Greece, deal with this issue by making voting compulsory. There is also an argument that low voter turnout does not matter. If people choose not to exercise their right to vote they are presumably content with the status quo. They are empowered to make change if they want to and that is the only important thing. This is a weak argument. Counting the silent middle ground as supporters is unsound. Absence of negative does not mean positive. Apathy is not the same as contentment. If you win a small majority in a country with fifty per cent voter turnout then, in effect, only one quarter of the eligible voters chose you. Do you really represent the will of the people?

What is behind this decline in voting? Opinion polls show that people often claim to be 'too busy' to vote. This does not really explain anything. It's just another way of saying 'voting is not high on my list of priorities' which the figures already tell us. Others point to a decline in civic activities generally: membership of social associations like bridge clubs, church groups and neighbourhood associations is also falling. They see the decline in voter turnout as part of this general antisocial trend as people retreat to the electronic cocoon of their homes to watch TV and play computer games. Right-wingers argue that the welfare state is to blame. Government interference in people's lives has eroded social capital. People no longer support each other in their community but apathetically expect the government to do it for them. This argument is not really supported by the facts. The welfare state is far larger in Germany than Japan, but the voter turnout rates are eighty per cent and fifty per cent respectively. The one common theme everywhere is that the decline in voter turnouts is concentrated amongst the young. Older generations still vote enthusiastically. The young seem disconnected from the process.

This leads us to the second troubling issue: the growing distance between the elected and the electorate. The sense of disconnect between the youth and the candidates may come from a feeling that politicians are a breed apart. They don't speak the same language as us. Looking at it from this perspective, voter apathy may reflect the supermarket problem: variety but no choice. There is no point in voting because they are all the same. The pithy slogan of the anarchists puts it best: No matter who you vote for, it's always the government that gets into power.

In earlier times, politics was not a full time job. It was not a career, but a temporary calling: A chance to take some time out to do your duty in public service and then, afterwards, get back to your other interests. In Britain, Members of Parliament did not start to receive salaries until 1911. In other words, Britain acquired and ran its vast empire with a bunch of part-time, unpaid gentlemen amateurs in charge. Even twenty years ago, almost all members of the cabinet in Britain had previous experience outside politics. Margaret Thatcher, for example, was a research chemist. Today, politicians are more likely to have spent their whole lives in the political bubble. They are career politicians through and through.

On the other hand, the rise of the professional should be no surprise. The shift from amateur to professional has been a general theme of the nineteenth century and has happened in many fields; science, sports, education and medicine. So what is all the fuss about? Isn't professionalism a good thing? In politics, it is probably not a good thing, for a number of reasons. First, voters live in the real economy so if you have never worked there how can you relate to them? You will inevitably be more distant from them. Second, experience outside politics should help you to make wiser decisions when pondering legislation inside. Lastly, and most importantly, there is an underlying conflict of interest. If politics is your career, then getting elected becomes your number one priority. Once you have achieved that, the next priority is getting re-elected. Your focus shifts from serving the people to serving yourself.

Getting re-elected means having a professional organisation and a well run political party. And a well run political party means focus groups. You can test out your policies in these laboratories of opinion and find the ones that play best. This insidious feedback loop has changed the dynamics of the process. What you believe becomes less important than what the public believes as determined by the focus group. It's like the Groucho Marx joke: 'Here are my principles. If you don't like them, I have others.'

This is why there is variety but no choice. Cars all look the same these days because they are designed in wind tunnels. The same eventual design emerges because it's the same set of physical constraints. There is no difference between designing cars and political policies. The focus group is the wind tunnel. In the election, voters are just getting an aerodynamically shaped, bullet-like projectile of their own views fired back at them. Maybe voter apathy is a completely rational response. Why bother voting when they already know what you think?

Unrepresentative democracy

The growing professionalism of party politics exposes the flaw at the heart of representative democracy. It is this: who are you representing? Who comes first, the voters or your party? Party politics effectively inserts an extra level into the hierarchy. In direct democracy, everything is on level one. Citizens directly participate themselves. Representative democracy creates level two. Citizens elect a representative who participates. Party politics adds level three. The party puts forward a candidate who the citizens then elect as a representative. So the three levels are these: the citizens, the candidate and the party. There is plenty of cataxic friction between these levels.

Let's take a simple example. Your party wants to expand the use of nuclear power. They want to build a new nuclear power station in your constituency but the locals are understandably against it. As their elected representative do you oppose the nuclear power station? Or as a party member do you support it? There is a clear conflict of interest. If you are a professional politician and the party funded your election campaign then you probably back the power station, even if it is against the wishes of your local voters. If you raised money locally yourself, then you would do the opposite. As they say in politics; follow the money. The power of the Party Whip is much stronger in the UK than the USA partly because of the differences in the source of funding.

We should note here that there are pros and cons with each method. If you raise money yourself locally then you will put local interests above national ones. This path leads to corruption and pork barrel politics. If the funding is done through a party mechanism and they appoint you as a candidate in a safe seat, you are more likely to put national or party interest above local ones. This makes politicians more distant from the local community and therefore less representative. It is reminiscent of the unit of selection issues in biology that we discussed in Chapter 4. Does selection happen at the level of the local voters or at the higher party level? In this case neither is particularly edifying. Local funding makes the US system prone to pork barrel politics. Party funding makes the UK system less representative.

The difference between a professional and an amateur is that professionals work for whoever pays them. And not only that, for professionals are also trying to build a career. Success means promotion to important posts; committee memberships or a cabinet position. Party whips use the promise of promotions or demotions to bully and cajole. Again, in the UK the party whips have more power in this respect because the legislative and executive branches of government are not separate. Promotion to the cabinet is a powerful lever. An amateur politician may happily spend some time as dissenting voice on the back benches. A professional one is more likely to follow the party line to get a senior position in government.

Party politics and politicians' growing professionalism means representative democracy is in danger of becoming unrepresentative democracy. This disconnect of the elected and the electorate has flipped the debating table on its side. The old defining vector of politics was horizontal: the battle between left and right. The new vector is vertical: the friction between politicians above and the populace below. Catataxis is the new political zeitgeist.

The recent elections in the UK and the USA in 2010 might lead you to believe that the two countries are on diverging paths. This is how it looks if you frame it in the old paradigm of left wing *v.* right wing. In Britain, the conservative party failed to gain a majority and were forced to dilute their right-wing policies by entering a coalition with the Liberal Democrats. So the pendulum of British politics is swinging to the left. In the USA mid-term elections the republicans triumphed, boosted by a grass roots rebellion from the Tea Party.

So the pendulum of US politics is swinging to the right. But this old horizontal framing device does not tell the real story. If you reframe it in catataxic terms, you will see the real issue is a vertical one.

In the 1980s the ideological battle between left and right was in full swing. In Britain, it was most forcefully expressed in the fight between Thatcher and the miners. Since the 90s and New Labour, politics has become ever more centrist. Whoever controls the centre rules the country. There is little difference between the policies of the three main parties because they are all sculpted in the same wind tunnel of public opinion. The coalition government between the right-wing Conservatives and the left-wing Liberal Democrats is the ultimate centrist construct. It is an un-opposable monolith because it internalises dissent. Since no party won out-right, both parties are free to change their manifestos and introduce policies that were not those that the electorate thought they were voting for. As a result, the electorate feels that promises have been broken. There is a growing sense of grievance that the coalition does not represent anyone and can do what it likes. Coalition governments have been commonplace for many years in Europe and elsewhere but, in Britain, this new type of government is an unfamiliar shock: A bucket of cold water in the grey dawn of a morning after. Once again, maybe the anarchists were right all along; no matter who you vote for it's always the government who gets into power.

In the US, this dissatisfaction with an unrepresentative government has a longer history. Newt Gingrich's *Contract with America* in 1994 channelled the anti-political mood of the voters and swept the Republicans back into Congress to execute a raft of reforming legislation. These reforms were aimed at making the government smaller and more accountable. They lowered taxes and promoted entrepreneurial activity. Nine of the ten bills in the contract were passed. Unfortunately, the one that was blocked was the proposal for term limits on congressmen. This would have devastated the political elite of incumbents. A twelve-year limit on the length of time served would have stopped professional politicians from having a lifelong career.

The frustration with 'beltway insiders' and the desire to sweep the scoundrels out of office is a common theme in US politics. It was the powering fuel behind President Obama's election campaign in 2008. His anti-incumbent message of hope and change caught the public imagination and he won office with sky high approval ratings. How ironic that two years later, in an echo of the 1994 Contract with America, he suffered so badly in the mid terms. In that short time, he had gone from being the reforming outsider to the incumbent target of the Tea Party movement. The message of this loose grass roots affiliation is a familiar one: smaller government, more accountability, lower taxes and back-to-basics constitutionalism.

So, both in the UK and the US, the dominant feeling of voters is disconnection: those in power don't represent us. They are in their own world and out of touch with what we want. The real question is what can be done about it? Direct democracy is a purer way of expressing the people's will but is unfeasible given the numbers and scale of a modern democracy. Many proposed solutions revolve around shrinking the scale and bringing things back to a local basis. But maybe it is time to turn the torch around and point it at the electorate and not the elected. Is it possible that voters' expectations are too high? Scale *is* an issue and it's *not* reversible. Maybe voters are luddites in a destructive rage, foolishly dreaming of an earlier, simpler time that we can never return to. Government is remote, self obsessed and unrepresentative of our views because that is the natural way of things. At this scale, that is how it is supposed to be. To complain about it is to make a catataxic fallacy. Government will never be the perfect reflection of the will of the people. It is made from voters' wishes, but it is a different thing entirely. It lives on a different level and therefore has different rules. We can state the proposal like this: Representative democracy is *not* the same as the will of the people. We can find evidence to support it by looking at the referendums on the EU constitution.

The battle for the EU Constitution

In 1957 the European Union is born when six countries sign the Treaty of Rome. Over the next fifty years, the treaty is amended many times through acts of accession as new countries join and formal agreements are signed in Schengen, Maastricht, Amsterdam and Nice. By June 2004 the EU has expanded to include twenty-five countries and its underlying treaties are a ramshackle patchwork of prolix legalese. So a plan is conceived to replace them with a single new treaty that will simplify and make more transparent the underlying principles of the union: a new European Constitution.

The new EU constitution is drafted by the former French president, Giscard d'Estaing. It is surprisingly long, in fact much longer than the patchwork of treaties it is designed to replace. The founding fathers of the USA managed to express themselves in a constitution of seven articles and a terse 4,600 words. In contrast, the EU constitution is thirty-five times bigger with 465 articles and 160,000 words. Buried in this thicket are some fairly major changes. It proposes that the EU should acquire all the symbols of statehood: a president, a foreign minister, an army, a judiciary, a national anthem and a flag. Most contentiously, it says for the first time that the laws of the Union take precedence over the laws of the nations beneath. The new treaty is signed on the 29 October 2004 by representatives of all the twenty-five member states. It then needs to be ratified before it can come into force. In some states, it can be just signed off by parliament. Others require a public referendum. A total of eight nations put the constitution to the vote: Spain, Portugal, France, Netherlands, Britain, Denmark, Ireland and Luxembourg.

Copies of the enormous document are sent out for the citizens of Europe to study. Some can't be bothered to read it, others receive it enthusiastically. In French Guiana (part of the EU as a *département d'outre-mer* of France) the Wayampi Indians are delighted. Shipped by helicopter and then canoe into the South American rainforest, the bulky documents are great for starting fires and wrapping tapir meat.[42] In France, books about the constitution top the bestseller lists with over a million copies sold. Finally on the day of the referendum, both in France and then the Netherlands, the opinion of the public is a resounding 'No'.

This is an astonishing defeat. The Eurocrats in Brussels can't believe it. Both countries were founder members of the EU. France is at the centre of the European project and the constitution was drafted by a Frenchman. Both governments spent millions of Euros of taxpayers' money on advertising to persuade the public to vote yes. Even more extraordinary is the fact that all the mainstream political parties in both countries were strongly in support of the

42 *Sunday Times*, 22 May 2005

constitution. Even the opposition parties were urging members to vote in its favour. The conclusion can only be that the votes in the referendum are a clear rebuke to the political classes. The will of the people is opposed not just to their elected government but also to the unelected opposition parties too.

To some, this is seen as a victory for people power. The EU is often cast as a gigantic anti-democratic monster because its officials are unelected and therefore unaccountable to voters. So to see the dragon slain by the shining knight of public opinion is a fairytale come true: democracy triumphant. On reflection, this needs qualification. It is a triumph for *direct* democracy but a failure for *representative* democracy. The elected governments supported the EU constitution but the referendum showed the will of the people was against it. So clearly, representative democracy is *not* the same as the will of the people. The EU referendum proves our original proposal.

How does the EU cope with this bombshell from the electorate? Some Eurocrats try to argue that the 'no' vote was really a 'yes'. They claim that some voters may have rejected the constitution because it does not go far enough down the path of a united Europe. Jean-Claude Juncker, the EU Council President, claims that if you add up all the votes of those who wanted 'more Europe' they would outnumber those against it. But the bureaucrats take a more pragmatic approach. They reformulate the constitution as an amending treaty: the Lisbon Treaty. This is duly signed and comes into force in 2009.

So did the public referendums of 2004 make any difference? Not really. The EU as a higher level entity follows its own rules. If national democracy is not really that representative then why should you expect a supranational entity, which is one step more removed, to be so. Accusing the EU of being unrepresentative is like complaining that a ruler is too straight or a lake is too wet. That is what it is. It is an entity that arises from the wishes of the people, but like all emergent phenomena it is not the same thing as the stuff that it is made of. By moving up a level it becomes something different. If you complain about that, you are making a catataxic fallacy.

As we saw in the last chapter, the will of the people is like a murmuration of starlings. It is not static and very hard to pin down. It flits and soars. It shatters, coalesces and then re-fragments. So if you want a referendum to come up with the right answer you just need to get your timing right. It's like a photographer waiting for that perfect shot. If you sit there looking through the viewfinder long enough, sooner or later you will get it: that perfect pattern of starlings against the sullen evening sky. Then, *snap*, and it's yours.

Consider Ireland. It has rejected EU treaties not once, but twice. And both times, a later second referendum came back with the opposite result. To the envy of citizens in many other countries, the Irish Constitution requires a referendum to ratify any changes in EU sovereignty. In 2001 the Treaty of Nice proposes changes to better integrate Eastern Bloc countries. Ireland is the only country to hold a referendum. In June 2001, Irish voters reject the treaty with a small majority and thirty-four per cent turnout. Just over a year later, in October 2002, a second referendum on the Treaty is held. This time over half the country turns out to vote and it passes with sixty per cent in favour. So when the Lisbon Treaty is rejected by Irish voters in June 2008, the Eurocrats know what to do: wait and try again. Sure enough, in October 2009, when the Treaty is presented again in a second referendum it passes. The vote has swung from fifty-three per cent against to sixty-seven per cent in favour in just over a year.

Critics of direct democracy point to this fickle behaviour as evidence to support their case. How can you run a country if you keep chopping and changing like that? The unstable whim of the general public is not a good basis for policy. You need consistency and long term vision to govern. The public is whipped up by short term emotionalism; better to leave government to the considered judgement of elected representatives, they conclude. In this argument, representative democracy provides a vital smoothing function. The government acts like a statistical moving average that evens out the sudden irrational lurches of public opinion. Statistics is like democracy in that you are getting one thing to represent many. In statistics, it is a numerical average: in politics, it is an elected representative. Both smooth out the churning chaos of the level beneath.

There is a problem with this. As we saw in Chapter 3 with the Climategate scandal, calculating the average is always contentious. It may not be wrong but it is always controversial. The presentation of statistical evidence to support the case for global warming soon descended into a bitter argument about statistical methodology. Had the numbers been doctored? In politics, similar debates about numerical methodology are common. The mathematics of voting is more complicated than you may think.

Four men, one vote

In 2009, Andy Roddick plays Roger Federer in the Wimbledon men's finals. Roddick has lost to Federer in these same finals twice in the past, so he hopes it will be 'third time lucky'. He plays the game of his life. It lasts for over four hours and is the longest final in Wimbledon history. Roddick has not lost his service once; but then in the 77th game of the match, Federer breaks his serve and wins the fifth set 16–14. That means Federer is Wimbledon champion again for the fifteenth time. The cruel twist is that Roddick has lost the match, despite winning more games. He won 39 games and Federer only won 38. That's how scoring works in tennis. Games are grouped into sets. You have to win the most sets, regardless of how many games beneath them you have won or lost.

In 2010, in the first round of Wimbledon there is an even more epic match which lasts for three days. In the end, John Isner beats Nicholas Mahut with the final set tie break going to the un-precedented score of 70–68. If you add up the total number of points scored, Mahut wins 502 to Isner's 478. But despite winning more points, Mahut still loses. Those are the rules. Four points make a game, six points make a set. A simple majority does not win because of the way points are broken up and grouped.

Voting in elections is like that too. Just like tennis, you can win the most votes and still lose. Tennis has sets; representative democracy has seats. All points don't have the same value, and all votes don't have the same value. This comes as a shock to those who believe democracy means 'one man, one vote'. In Britain, a recent study[43] showed that the average power of a single vote is more like 0.25 per cent. In other words, 'four men, one vote'.

It all depends on how you add the votes up. A proportional representation method tries to even out the votes by matching seats to overall totals. In contrast, a 'first past the post' method, used in the UK, USA, Canada and India, just looks at the majority in each

43 New Economics Foundation, Voter Power Index 2005

seat. Tennis is a first past the post system. You only count the games and the sets, the actually number of points does not matter. Likewise in an election, you count up the seats. In a first past the post system, you discard the number of votes beneath. Let's look at an example. Imagine there are two parties, red and blue, and three seats. The blue party wins two of the seats with a small majority of fifty-one per cent in each case. But it loses badly in the third seat only getting ten per cent of the votes. It becomes the elected government because it has the majority of seats; it has two and the red party has one. But the red party got the most votes overall. It narrowly loses in two seats and wins by a huge majority in the third. In total, it wins sixty-three per cent of the vote but still loses the election. This result is clearly against the wishes of the general public, so you can see why some observers think the 'first past the post' system is profoundly undemocratic.

Proportional representation (PR) tries to redress this balance. The party list system, used in over seventy countries, allocates seats based on the percentage of votes each party receives. The party makes a list of candidates in a preferred order. Its share of the vote determines how far down the list it gets. Critics of this system say it's undemocratic because you are voting for a party and not a person. It gets a representative result at the national level but not at the local level. Other PR systems try to keep the link between votes and specific candidates. The 'single transferrable vote' system used in Ireland, Malta and Scotland has multiple candidates for each constituency. In effect, it turns each constituency into a mini-nation. Voters rank their preferences, each preference is counted and more than one candidate is elected. The downside is that it is very complicated to work out.

Another variation is the 'alternative vote' system. This is used in Australia and requires candidates to get fifty per cent of the vote to get elected. If no one gets this in the first round, the least popular candidate drops out and the vote is recalculated including second preferences. The process continues until someone gets more than fifty per cent. The benefit of the system is that winners have to have a clear majority. The downside is that, like the first past the post system, minority votes are discarded at the very end of the process.

The ideal system would be the best of both worlds. The best thing about 'first past the post' is the strong link between the voter and the candidate at the constituency level (level one). The best thing about proportional representation is that the will of the people is properly reflected at the national level (level two). There is cataxic friction between these two levels. The 'additional member system', used in Germany, New Zealand and Mexico, tries to get around this by combining both systems. Members who are elected in a straight constituency fight are then topped up with others through a proportional system. It may be theoretically the best system, but in practice it is very confusing for voters.

Identity politics

As you can see, the mathematics of voting systems gets quite complicated. Each different system has enthusiastic supporters and vocal critics arguing about how representative it is. But there is another angle to representation; not mathematical but human. You want the person representing you to have similar views and opinions to yourself; you want him to be *someone like you*. This introduces another area of cataxic friction, often known as identity politics. It is summed up in a question like this: why aren't there more female, black, Asian or gay members of the government?

The intentions behind identity politics are wholly laudable: to give a voice to an oppressed minority that is excluded from the mainstream. It is hard to find any grounds to argue against that sentiment. The problem comes when trying to do this in practice in a representative democracy. Identity politics makes two implicit assumptions. First, that the representative must come from that minority, and second, that all members of that minority think the same way.

This is similar to the taxonomy issue we discussed in Chapter 3. By classifying something, you are throwing away information. A taxonomist creates a new species by identifying a type specimen. This individual plant or animal is then preserved in the library as the representative of the species. Other members of the species are similar to this type specimen but not identical. When the taxonomist is asked to classify a new plant, he will look at the different type specimens in the library and decide which one it is closest to. By classifying it, he is emphasising the similarities and ignoring the differences. So by informing us that: 'This plant belongs to the species *Fritillaria meleagris*,' he is in fact eliminating information.

We have two levels here. The physical plant (level one) and the conceptual category of the species (level two). The type specimen is the representation of the species in physical form: level two made manifest in level one. We can contrast this with a map which is the reverse of this situation. There is the physical landscape (level one) and the conceptual representation of it in the form of a map (level two). Moving from level one to level two still involves discarding information: the cartographer only selects certain features to put on his map and discards the others. The resulting map is, in effect, level one made manifest at level two. This is the inverse of the type specimen. To summarise, a type specimen and a map are both representative objects but on different levels. A type specimen represents *down* and a map represents *up*.

The problem at the heart of identity politics is catataxis. It requires the representative to be both a type specimen and a map, therefore confusing the two different levels. The first assumption that identity politics makes is this: only members of the minority group can speak for the minority group. In other words, the representative must be a type specimen. The flaw in this logic is that the representative must speak for all the voters, not just the minority voters. That means that the minority group member, when elected, must also speak for the majority. If a minority group member is able to do this, then why can't a majority group member do so too, but the other way around. Either representatives speak for everyone, in which case it does not matter which group they are from, or they don't speak for everyone, in which case they are not representative. The second flawed issue for identity politics is the idea that members of a minority all think the same way. In this case, the representative metaphorically becomes a map. But the identity politics map is monochromatic and covered with a single repetitive symbol. It is not a good representation of the richness and diversity of the landscape.

The contorted salamander

So representative democracy has many problems. Some of them are mathematical because not all votes are equal. Some of them are human because the representative may, or may not, properly represent your views. But at least there is one good thing we can all agree on: in a democracy we have the right to chose. We, the general public, pick who our elected representatives will be. The underlying principle is that *we* select *them* . . . Unfortunately, this is not always the case. In fact, some argue that *they* select *us*. How does this travesty take place? It happens through a process known as gerrymandering.

In 1812, Governor Eldridge Gerry is redrawing the boundaries of the districts in a Massachusetts state senate election. By carefully deciding where to draw the boundary lines he can ensure that his party has a majority. The electoral map ends up with an extraordinary elongated shape. This curious object looks a bit like a contorted salamander. The local press, the *Boston Gazette*, writes a mocking article about 'Governor Gerry's Salamander' which becomes shortened to 'Gerrymander'. In the election, Governor Gerry is voted out of office by voters who are enraged by his blatant cheating. But the name sticks and comes to mean any electoral district where the boundaries have been manipulated for political gain.

Regular states, irregular districts
A bad case of gerrymandering in Arizona

Redistribution or redistricting of the boundaries of electoral districts happens on a regular basis, typically every ten years or so. There are sound demographic reasons for this. Populations move, towns grow, cities wax and wane. As a result, boundaries need to be redrawn to make sure there are a similar number of voters in each district. Towns that have grown may be subdivided. Those that have shrunk will be lumped together with others. The committee that oversees the redrawing of the boundaries is supposed to be impartial. But it will not surprise you to know that the process is often rancorous and bitterly fought, ending in political horse trading and back-room deals. There is so much at stake. A small detour of the boundary line can transform a safe seat into a majority for the opposition.

In a perfect world, with no political manipulation of the boundary line, electoral districts would be rectangular, or at least simple, smooth-sided polygons. A simple mathematical algorithm can generate a map that splits a region into districts of equal population density. In the real world, particularly in the USA, electoral districts look nothing like this. Arizona is a good example. The shape of the state itself is childishly simple: straight lines on three sides and the Colorado River on the fourth. But even though the state boundaries look as though they have been drawn with a ruler, the congressional boundaries inside are an extraordinary meandering maze. It should be a simple task to divide what is essentially a rectangle into eight parts, but these boundaries look like some beetles were dunked in ink and left to crawl randomly across the page.

A more egregious example is the reorganisation of the thirty-two congressional districts in Texas in 2003. The boundaries are completely redrawn with some ending up as long, thin winding strips. District 25 becomes 250 miles long from north to south, but at one point only three miles wide. It delivers the required result. Previously, the Democrats had a 17 to 15 majority. After the gerry-mandering, the Republicans lead by 21 to 11. This manipulation is so brazen that it is later struck down by the Supreme Court in 2006. In the most extreme examples of gerrymandering, the congressional district is in two completely separate parts. District 4 in Illinois and District 13 in New Jersey are examples. They don't even have the integrity of being contiguous wholes. Clearly the politicians are picking the voters and not the other way around.

The best of a bad bunch

Most of democracy's flaws are catataxic and revolve around the problem of getting an individual to represent the group. Having spent so much time criticising democracy, it is worth looking at other political systems in comparison. Winston Churchill once said: 'Democracy is the worst form of government apart, of course, from all the others.' How do the others stack up? Is democracy really the best of a bad bunch?

The alternative to democracy is totalitarianism which comes in two flavours: communism and fascism. Historically, these have been seen as two extremes on a horizontal scale. Communism is on the extreme left, democracy in the middle and fascism on the extreme right. This is a slightly awkward model because communism and fascism have many things in common. So it is sometimes refined from a straight line to a horizontal ring. You travel round the curve and eventually extreme communism and fascism meet each other in a totalitarian hell somewhere round the back.

I think it is time to junk this model and replace it with a vertical one; a catataxic one. We can start by observing that the roots of fascism are not right wing but left wing. In 1919, Mussolini is a prominent Italian socialist. When he founds his *Fasci di Combattimento* in Italy, it is not a renunciation of socialism but a rejection of internationalism. The same distinction is made by Hitler with his National Socialist, or Nazi, party. This is the first distinction on the vertical axis. Fascists and Nazis have a national focus while Communists are international (the clue is in their anthem *The Internationale*).

The second distinction on the vertical axis is class. Communism is an expression of working-class idealism. Sharing in times of adversity is an effective survival strategy. Hardship brings people together. The rule of the commune is 'from each according to their ability, to each according to their need'. The vision of communism was to take this small scale kernel of truth and expand it into an international movement. It is the scaling up that is the problem. It is a catataxic fallacy. What works for a small group of people does not even work at a national level, let alone an international one.

Fascism is an expression of middle-class idealism. If hardship brings people together, then prosperity tends to make them more selfish. The focus shifts from what you are giving to what you are getting. The sense of 'us *v.* them' intensifies. Foreigners and other undesirables fall into the 'them' category. You become more convinced of the righteousness of your personal view. You crave order and tidiness and long for 'common sense' solutions to be forcibly imposed to cut through all the bullshit. (The 'bullshit' here being the messy debate with minorities who don't share your view.) Sooner or later come the book burnings, concentration camps and gas ovens. The catataxic fallacy here is the expansion of the sense of individual righteousness to encompass the whole nation.

So you can see two sets of vertical conflicts between Communism and Fascism here: international *v.* national and working class *v.* middle class. Underlying both is the third, which is individual *v.* group. Both systems claim their acts to reflect the will of the people. It's right there in their names. Communism means 'the way of the commune' which is synonymous with 'the wishes of the group'. Fascism takes its name from a bundle of sticks; the Roman *fasces*. It is emblematic of strength in unity. One stick may be broken easily where many bound together in a bundle may not. It is the symbol of the will of the people of Rome.

Neither Communism nor Fascism has any explicit mechanism for determining the will of the people. The rulers merely assert that they act in their name. To those brought up in a democratic tradition this seems illegitimate. Democracy, at least, has a demonstrable mechanism for discovering the will of the public, even though it is flawed. In the 1930s Fascism was seen as an improved form of democracy; one where the flaws had been removed. It is worth remembering that Hitler was actually voted into power in 1933. Though totalitarianism is seen as the ultimate system of top down control, Hitler thought of it as a bottom up expression of the people's will. 'The state does not command us, we command the state,' he famously says in *The Triumph of the Will*, the documentary film of the 1934 Nuremberg rally. Read that line again and it sounds like a perfect encapsulation of a democracy. It's just democracy without the voting: non-suffrage democracy.

The mandate of heaven

Non-suffrage democracy? It sounds ridiculous, like bubble free champagne or a decaffeinated double espresso. But the idea still has some traction in Europe. In fact, that is the best way to describe the EU. European countries are all democratic, but the leaders of the EU are unelected. The EU is a symbol of democracy without the voting. It is a supranational entity. As we discussed earlier, the voting process is an irrelevant inconvenience that can be bypassed and manipulated by the technocrats. Catataxis means recognising that different rules operate at different levels. Maybe, at the EU level, voting *is* irrelevant. We can buttress this argument by looking at another entity of similar size on the other side of the world: China.

Some western observers are still obsessed with the notion that China is a 'communist' country. That may be what the label says, but labels are often misleading. The Holy Roman Empire[44] was neither holy, nor Roman, nor even an empire. The same criticism can be made for Japan's Liberal Democratic Party. Nobody could think that North Korea is really a Democratic Republic even though that is its official name. China is communist in name only. The vigorous dynamism of its capitalist economy bears no resemblance to the old Soviet model. This has prompted some to go to the other extreme and label China as a fascist state. They point to the rampant nationalism, the racism, concentration camps and the suppression of free speech and draw parallels with the Third Reich.

There is the third and more ingenious argument: China is in fact a democracy. There is vigorous political debate in China but you have to be a communist party member to participate. Every five years at the National Congress, committee members are elected and there is voting on the direction of policy. There are eighty million members of the Communist party, which means there are more voters in China than in any country in Europe. If you look at it on a proportional basis, five per cent of the population is eligible to vote. In ancient Greece only a certain type of male citizen could vote; women, slaves and foreigners were excluded. In effect, this meant suffrage extended to only five per cent of the population. So China's democracy is similar to that of ancient Greece, democracy's birthplace and arguably its purest expression. It is also worth

---

44 The Holy Roman Empire was a loose collection of German principalities in the Middle Ages.

pointing out that universal suffrage is a fairly recent phenomenon. For most of democracy's history, voting was restricted to property owning males. For example, in Britain as late as 1850 only fourteen per cent of the population had the right to vote.

As you can see, you can call China many things: Communist, Fascist or Democratic. But these are external labels and western concepts and it is better to try and understand China in its own terms, through the concept of the 'mandate of heaven'. In the past, emperors in China are seen to have this mandate. The 'heaven' in question is not the domain of a Christian God but one based on Confucian ideals of justice, harmony and social order. A good emperor has the mandate of heaven because he rules justly. A bad emperor loses the mandate and injustice, social upheaval and disorder follow. Then, of course, a good emperor comes along, claims the mandate of heaven and founds a new dynasty. The important point to note is that the mandate does not come from God but from the people; if they are unhappy then the emperor loses his mandate.

Chairman Mao founded the Peoples Republic of China on 1 October 1949. In his speech in Tiananmen Square he famously said, 'The Chinese people have stood up'. With these words he was claiming the mandate of heaven, and in effect founding a new dynasty. The location was highly symbolic. Tiananmen literally means 'the Gate of Heavenly Peace' or in other words, 'the place for receiving the mandate of heaven'. Since 1420, emperors have legitimised themselves upon this spot. That is why it is also the favoured place for political protest, as in the televised riots of 1989. If the mandate comes from the people, then this is also where it can be revoked.

The 'mandate of heaven' is different from the similar sounding western concept the 'divine right of kings'. Both attempt to claim legitimacy in the name of a higher power. The divine right of the king is unconditional; he can do whatever he wants because he is appointed by God.[45] In contrast, the mandate of heaven is conditional upon the just ruling of the emperor and can therefore be removed. However, there is no explicit mechanism for its

---

45 In practice, of course, as Charles I and Louis XVI found out, monarchs who push it too far get their heads chopped off by revolutionaries.

removal. It can only be recognised retrospectively. If a revolution is successful then the mandate is deemed to have been passed on. This makes it a very fluid and pragmatic type of legitimacy, almost 'might is right'.

The shogunate system in Japan is an interesting fusion of the hereditary divine right and the mandate of heaven. If legitimacy comes from a divine being, then it passes down the blood line. But if you have a hereditary emperor then how can the mandate of heaven be revoked? The answer is the Shogun system. The emperor retains an unbroken bloodline but has no power. The shogun has the power, but can be overthrown by the people. It's just like a constitutional monarchy apart from the fact that the Shogun is not elected.

The mandate of heaven is a type of non-suffrage democracy whose basic tenets run like this: An individual should not oppose authority. To do so is to be selfish and to put yourself above others. The interests of the group are more important than yours. The purpose of authority is to keep harmony and order. Disorder is a sign that the interests of the group are not being upheld. Therefore those in authority have become illegitimate and it is time for the mandate to pass to someone else. My local beekeeper tells me his hives are run on the same principal. Normally, bee hives are an environment of order and harmony. You see it in the perfect stacking hexagons in the honey combs, the busy workers humming contentedly and the efficient separation of allotted tasks. But once the Queen begins to do her job badly, the workers will kill her and create a new one.

The most important point about the mandate of heaven is its pragmatism. The early years of the Peoples Republic of China were ones of harsh totalitarian control. Mao chillingly says in 1956 that the Chinese people are 'a clean sheet of paper on which only the newest and most beautiful words will be written'. But this proves to be only a brief passing phase. History soon reasserts itself and it is clear that traditional Chinese culture has not been erased. The astonishing economic growth in China in the last twenty-five years is a sign that the government is fulfilling the mandate of heaven; not through applying top down control but by relaxing it. The government's task is to deliver economic growth to keep the people happy, just like everywhere else. This only comes by freeing up the natural entrepreneurialism of the Chinese. This bottom up pragmatism is best summed up in the motto, as true now as in ancient times: heaven is high and the emperor is far away.

Democracy of the elders

There are many other cultures besides the Chinese where group harmony is valued more than individual interests. Africa is a good example. African culture has a strong tradition of respect for elders. You can see this in the way a typical village is run: when there is a problem the village elders sit around and talk about it until they agree. Western style democracy sits uneasily in this context because majority rule ignores the minority. In an election, if the winner gets fifty-one per cent of the votes and the loser forty-nine per cent, then that is not necessarily a mandate. How can you run a village when just under half of it is unhappy? Western observers view the many one party states in Africa as undemocratic. African leaders respond that absence of an opposition party does not mean absence of democracy. In fact, it is a better form of democracy, for Africa at least, because the will of *all* the people is being expressed, discussed and accommodated for. The elders, through their experience and wisdom, are able to balance out differences in opinion and forge pragmatic compromises.

This government by consensus filtered through the oldest and the wisest is extremely effective in a village. The difficulties come when you try to scale it up to a national level. In that sense, African democracy is a cataxic problem. A nation is too big to run on village lines. The larger the scale becomes, the greater the risk of greed and corruption: there is less scrutiny and a bigger jackpot. In a village, your elders live amongst you. You can see what they do every day. In a presidential palace, surrounded by armed guards, they can do as they please. Without the checks and balances of a formal opposition party, who will do the scrutiny?

In answer, in some cases, is a supranational group of elders. These 'global village elders' have had some success on the global stage. The African Union sponsors a 'Panel of Eminent Africans', headed by Kofi Annan, which successfully mediated a ceasefire and power sharing deal in Kenya in 2008. Likewise, Nelson Mandela's group, 'The Elders', has helped ease tensions in Sudan and Zimbabwe. These groups have no formal power but can have a lot of influence. They have moral authority.

The fourth estate

In China and in Africa we see two possible examples of non-suffrage democracy, where the will of the people is expressed without voting. But there is another example of a group that claims to reflect the will of the people without being elected: the press. This is sometimes referred to as the 'fourth estate'. There are three estates in the British Parliament: the Lords Spiritual, The Lords Temporal and the Commons. Thomas Carlyle pointed out in 1840 that there was a fourth estate, more important than the other three, in the Reporter's Gallery. The press scrutinises the government and therefore acts in the public interest. Like the village elders, it has moral authority. By acting in the public interest, it claims the mandate of heaven.

Is the fourth estate more powerful than the other three? If you look at the Watergate scandal, the answer should be yes. President Nixon was forced out of office through the patient investigative reporting of the *Washington Post*. If you look at the row in Britain over the Iraq dossier you may be not so sure. This was a report about Iraq's Weapons of Mass Destruction published by the British Government in 2002. Its startling contents helped sway parliament into voting to go to war. A BBC reporter claimed it had been 'sexed up' by spin doctors. In the subsequent row, the journalist's source, David Kelley, committed suicide and the journalist, the Director General and the Chairman of the BBC were all forced to resign. Later inquiries have shown that the dossier was indeed 'sexed up' and we now know that all the allegations about WMDs were untrue. So, in effect, the government lied and got away with it and the press were beaten. The difference between the Watergate scandal and the Iraq WMD scandal is the power of the spin doctor. (This is something we will examine further in Chapter 9.)

The press acts in the public interest and is unelected. But there is a feedback mechanism that legitimises them: viewers or readership figures. The public is effectively voting with its money or its time. So a widely read newspaper or a popular TV programme can legitimately claim to represent the general populace. If people disagreed they would not read or watch it. That's why a free press is recognised as one of the bulwarks of democracy. In fact, press freedom is probably more important than voting. A one party state may claim to be acting in the interest of all the people, but if the press is not free, then how do they know what the people think? China or a one party African state are undemocratic, not because there is no voting, nor because there is no opposition, but because the press is not free.

A free press is powerful. But the feedback loop between the press and the public makes it very hard to determine where that power lies. Some see the newspaper proprietor as a shaper of public opinion, as depicted in *Citizen Kane* when Orson Wells' monstrous press baron says: 'The people will think what I tell them to think'. This fictional character was modelled on William Randolph Hearst, the biggest press magnate of all time. When told by one of his reporters in 1897 that there was no war in Cuba, he replied: 'You furnish the pictures, I will furnish the war'. Rupert Murdoch was once popularly believed to have the power to make or break British governments.

Others recognise that editors of newspapers are desperate to increase circulation, and therefore not the masters of public opinion but their servants. They print what is popular and are always chasing the zeitgeist: not leaders but followers. Both this bottom up argument and the top down one are partially true. The main point is that this creates a feedback loop, like the howl on an unguarded microphone which distorts issues beyond their natural perspective. A small issue can easily be blown up out of all proportion. Journalism is an amplifier that both speaks for the people and fuels the mob.

The madness or wisdom of crowds

In these last two chapters we have been discussing the will of the people. The prices in the marketplace reflect their aspirations. The votes in a referendum reflect their opinion. A democratic election reflects their considered judgment. But down in the basement something sinister lurks: the mob that reflects their brutish lust. An angry mass of protesters can be a terrifying thing. The barriers of individual responsibility melt away like wax in a honeycomb leaving a sticky inchoate mess of emotional energy. From defenceless minorities to dictators and kings, all know that the mob is something to be feared.

Mob rule is the opposite of civilisation. It is the triumph of passion over reason: A beast-like collective that amplifies the lowest in all of us. In Ancient Rome, emperors can only rule by keeping the mob fed and distracted by brutal games in the coliseum. When the mob demands the head of a public official they mean it literally. They will only be appeased when that decapitated object is thrown into their mass. Likewise with the *sans-culottes* in the French Revolution, and the spontaneous lynch mobs of the American West. The Salem Witch Trials in 1692 are a more spiritual expression of mob rule but still end in nineteen people being executed in defiance of all law and logic.

There is, however, another side to the mob: One that expresses not popular delusions and madness, but wisdom. Frances Galton, a British statistician and cousin of Charles Darwin, first notices the effect in a country fair in 1906. In a competition to guess the weight of an ox, the average of all the uninformed guesses is remarkably accurate. Using the estimates of a random sample of people proves more accurate than listening to the experts. This effect is linked to our old friend the bell curve. The peak of the curve coincides almost exactly with the actual weight of the ox.

How is it that a mass of uninformed people can beat the acknow-ledged experts? That's the power of statistical aggregation. The general public may be uninformed, but that does not mean they are stupid. In fact, collectively they are very wise. It is that wisdom that is expressed in a democracy or in a marketplace. Politicians know they won't last long if they go against the public will. So do punters in the stock market. The most effective strategies when investing are often just following the momentum of the crowd. Don't try to outsmart the market, go with it. Or as the traders put it more succinctly: 'the trend is your friend'.

The accuracy of collective intelligence is put to good effect in prediction exchanges, like the Iowa Electronic Markets. These operate like a stock market but people bet on non-financial items, such as the outcome of a political election or what next week's unemployment figure will be. It's like a fusion of an opinion poll and a betting shop. The results are remarkably accurate and seem better predictors of the future than either of those other two methods.

There is one important caveat. The 'wisdom of crowds' effect only works when people have independent views. In other words, people need to be expressing their own thoughts rather than being swayed by the opinion of others. Throw an acknowledged expert into the mix and she is likely to distort everyone else's view, bending them towards her own. So the expert, if he is allowed to pontificate, will make the results less accurate. A statistician would put it this way: if the data samples are not independent, the aggregates will be distorted. In other words, experts make things worse.

This highlights the danger of the journalistic feedback loop. If people's opinions are being fed back to them through the press, their views become less independent. The wise crowd becomes more stupid and eventually turns into a mob of like-minded bigots. The best results come from a diversity of individual views bubbling up from below. The press reflects the opinion of the people, but in doing so ends up manipulating it too.

There is a tendency for the press to be nationalistic. Since they only publish things of interest to their readers, and the readers always have nationality in common, newspapers tend to be engines of nationalism. The nation state is the topic for our next chapter.

CHAPTER 7

The Death of the Nation State

A trip beyond Pale

Bosnia. You are in a taxi going from Sarajevo to Pale eleven miles away. You are taking the scenic route, up through the mountains that hosted the Winter Olympics in 1984. Half way up the steep, winding road the taxi comes to a stop. The driver turns his head to look over his shoulder. His wrinkling face gives you an apologetic, gap-toothed smile. He gets out of the car and starts rummaging around at the back of the vehicle. First you think it's some sort of breakdown. Has the mountain road proved too much for the car? Then you realise what he is doing. He is changing the number plates.

Since the Dayton Accord ended the war in Bosnia, the country has been run by the Office of the High Representative under the auspices of the EU. Over the last fifteen years there have been seven High Representatives: two Austrians, a Slovak, a Swede, a German, a Brit and a Spaniard. Beneath this High Representative is the President of Bosnia and Herzegovina; elected by the populace, this is the official Head of State. However, there is not a single president, but three of them: a Bosniak, a Serb and a Croat. This matches the main ethnic divisions of the country. On the next level below this, the country is split into two parts of roughly equal size: the Republika Srpska and the Bosnian Federation. Their territories match the ground held by the Serbs and the Muslims at the end of the war. Each of these two entities has its own presidents and government structures which in practice are stronger than those of the State. The Bosnian Federation is then further spilt into ten Cantons which, like Switzerland, have independent government structures.

This complex multilayered political confection could only have been cooked up by bureaucrats. Take the Canton of Una-Sana. Its capital city is Bihac and its Head of Government is Hamdija

Lipovača. It has its own flag, coat of arms, airport and ten different local municipalities. To the outside observer it looks like a country in its own right, but there is still a federation and then a state above it. Then there are two layers of elected presidents higher up the cake and an EU bureaucrat as a crowning cherry on the top. So many hierarchical levels in such a tiny region: Bosnia is smaller than Scotland, both in area and population.

To be fair, the EU is keen to pass the powers of the High Representative downwards but there are so many unresolved issues, this is proving difficult. The Dayton Accord brought a bitter ethnic war to an end with a political structure that was designed to promote multiculturalism. If anything, the ethnic boundaries have become more entrenched. Serbs have relocated to the Republika Srpska and Bosnians likewise to the Bosnian Federation. These two entities are becoming ethnically homogeneous nations inside the larger state, a bit like Belgium. But at least in Belgium taxi drivers don't have to change their number plates as they drive around the country. Not yet, anyway. In Bosnia, if your car looks like it comes from the wrong part of the country it is likely to get vandalised.

The sovereignty of the nation state

Bosnia is so complicated it is hard to figure out what to call it: country, nation or state. These three words are often used inter-changeably. For example, the United Nations' website describes itself as being 'founded by 51 countries in 1945 . . . and now provides a forum for 192 member states'. In fact nation, country and state all mean different things as the Latin roots of these words illustrate. Nation comes from the Latin *natio* meaning 'to be born', and refers to a group of people. Country comes from the Latin *contra* meaning 'against' and refers to an area of land with a defined border. Why against? Because at the border, two countries lie against each other. State comes from the Latin *status* whose meaning in English is the same. State refers to the status or power of the government. So a State is an organised community living under one government.

You can have a nation without having a state; think of the Cherokees, the Roma or even the Celtic Fringe.[46] These groups

---

46 The Celtic Fringe is Scotland, Ireland, Wales, Cornwall, Brittany and
    Galicia which share Celtic cultures and languages.

are defined through cultural and racial ties rather than land ownership or government. You can have a state without a country; think
of Palestine or the Free French government in exile, based in
London in World War II. You can be a country without being
a state; Scotland and Wales are countries that are part of the
sovereign state of the United Kingdom. But not all states are
sovereign. A state may transfer some of its sovereign powers to the
higher entity of a federal government. If so, it becomes a federated
state as in the USA or Germany.

Each of the three words is an attempt to describe the fourth
rung on the ladder of society. The bottom three rungs are the
individual, the family and the local community. What should you
call the next rung up? If you are considering race or culture as the
defining characteristic you would call it a nation. If your concerns
were territorial you would call it a country. If you were focusing
on who rules the people you would call it a state. In this chapter,
in an attempt to combine these issues together, we will call it the
nation state.

There used to be an easy certainty that people of the same race
lived in the same place and were ruled over by their unique sovereign.
Nation, country and state were the same thing and they were
embodied in a single person; in the words of Louis XIV, the Sun
King of France, 'L'etat c'est moi'. But in the modern world,
multiculturalism and globalisation make things much more complicated. The three terms are drifting apart. Like poor registration
in a newspaper picture, the three 'colours' are misaligned and the
image is blurred and confusing.

A second historical trend is the shift in the seat of sovereignty.
Over time it passes from God to the State and then from the State
to the Self. In the mediaeval era, God is sovereign and Kings rule in
his name. The Protestant reformation and subsequent civil wars
and revolutions put God to one side and make the state sovereign:
the divine right of kings is ended. Later, in 1859, John Stuart Mill
publishes *On Liberty* which proclaims the individual sovereign over
himself. This hugely influential work is the wellspring of liberal
political thought. Liberal democracies with universal suffrage are
widespread today; the individual is self-sovereign.

As we saw in the last chapter, the self sovereign individual cedes
his power to the government through various flawed mechanisms,

some democratic, some not. But in all cases, the sovereignty of the nation state stems from the people. In this chapter, we examine the nation state and the catataxic issues of this fourth rung on the social ladder. A nation state is a geographic, political and cultural entity. It functions as a sovereign territorial unit. International relations between nation states occur at a different level from personal ones. They are overseen by diplomats and have a separate set of conventions and practices. These are different from the normal codes of personal intercourse. When two diplomats chat informally, they are interacting on level one. When they discuss things formally, they are interacting on level four.

We will look at the history of the nation state: how it came to be, why it is under threat and what comes next. We will also examine issues such as: What power does the nation state have? Is the nation state is past its sell-by date? How serious is the threat from above with supranational bodies such as the EU. What about secessionists pulling things apart from below, as in Bosnia or Belgium?

Mayan Glyphs on Capitol Hill

Nation states need to establish a critical mass. In order to move up the catataxic ladder from group to community to state, they need to have the right scale. The Mayans provide an interesting example of the issues here. The Mayan civilisation is first established in Central America in 2000 BC and collapses three millennia later around AD 1000. There are many different reasons given for this collapse: drought, war, overpopulation or other environmental issues. But underneath these is a more fundamental one which is the relative size of the different kingdoms.[47] The civilisation consists of numerous small city states which are in a constant state of rivalry with each other. Imagine you are the ruler of one of these kingdoms. To beat your rival city states you need to invest heavily in two areas: war and infrastructure. By building fabulous architectural monuments you promote your culture and can attract more people to your city. You also need to build up a big army to defeat your enemies. But then again, everybody else is doing the same thing. No one city state achieves dominance over the others. In the end, the

---

47 This is the main conclusion of Arthur Demarest from Vanderbilt University Tennessee, the world's foremost Mayan expert.

collective level of spending is too high for the existing resources to support and the whole civilisation collapses. Today, only the fabulous crumbling monuments remain. That's what happens when competing little kingdoms do not achieve critical mass.

On the other side of the world, the classical civilisations of Europe have a similar beginning but a different ending. Greek city states emerge in 800 BC from the dark ages, following the fall of the Mycenaean civilisation. Like the Mayans, there are many small units. Each city state has its ceremonial buildings: temples, city walls and an agora where people can meet to do their business. The city state includes both the farmland and the city. There is no distinction between the two, although the land is the economy and the buildings supply the cultural identity. The crucial difference is that these city states are egalitarian. Citizens own their own land and see working for others as shameful. This stands in marked contrast to the large Persian empires of the Near East where the King or Emperor owns everything and the people are his vassals. A Greek city state is an expression of independence. Citizens are equals with a strong sense of local identity. You can see this from the collective names of the period: Trojans, Corinthians, Spartans and, later, Romans. They are all named after their cities because countries do not yet exist.

In Ancient Greece, the only symbol of a uniting 'Hellenic' culture are the games held in Olympia every four years. The city states compete against each other in Pan-Hellenic games dedicated to the Gods. Did the participants feel more 'Greek' after the games? It's an open question. The modern Olympics has countries rather than city states competing. When you watch them do you feel more global or more nationalistic? It's probably a bit of both. One thing is for sure. The medal winners bring back glory to their city states.

Like the Mayans, with Greek city states it's still all about war and infrastructure. The two are exquisitely combined on the marbles that decorate the Parthenon in Athens. Running around the top of the columns is a frieze of metopes that depict legendary battles. The south side shows the fight between Lapiths and the Centaurs,[48] the

---

48 These south side metopes are known as the Elgin Marbles and are held in the British Museum in London. They are at the centre of dispute between the UK and Greece who would like them returned to the Acropolis

north side depicts the Trojan war. The west side illustrates the invasion of Athens by the Amazons, while the East side takes as its theme the cosmic battle between the Olympian Gods and the Giants. This symbolic monument defines the Athenian identity through war. You are united by what you fight against. It is a lowest common denominator sentiment expressed in the highest artistic terms.

The irony is that the Parthenon is built with money extorted from other Greek cities. In 480 BC Athens leads the Greek city states in the wars against the Persians and soon began to dominate them. In time, they become satellites in an Athenian empire. Athens demands protection money from the other city states and uses it to build its temples. So unlike the Maya, in ancient Greece Athens achieves critical mass in the fifth century BC and makes big advances in philosophy, science and the arts in this golden age. Later, though the power of Athens is broken by a war with Sparta, Alexander the Great picks up the Hellenic torch and conquers the known world.

Mayan culture disappeared until astonished explorers stumbled over their overgrown temples in the jungles of Central America. Greek culture triumphed even on the American continent. The architecture of power expressed in the Parthenon is mirrored in the fluted columns that front the New York Stock Exchange and most of the official buildings in Washington DC. If you want to look authoritative, then use Greek columns in your buildings of state. If heritage was territorial then Capitol Hill would be covered in decorative step pyramids and intricate Mayan glyphs which are the traditional architectural vernacular of that continent. If one Mayan city state had achieved critical mass over the others as Athens did, imagine how different things could have been.

Strong barons, weak kings

A strong state requires a dominant ruling city, but it also needs a strong ruler. The curse of some countries has been the strength of the nobles relative to the king. Poland is a good example. It is often observed that Poland's misfortune is to be sandwiched between two bigger and often unfriendly powers: Germany and Russia. Both

museum. There is a cataxic angle to this argument. Do the sculptures belong to a country or are they so exquisite and important that they transcend nationality and belong to the world?

those countries have twice divided up Poland between them, in 1795 and in 1939. But looking further back in history, it is clear that a more fundamental reason for Poland's weakness is the power of the nobles, or Szlachta, relative to the king.

In 1355, King Casimir the Great has no male heirs and so strikes a deal with the nobles; if they allow his nephew Louis to become king he will make them exempt from land tax. This is the beginning of the period known as the 'Golden Liberty', or the commonwealth of the nobles. Since the king is appointed by election rather than hereditary right, the nobles are able to extract greater and greater concessions for their support. There are many positive consequences to this. By the sixteenth century, Poland is the dominant power in central Europe. It is a state with an extraordinary degree of religious tolerance. Protestants and Jews are welcome, and science and culture are flourishing. In the northern city of Frombork, Copernicus triggers an intellectual revolution by demonstrating that the earth revolves around the sun.

All these advances mask a big underlying problem: the nobles have grown too powerful. They effectively own the whole country, are not subject to the King's law and are free from tax. The nobles are like little kings in their own right, protective of their own self interest and easily bribed or influenced by foreign powers. This makes it easy for the country to be broken up. Partition comes in three waves between 1772 and 1795 as the little fiefdoms of the nobles are swallowed up by Austria, Prussia and Russia. Poland effectively ceases to exist. This is a catataxic takeover. The nobles are at level three, and Poland has plenty of them. There are plenty of Prussian, Austrian and Russian nobles too, but those countries also have a strong centrist monarchy. Poland does not. There is a vacuum at level four. It's like a game of monopoly where one player has left the table. The level three cards can be easily redistributed amongst the other players.

Another country where the nobility has historically been stronger than the monarchy is Scotland. The country's roots lie in the warring clans of Picts, Gaels, Norse and Scots where the allegiance is predominantly to the clan chieftain.[49] The King is the first

---

49 This title is still recognised in Scottish law although it is purely ceremonial these days, with no legal jurisdiction. My clan chieftain is Godfrey

amongst equals chosen from the ranks of these chiefs. As Shakespeare shows in *Macbeth*, those with enough strength and ambition can become King. But the King needs the support of the chieftains to raise an army because the men still fight in their clan units. So the clan chieftains are more powerful than the King.

The death of King Alexander III in 1286 illustrates the problem. He has no heir and there are fourteen different rivals for the succession. Edward I of England is asked to arbitrate and he exploits this position of authority by appointing himself Scotland's feudal overlord. The subsequent wars between England and Scotland and between the different Scottish nobles are the stuff of legend. Robert the Bruce, William Wallace and Edward Longshanks are all vividly portrayed in the Hollywood movie *Braveheart*. From this maelstrom of these wars comes the Declaration of Arbroath in 1320, a letter to the pope from fifty-one nobles which specifically claims that the king is to be chosen by them. Ironically it is Scotland's King James VI, transplanted onto England's throne as James I, that brings the countries together. It is the power of the English institution of monarchy, centrist, single and absolute that cements the two in a United Kingdom.

All roads lead to Rome

The point is this: the governing institution must be vested with enough power and authority to pull the nation together. Warring city states need to coalesce. The Mayans did not manage this, the Greeks did. Bickering nobles must give the King enough power to discipline them. Poland and Scotland struggled with this, other countries such as England and France did not. Unless both these conditions are met, there can be no transition from level three to level four; from tribe to nation. When they are met then astonishing things can happen . . . as the lessons of the Roman Empire show.

We left the story earlier with Alexander the Great conquering the known world. The empire he creates is an empire of culture. He is exporting philosophy and art, which the Greeks have developed to astonishing heights. But culture is not enough to keep an empire together. Alexander's empire falls apart when he dies, leaving a

---

Macdonald of Macdonald, 34th hereditary chief of the Clan Donald, who runs a hotel on the Isle of Skye.

cultural footprint but little else. As he dies in Babylon in 323 BC, a new power is rising in the west. Rome, a small Italian city state, is busy conquering the neighbouring cities of the Etruscans, Samnites and Umbrians. What Rome is exporting is not culture but civilisation; not art, but infrastructure, systems and laws. What they introduce is *civitas*, in other words, citizenship and a civilised way of living.

The success of Rome is all about bureaucracy and engineering. The Roman legal system is the cement that keeps everything together. The twelve tables of Roman law are written down on bronze tablets and posted in the Forum for everyone to see. Even slaves have rights and do not have to remain slaves forever. They can win their freedom and rise to positions of wealth and prominence. Public infrastructure is another important binding mechanism. Their network of roads that are still in use today are the arteries of commerce and control. Aqueducts bring water from afar for public baths to improve everyone's quality of life, not just the rich. These buildings are functional; not ostentatious pyramids and temples, but practical civic engineering.

When Roman legions defeat their foes their intent is not to pillage and enslave, but to conquer and assimilate. They convert their enemies to the Roman way and then conscript them into their armies. This process of assimilation has a momentum all of its own, a positive feedback loop. By the second century BC, Rome has conquered Greece and Alexander's Seleucid Empire. Egypt and North Africa soon follow. By this stage, half of their army is non-roman.

Up to this point Rome is still a Republic. But the political machinery of the republic is not really fit for the purpose of running a huge empire. Rome is consumed by internal strife and civil wars interspersed by the dictatorships of Sulla and later Julius Caesar. Despite the theoretical benefits of the republican system, it is clear that it does not work in practice because of the corruption and greed of the senators. A single strong authority figure is required to pull it all together. The heir of Julius Caesar is Octavian, who renames himself Caesar Augustus when appointing himself emperor in 31 BC. From then on, 'Caesar' becomes the Emperor's traditional title.

It is the change in scale that drove the change from Republic to

Empire. At first, this transition from the rule of many to the rule of one may seem like a backward step. After all, Rome was originally ruled by Kings. It was only after they were deposed and the Republic founded that the city state began its march to dominance and glory. But an Emperor is not the same as a King. Caesar is not just a man, but a divine being. The Imperial Cult, where the emperor is worshipped as a demigod,[50] proves an effective way to communicate power and authority to the millions of subjects who will never see Caesar in person. He is not a man but a concept. The institution is much bigger than the individual who occupies it. So the emperor can be mad, bad or dangerous to know (often all three) but the machinery of empire will run on regardless.

There are famous and great roman emperors: Trajan, Hadrian, and Constantine. There are plenty of dispensable ones too. In AD126, Pertinax, a city prefect, is proclaimed Emperor by the Praetorian Guard. Three months later the same guards murder him when he tries to impose stricter discipline upon them. The guards then sell the title of Emperor to the highest bidder in an auction. Didius Julianus wins, but only lasts three months before he too is executed. In the third century AD, a period of fifty years saw twenty-five different emperors. Some served only a few months, just long enough to get their head on the coinage. Those few coins are the only relic of their existence today. Just as the system is about to collapse, the good emperor Diocletian comes along to introduce much needed reforms and to give the Empire a new lease of life.

The Roman Empire is a tax-collecting and law-dispensing machine; a bureaucratic supertanker. At times, it is driven only by the force of its own momentum, at other times by a wise helmsman. It is vast, covering 5 million km². It extends from Spain to Iraq and from Britain to Egypt. It is supremely efficient. The Empire is run by only 10,000 bureaucrats. This is a surprisingly low number when compared to the half a million required in Britain today, which has a similar population in an area twenty-five times smaller. The Roman Empire is polytheistic. Citizens can believe what they want so long as they pay their taxes and don't rebel. The power of the

---

50 Emperor Hirohito of Japan, the last emperor on earth to be recognised as divine died in 1989.

name 'Caesar' resonates down the centuries as an imperial title of supreme authority. It becomes 'Kaiser' in Germany and 'Tsar' in Russia. The idea embodied in the name is too powerful to ignore.

Traders in the city

The Roman Empire finally ends in 1453.[51] The last Emperor, Constantine XI, dies when Constantinople is taken by Mehmet II, Sultan of the Ottoman Turks. So the end of one empire is the beginning of another. It is less a full stop and more a passing of the torch. Mehmet makes Constantinople his new capital, and takes the title *Kayser-i Rum*, which is Arabic for 'Caesar of the Romans'. He absorbs much of the bureaucratic mechanisms of the Eastern Roman Empire and uses it to run the Ottoman lands. Like the Romans he is religiously tolerant, allowing the Byzantine Church to continue. Also like the Romans, he conscripts the conquered into his armies. His elite troops, the fearsome Janissaries, are recruited from Christian families.

It is important to note that at this time there are cities and there are empires, but there are no countries, at least not in the modern sense. Italy is a geographic expression but not a political one. It is simply the name for a peninsular. Cities, filled with merchants focused on trade, are the key political units. The Italian city states are fiercely independent. Venice and Genoa are bitter commercial rivals who are often at war with each other. In Northern Europe, the Hanseatic League is a confederation of free cities stretching from Flanders to Russia. The League has its own armies and ships and the cities cooperate to develop trade routes and profitable monopolies. England has a similar but weaker version of this in the Cinque Ports. Along the Silk Route lie the great trading cities of Central Asia, like Samarkand, Kashgar and Bukhara. Since there are no sea routes yet, they get rich from all the east-to-west trade passing through their hands.

These cities are set like fat jewels in a boring agricultural landscape. In Europe, there is little on the level above them. The most significant political structures, at a larger scale, are the empires of

---

51 The empire was split into two parts by Diocletian. The Western Roman Empire falls in 476 to the Hun Odoacer. The capital of the Eastern or Byzantine Empire is Constantinople.

the orient: the Ottomans, the Safavids in Persia, the Mughals in India and the Ming in China. These are empires of the mind; spiritual, cultured and refined. Their arts are scholarly pursuits like calligraphy and poetry. Their architecture has an exquisite and dreamy beauty; think of the Selimiye Mosque, the Taj Mahal and the Forbidden City. The European colonial empires, when they arrive several centuries later, will not be like that. They will be empires of trade; pragmatic, exploitative and mercantile. They will express themselves with a squat architecture of taxation and control.

In Medieval Europe, sovereign states have yet to coalesce. Monarchs at the time rule over a patchwork of territories, not the coherent countries we recognise today. King Richard the Lionheart, a heroic English icon, is a good example. He is the 'good king' that appears at the end of the Robin Hood stories. In a later era, the Victorians erect a huge statue of him outside the Houses of Parliament, cementing his reputation as a pillar of the English state. In fact, he is not really English at all. He was also the ruler of Normandy, Brittany, Aquitaine, Gascony, Anjou and Nantes; in other words, half of modern day France. He spoke no English, only *langue d'oc* [a form of medieval French spoken south of the Loire] and French. He spent only six months of his ten-year reign in England. He died suppressing a revolt in Limoges, and parts of his body were buried throughout his scattered kingdom: the heart in Rouen, the entrails in Chalus and the rest of the body in Anjou. England was clearly not important enough to be a final resting place for even a small part of his remains.

The medieval world had many overlapping authorities in a patchwork of non-exclusive arrangements. England is probably the most organised, centrist and coherent state of the time, but even there things look a mess to the modern eye. There are three different types of local government boundaries: parish, manorial and hundredal. The parish boundaries are set by the church, the manorial boundaries are set by the aristocracy, and the hundreds are a judicial boundary system inherited from the Saxons. The boundaries do not necessarily overlap. A farmer owes tithes to the church, heriot to the manor and frankpledge to the hundred. Neighbouring farmers may be in the same parish but belong to different manors and attend different hundred courts. Scattered like raisins through this mixture are the self-governing boroughs or towns, the whole making a rich and complex fruit cake. It is not until the nineteenth century that a unitary system of local government is created and the boundaries harmonised.

The city is the primary political unit. Walled cities with a cathedral at their heart dot the landscape of Europe. They are self-governing entities, sometimes operating under a royal charter, at other times a state in their own right. Above this there is a shifting web of kings, lords, dukes and counts. Through wars or marriage, the kingdoms, duchies and counties change hands. When one player amasses too much territory the others unite against him. The wars are a constant background, hence all the city walls, and are so complex that they are known only by their length: the Hundred Years War (1337 to 1453), the Thirteen Years War (1454 to 1466), the Eighty Years War (1568 to 1648) and the Thirty Years War (1618 to 1648). It is the cities that provide the stability and continuity. Rulers may quarrel and change but behind the city walls, bar the occasional sacking, life and trade goes on regardless.

The birth of the nation state

The Thirty Years War ends with the Treaty of Westphalia in 1648, seen by most historians as the moment that the nation state is born. It is a series of peace treaties agreed in a diplomatic congress between Austria, Spain, France, Sweden, Switzerland, the Dutch Republic and the Holy Roman Empire. It creates the 'Westphalian System' that still underpins international relations today. The treaty establishes several key principles of territorial integrity. First is the principle of state sovereignty and the right of political self determination. In particular, the right of the ruler to choose the religion of the country is recognised, much to the annoyance of the Pope. Second is the principle that all states are equal in a legal sense. Third is the principle of non intervention. One state should not interfere in the internal affairs of another. International relations becomes all about the balance of power between these sovereign states.

And so there you have it. The concept of the state is established as an entity in its own right. For the first time, it is something more than a set of land holdings acquired by a king through war or marriage. A state has an existence separate from the ruler who reigns over it. Territorial boundaries become more significant and are unlikely to change just because the king's daughter marries someone else. State boundaries mean that internal systems are harmonised: taxes and customs duties become national rather than city based. National transport networks knit the country together; toll roads, canals and later, railways. The first newspapers begin to circulate, promoting a sense of national identity. Gradually the state becomes the nation state, driven by the swelling tide of nationalism in the nineteenth century. Nations that previously were only linked through culture, such as Germany and Italy, become unified political entities.

The concept of the nation state is buttressed by Hegel when he publishes his *Philosophy of Right* in 1820. In this book, he illustrates the workings of his dialectic on the individual and the state. The dialectic has three steps: thesis, antithesis and synthesis. For his political argument, these entities are renamed like this: 'undifferentiated unity', 'differentiated disunity' and 'differentiated unity'.[52] The long words make it sound more complicated than it really is; it's just a riff around whether things are united and distinct, or not. The first case is the undifferentiated unity of the family. This is a group of people who are the same (i.e. undifferentiated) and together (i.e. a unity). The antithesis, the opposite of this, is differentiated disunity which is a group of competing individuals, all out for whatever they can get. They are disunited and selfish. People fight, might is right and the strongest survive; the very opposite of a family. The synthesis is differentiated unity, which is the crux of Hegel's argument for the state. It combines the best of both worlds. The state sees us as separate legal individuals but its laws keep our actions focused on the common good. People are different but also united; distinct, but not selfish. In Hegel's view, the state is the logical solution to the problem of human society, a perfect synthesis of rights and power.

So the state is the answer; power must be vested in this unitary

---

52 Those of you of a logical bent will notice that there is one quadrant missing here: undifferentiated disunity. In other words - all the same but not together. This may be the most interesting quadrant; the catataxic quadrant. Undifferentiated disunity is another way of saying more of the same is different.

building block of international relations. What about religion? The Pope in medieval times held sway over kings and princes through-out Western Europe. The Treaty of Westphalia releases those newly formed states from his political authority. The growing statism of the nineteenth century diminishes his power further. The newly unified Italian state makes Rome its capital in 1871, which creates a big problem: where do you put the Pope? In what entity does his power reside? The eventual answer is to make a little mini-state just for him. Vatican City is the smallest state in the world, with a population of only 800 people and an area of one square kilometre. It mints its own highly collectible coins. So religion is translated into a unit that other states can understand.

At the same time, the dark side of nationalism is beginning to appear.[53] The appalling barbarity of World War I makes people question whether nationalistic fervour is a good thing. Can the Hegelian nation state actually be evil? No one really knows the reason why they are going to war, but it is a consequence of inter-linked treaties between states. The momentum of killing can only be sustained by jingoistic appeals. So the war is the child of statism and nationalism. Worse is to come. Hegel's Dialectic spawns the Marxist Dialectic and also, some scholars argue, Hitler. The totalit-arianism of the twentieth century is the concept of the state taken to its ultimate extreme. And World War II is the nation state's apogee.

The Suprastate and the Multination State

The end of World War II saw the birth of some supranational entities. These organisations are on level five, one level above the nation state on level four. Their aim is to reduce the risk of future conflicts. The nation state has blood on its hands: 16 million killed in World War I and 60 million killed in World War II – all this death because of belligerent nation states. The United Nations is set up as a forum above the level of the nation state where differences can be resolved. The European Union is founded for the similar reasons: a supranational entity should be able to mediate differences in a civilised way, avoiding warfare. There are also

---

53 In fact the Vatican City was not created until 1929, finally resolving a sixty-year-old problem.

commercial benefits. By removing all the internal tariffs and customs barriers, trade booms and everybody gets richer. It's the same process as the unification of the free cities into a German state one century before. This time it is happening one level higher up; between nation states rather than city states. Similarly, on a global scale, international bodies such as the World Bank, the World Trade Organisation,[54] the World Health Organisation and the International Court of Justice. So the post war period sees the creation of a complete set of government functions on level five: health, trade, finance, justice and a debating chamber for representatives. In short: everything that a suprastate could need.

While these forces are pulling power away from the nation state from above, there are also forces of fragmentation working from below. The nation state concept is weakened because it is no longer a single nation. As discussed previously, the word 'nation' implies monocultural unity as in the 'Cherokee nation'. All those deaths in the war have created labour shortages that are filled by immigration, often from previous colonies. The state is no longer monocultural, but multicultural. For many European countries, their old empires have been distilled down from a vast global mishmash to a single, concentrated, blended essence in the home country; a multinational state. The Americans, of course, were doing all this two hundred years earlier.

The multinational state brings its own problems. First, you can no longer take social cohesion for granted. If there is no shared communal history, there will be little common culture: Even less if there are language barriers too. This means some sort of legislation to enforce cohesion is required. Respect for the feelings of others is a personal virtue. It is instilled in almost all societies at a community level. But this bottom up propagation has a flaw. The respect is for others in *our* community, respect for others *like us*. It is much harder for a community to teach respect for others not like us, since a community is a statement of common togetherness. By defining an 'us', you also define a 'them' who are, therefore, not like us, so why should they be worthy of the same respect? This is where the government steps in and tries to impose respect for

54 originally called General Agreement on Tariffs and Trade (GATT) in 1948

others in a top down way. Personal virtues become public policy. But then once the government tries to introduce rules to respect peoples' feelings, the door is open to all sorts of curtailment of liberty in the interests of social cohesion. Of course, laws should curtail certain actions; few would argue that murder, or theft, are wrong and that laws should reflect that. But respect is something that comes from the inside and cannot be imposed externally. So the concept of legislating respect is flawed. Yes, just like the popular press complain, this is political correctness gone mad!

In the nineteenth century the state is sovereign ruler and confines itself to the legislative concerns. Everything else is handled with a casual, laissez-faire liberalism. But in the twentieth century, the state becomes bureaucratic and administrative as well. These new self-appointed responsibilities go hand in hand with a huge increase in size. Gladstone, four times UK Prime minister between 1868 and 1894, used to answer all his correspondence personally. Today, the state has grown so large it is impossible to imagine a current Prime Minister being able to do the same thing. The apparatus of power has swollen dramatically. In the UK it has grown from several thousand Civil Servants in Gladstone's day to half a million today. In France, over the same period the state civil service has grown by ten times to over two million employees.

As it gets bigger, it gets more intrusive, particularly in the personal arena. The attitude towards children changes. They are no longer seen as the property of their parents but as citizens with rights protected by the state. This seems like a wholly good thing as the evils of child labour and abuse are stamped out. But take it too far and it gets disturbing. Totalitarian states often attempt to break the backbone of the nuclear family because it is the thing most resistant to political indoctrination. Whitney Huston believes that 'children are the future' but so does Hitler. He once said: 'Your child belongs to us. You will die and your descendants will only know our way.' Hence, the Hitler Youth. The Soviets believe it too. In 1932, a thirteen-year-old boy called Pavlik becomes a Hero of the Soviet Union for denouncing his parents to the authorities. Loyalty to the state is held up as a higher virtue than loyalty to the family.

Hold on, you may say, that happens in a totalitarian state but surely not in a democracy? The trouble is that in a multicultural state the best way of forging a sense of national identity is through educating the kids. Controlling what children are taught can break immigrant mentalities and help their absorption into the cultural mainstream. Education is the fire under the melting pot. What children are taught is highly significant politically, both in a dictatorship and a multicultural democracy. That's why there are always such vicious debates about the school curriculum.

It's not just education, it's health too. The state is treating children like little adults, but it is treating adults like little children also. Health should be a private concern but almost every government in the developed world runs anti-smoking and, more recently, anti-obesity campaigns. Alcohol and recreational drugs are either illegal or heavily controlled. This is so commonplace it is easy to forget how recent a development this is. One hundred years ago you could drink, snort and smoke whatever you wanted to your heart's content. State regulation in the health arena is a well meaning intervention and it's not all one way. Here is a good example of changing social mores. In the 1960s, homosexuality is illegal but you can smoke anywhere you want. Fifty years later, you can have sex any way you want but you can't smoke. The government is still legislating fags,[55] just a different type.

Part of the problem with political correctness at a deep level is this: a statement of equality is a statement of difference. So, for example, a mathematician can say $10 \div 2 = 4 + 1$. They both equal five. It's just two different ways of expressing the same thing in mathematical form. But by expressing the fact that these two things are equal, you are also highlighting their differences. In order to make them equal, you have to make them separate. After all, $5 = 5$ is so facile a statement that you would not even bother saying it. So, looking across to the political field, we can say that anti-discrimination law is itself discriminating. By legislating equality you are emphasising difference. Quotas and positive discrimination distort the meritocracy and can sometimes have the opposite effect than that intended.

That's all very well, some will reply, but if you have a grossly unjust system then you need to introduce legislation in order to change it. None of the major steps forward in social justice during the last hundred years would have occurred without brave

55 for American readers, fags is slang for cigarettes in Britain

campaigners and enlightened legislators forcing change. You, dear reader, may take any side in this debate you like. My only point is legislating personal values are a good example of catataxis. It's a level four entity trying to impose rules at level one.

Those who thought that World War II and the Cold War put an end to totalitarianism are disheartened to see it return, like Banquo's ghost, in the form of political correctness. Maybe the more multicultural a state becomes, the more intrusive it must be in response. If there is no commonality of feeling among the citizens, the state feels it should impose it from above by stealing a few tricks from the totalitarian play-book. The concluding thought is this. The disgruntled citizens who moan about EU (or UN) meddling and 'PC gone mad' may be old fashioned but a least they are consistent. Both are caused by a catataxic bifurcation of the old nation state. The EU acts to its member states as the states act to the many 'nations' inside them. It's an old story: your boss gives you a hard time, you go home and kick the cat.

Rethinking the nation state

If you step back and look at the pattern of nation states in the world today you are struck by the sheer diversity in scale. In South East Asia, you have a tiny island city state like Singapore right next to the Indonesia, a state with 17,000 islands and a population of 238 million. So Indonesia is 100 or 1,000 times bigger than Singapore depending on whether you are looking at population or land mass, but in the Westphalian system of international relations, they are in the same category. Looming over both of them is China, which is five times bigger than Indonesia. This vast disparity in size could be held up as a triumph of the nation state concept: look how flexible and useful a notion it is. Alternatively, you could see it as the Achilles heel: an outmoded political accounting system well past its sell by date. If we apply our catataxic analysis to it, we must conclude the latter. Singapore is one city. China has 668 cities.[56] One tree is not a forest.

Picture an eccentric Victorian scientist showing you his 'collections' in one wing of his rambling country house. He points

---

56 Even this understates China's size. The majority of its population is still rural, in other words outside those urban centres

proudly through the dusty glass display cases at some very unusual objects. To his mind this sprawling assemblage of items, all carefully catalogued and labelled, makes a coherent whole. To you, it's a random mass of unrelated bric-à-brac. You surreptitiously look at your watch, smile politely, make your excuses and leave.

That Victorian country house collection is the United Nations today. Other than the fact that they are in the assembly, the countries in the United Nations have little in common. San Tome and Principe are two tiny volcanic islands off the West coast of Africa which are recognised as a state by the United Nations. Reunion Island, five times bigger off the East Coast of Africa, is not. That is because it is actually part of the European Union, as a *Région d'outre-mer* of France. In the diverse menagerie of the UN, some states are monocultural, some multicultural; some are huge, some tiny. Some are monolithic states, some are united states. The UN sees them all as equal. Can this really be right? Are Vatican City, East Timor and Russia, in other words a religious authority, a half-island ex-colony and a superpower, really all the same thing?

If you started with a clean sheet of paper you would organise things differently. You might decide to arrange things by size into three categories: metropolis, state and suprastate. So Singapore is no longer a state but a metropolis. China is also no longer a state, it's a suprastate, just like the USA and India which are already organised on federal lines. In this thought experiment, London, New York, Singapore and Hong Kong are equivalent level 3 entities or metropolises. France, Michigan, Rajasthan and Sichuan are states on level 4. At the top, on level 5, are the USA, the EU, China and India, along with the African Union and Mercosur, in Latin America.

Such a scheme looks very neat and tidy on paper but ignores a key issue: where does sovereignty lie? Are all the countries of the world forced to surrender sovereignty to a regional federal superstructure? Alternatively, could the world's financial cities like London and New York declare secession from their nations and form a global financial Hanseatic League? Both ideas seem fanciful. In the current status quo, no sovereign entity wants to cede power either upwards or downwards. Turkeys, as they say, don't vote for Christmas. But the closer you look at the nation state today, the more you realise it is not as powerful as it seems. That sovereignty is slipping away.

L'état ce n'est pas moi

One index of state sovereignty is the power vested in its leader. All power is borrowed, as the saying goes. You have as much of it as others think you have. Consider this group of leaders from the 1940s: Stalin, Churchill, Hitler, FDR and Mao. Now consider these leaders sixty years later: Obama, van Rompuy, Hu and Putin. Not much of a comparison, really, is it? Few could argue that the second group have the same stature as the first. But you might argue that it is an unfair comparison. After all, the first group were all war leaders. Just as a market crash collapses investment horizons, war collapses politics to a powerful nationalist core. Any leader borrowing that power will look impressive. The passage of time and history's varnishing brush add gloss and stature too.

Even so, today's suprastate leaders look unimpressive. Are they really their own men or are they ciphers? Do they lead or are they merely chairmen, forced to compromise and reflect the disparate views beneath. President Obama's election campaign in 2008 is built around the inspiring themes of hope and change. When elected, he is able to change very little. Only two years later, the Republicans humiliate Obama by making major gains in the mid-term elections. Their theme? Why, it's change, of course. It's a well worn political melodrama. The political opposition castigate the government and promise to transform things. After they get elected they change very little. The public lose faith and back the opposition and the cycle begins again. Why does nothing change? Because the leader has no power. Why does the cycle continue? Because the voters don't want to believe that. They vote for a person who embodies their hopes and fears. This is a catataxic error. An individual cannot run a modern suprastate. It's too big and too diverse. The head of state is a bureaucratic entity; a position, not a person. The rules at level five are not the same as level one.

Some view China as a monolithic state run by a powerful communist dictator called President Hu Jintao. In fact, he is in a worse position than President Obama. His main concern is to keep the country coherent and harmonious. There are powerful centrifugal forces. The provinces are getting richer and far harder to control. Power is leaching from the centre. This is not a new phenomenon, but a return to status quo. As we saw in the last chapter, the old saying in the provinces is 'heaven is high and the emperor far away'. President Hu Jintao may look powerful from outside but he is subject to exactly the same pressures as President Obama. Both positions require similar skills; consensus building, compromise and pragmatic deal making.

The European Union appointed its first full time president in 2009. Herman van Rompuy is a camera shy Belgian; a career politician whose hobby is writing Haiku. This charisma-free non-entity is the subject of many cruel jokes around Europe. He was deliberately chosen for his greyness and lack of profile because the countries in the EU are not keen for too much power to be vested in Brussels. They don't want a strong man in the top seat. But rather than being a laughing stock, maybe this is a glimpse of what the future holds. Not a lame also-ran, but a prophetic beacon? Could it be that both the USA and China will gradually become like the EU?

It is misleading for a suprastate to be represented by a charismatic commander in chief. A figurehead like that is unrepresentative. Implying a personal relationship exists between that individual and the citizens is a naive and cataxic fallacy. The machinery of realpolitik means it will end in disappointment; a feeling that the leader has let you down personally. The perfect president of a suprastate is a grey technocrat who concerns himself with suprastate matters; trade legislation, carbon emission proposals, bank reserve requirements and institutional protocols. Charismatic candidates should stand for local office like a sheriff or town mayor. You are much more likely to meet them and have some sort of personal interaction.

There is an alternative model to the leader as a down to earth, telegenic communicator with the people. We can call it 'Delphic power'. President Suharto, who rules Indonesia from 1967 to 1998, is a good example. Picture the scene. A group of cabinet ministers are arguing about whether the import tax on machine tools should be increased. After a vigorous debate amongst them, they decide to approach the great man for guidance. They nervously gather in his presence and ask, 'What should we do about the import tax problem?' Suharto's reply is opaque; he says something like, 'We must do all that we must to promote our economy.' The ministers all shuffle out again and begin to discuss what the great man actually meant by that. Does increasing the import tax actually benefit or harm the economy? Along the way they find a compromise that everyone is happy with. Problem solved.

The point of the story is that the more mystic and opaque the statement the more powerful Suharto seems. He appears to be dwelling at a different, higher level thinking deep thoughts about far more important problems. He is not a down to earth, direct communicator; he is distant, opaque and non-committal. Just like the Oracle at Delphi, that means he is rarely wrong. If the outcome turns out well, that is proof of his vision and genius. If it turns out badly, then the underlings must have misinterpreted his intent.

Real power does not communicate directly. It is a staple of mafia movies. The protagonist is trying to strike a deal with the mafia boss, arguing over a table in an Italian restaurant. But before the agreement is reached, the mafia boss looks over at an old, grey-haired guy sipping coffee at a table to the side. He is the real power. It is only when he nods his assent, that the deal is done. It is the same when negotiating a business deal in an office in China. You have spent a couple of hours talking and developing a rapport with the people across the table but the man in charge is that other guy sitting silently on the row of seats against the wall.

Real power communicates symbolically. Think of the statues of Emperor Augustus put up in temples and worshipped throughout the Roman Empire. Or British postage stamps; a single image of the head of The Queen with no writing, not even a name of a country. That is power. Maybe the reason that today's democratic leaders lack authority is that they engage too personally with the electorate. To be elected, they must be likeable; not aloof, but a regular Joe, just like you. Well, maybe not just like you. They need to be a bit more outgoing, better looking and a lot more charming. Here lies the rub. Besides politicians, there are other professionals who trade on their looks and personality: prostitutes, clowns and travelling salesmen. It should be no surprise that the public treat them all with the same level of respect.

Territory and resources

So today's political leaders may not have the stature of their fore-bears. So what? The state is still powerful. It intrudes into your personal space and affects every citizen. It still controls everything.

It has power over territory, citizenship, taxation, trade and legislation. But on closer examination, even here control is slipping. Let's look at these areas in turn.

Territory has been the key defining factor for a nation state. A state has to exist somewhere. It is an abstract concept anchored in the physical world by its geographical location. The territory is the state and the people are the nation. In pre-industrial times, that is all you need; land plus people equals wealth. Serfs toiling in the fields create agricultural surpluses that you can tax. You are sovereign over the people and the land. You own them both. As the economy develops and becomes monetised, there is a second way of getting rich; by trading things rather than making them. You don't own the traders since they move with their goods between territories, but you can license and control their activities. Then, with the industrial revolution another factor becomes important: technology. And so you have the four factors of production: land, labour, capital and technology. Of the four, land is the most fundamental. The other three can move, but land is fixed.

The Industrial revolution highlights the importance of technology but it also changes the attitude to land. Suddenly, what is underneath the land becomes much more important. Demand for coal, iron ore and other minerals increases dramatically. These resources differ from agricultural ones in one key way: they are not renewable. Once you have used them they are gone. They are not something that man can create through careful husbandry like beef or wool. They are a one-off bounty given to a nation by God. In that sense, they are more national assets than personal ones.[57] So, one impact of the industrial revolution is to strengthen the trend towards nationalism. Industry requires raw materials and raw materials are national assets. If your nation does not have those raw materials then you had better go and colonise another one. Hence the wave of colonisation known as 'The Scramble for Africa' in the late nineteenth century.

57 In Australia, a proposed Mineral Resource Rent Tax led to the downfall of Prime Minister Rudd in June 2010. He argued that Australia's abundant mineral resources were a national asset, so when commodity prices skyrocket the Australian people deserve to benefit. Powerful mining interests, alarmed by this proposal, funded an advertising war that brought his term to an end.

A colonial system has a basic economic equation at its heart. Raw materials from the colonies are transformed into manufactured goods in the mother country. These goods are then profitably re-exported back to the colonies. Coal, iron ore, rubber and cotton are the key commodities to start with, but in the twentieth century one commodity acquires an importance that dwarfs all others: oil. It redraws the geopolitical map and plays a significant part in both of the World Wars.

In World War I, oil first demonstrates its importance. The British Navy has moved from wind power in Nelson's day to coal and then oil. The greater range and speed of Britain's oil-powered Dread-noughts keeps the German coal-fired Navy bottled up in harbour for most of the war. Three new weapons of war make their debut and herald the future of conflict: the submarine, the tank and the aeroplane. All three are powered by oil. The latter two create the decisive breakthroughs that end trench warfare and make sure that all future wars are mobile ones. Oil fields become battle fields for the first time. My grandfather was wounded in Britain's ill-fated Mesopotamian Expedition in 1917. They were fighting to protect British oil supplies in modern day Iraq.

In World War II, Japan's attack on Pearl Harbor is a retaliation for the USA's oil embargo. Japan's invasion of South East Asia was an attempt to capture the oil fields there. Likewise, Rommel's war in North Africa and Hitler's invasion of Russia has the ultimate goal of securing oil supplies. Hitler diverted his tank divisions from the doorstep of Moscow south to the Caucasus. He viewed the oil fields there as the more important prize. That led to Stalingrad and his eventual defeat. It is easy to see why some historians view all conflicts in the twentieth century as 'Oil Wars'.

Thankfully, both colonialism and global warfare come to an end. There is a much easier way of gaining access to commodities than invading a country or colonising it. It's called the international trading system. It peacefully and efficiently reallocates resources to the highest bidder. Despite this, in recent years, nervousness about access to commodities is prompting a new trend: the 'rent a country' boom. The soaring price of several agricultural staples have made some states ponder their long term food security. South Korea recently leased 2.2 million acres, one third of Madagascar's arable land, to grow corn and palm oil. Saudi Arabia has a similar deal in

Indonesia for rice, as has Qatar with Cambodia. These deals look a bit like colonialism under another guise; indentured servitude rather than slavery. It remains to be seen, if famine strikes, whether starving locals will respect the fact that the rice in the paddy field next to their house belongs to a country far away.

These 'rent a country' deals compromise the territorial integrity of nation states and have a dubious aura. It's not an edifying sight to see rich countries short of arable land exploiting poor ones. There are plenty of examples of countries who willingly fragment their own territorial integrity. In fact, it is quite common. Why would a country want to separate out a part of their territory? In order to make a free trade zone: an area where normal laws, tariffs and customs don't apply. It can be a strikingly effective way to boost economic development. China has employed them with spectacular success. The tiny fishing village of Shenzhen across the border from Hong Kong was one of China's first special economic zones. In just twenty years, it has become a city with 15 million people.

The free trade zone has been much copied and is now a standard part of the script for poor countries looking to move up the development curve. In total, ninety-three countries around the world now have free trade zones. In fact, there are so many that competition between them is rife. It has become a buyer's market for multinationals looking for a cheap labour site to place their factories. Indeed, some free trade zones may have already peaked. Mexico's zones, called *maquiladoras*, boomed in the 1990s but are now declining because of competition from other cheaper sites in the Far East.

All this activity is happening outside the purview of the established nation state. It's the jurisdictional structure that is important, not the territory. In other words, a virtual state rather than a physical state: A set of laws that you can plonk down on any area of land and hothouse up some economic growth. This is the idea behind the concept of charter cities, as put forward by the Stanford economist Paul Romer. He advocates setting up a new type of city in an undeveloped part of an impoverished country. The legal and commercial infrastructure is provided under a charter by a western government. The physical infrastructure such as factories, plants, housing and roads is provided by foreign companies. The labour is provided by immigrants. This proposal effectively goes one step further than special economic zones; not just free trade but free speech too.

This is not a new idea but an old one. Romer developed his ideas by looking at Hong Kong. That barren rock with a British legislature on the southern edge of China became a hugely successful entrepot for global trade and finance. But the idea is even older than that. It goes right back to the first city states of the Hanseatic League such as Danzig. That city was set up in 1235 under a charter of autonomy, and immigrants soon came flooding in. Today, it is known as Gdansk and, ironically, the Polish Government made it a special economic zone in the 1990s. So it took around 800 years for the idea to come full circle.

The charter city is a virtual state. It is a legislative framework but it has no citizens. The immigrants who work there have whatever legal protections the charter lays down, but their passport remains that of their country of origin. The governor is not accountable to the people of the city. He is appointed from outside by whichever developed nation is sponsoring it. In a charter city, you don't vote with a ballot box, you vote with your feet.

People and Culture

Immigration is a major problem for most developed countries. In fact, the charter cities concept can be seen as a solution for that issue. If you want a developed country to sponsor a charter city then the sales pitch goes something like this: 'To stop people flooding into your country, set up something equally attractive elsewhere to divert them.' Having discussed some of the territorial and legal aspects of the nation state, it is time to consider the people and culture side. Let's look at the nation part of the nation state.

As noted above, wars are sometimes about access to resources. But another common cause is the mismatch between state boundaries and cultural boundaries. State boundaries are notoriously arbitrary; imposed from above by a bureaucrat with little sense of local geography. The most famous example is Winston's Hiccup. This is a huge zigzag on the border between Jordan and Saudi Arabia. Legend has it that Winston Churchill had a long liquid lunch on a Sunday afternoon in Cairo. When he came back to his desk, he hiccupped while drawing the new border for Transjordan.[58] Hence the dramatic twist in the line. Since it was mostly desert, no one really cared.

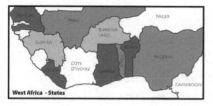 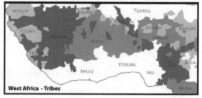

Spot the difference

Look at these two maps of West Africa. One shows the state boundaries, the other the boundaries of the different ethnic groups or nations. It is clear that the state borders are an arbitrary higher level intrusion into a complex ethnic landscape. This is one of the reasons behind West Africa's notoriously turbulent past. The bloody Biafran civil war in the late 1960s was caused by the secessionist desires of the Ibo in the south east part of Nigeria. The post colonial period has seen similar civil wars in Sierra Leone, Cote d'Ivoire, Guinea-Bissau and Liberia (twice). In addition there have been several military coups in Ghana and Burkina Faso. Maybe there would have been less strife if the state boundaries had followed the tribal boundaries. At least the true nation states created as a result would have been more stable.

A nation state needs to be defined around a culture. There was a fairly good mapping between nations and states in nineteenth century Europe but recently immigration has made most Western democracies multination states. An economist would look at this immigration with joy. If people want to move to your country, it is a sign that you have won. Your economy has out competed everyone else. Through vision or luck, you have figured out how to add economic value in your country and so people are flocking in to take up those jobs. Moreover, it's a virtuous circle. Labour is a key input to economic growth. The quickest way to grow your economy is to get more people. So you can see why, to an economist, immigration is a golden bounty.

---

58 In fact it is an apocryphal story. The border takes account of ancient incense trading routes and Britain's need at that time for an air corridor to India.

To the citizens in the country, immigration is the opposite; a blight, a curse and a source of friction. Western democracies now have a greater diversity of tribes than a West African country. No wonder people are getting nervous. Polls in almost all western countries show that 'too many immigrants' is a very common complaint. For a politician, to stand up and say 'we need more immigrants,' is political suicide. But if he stands up and says 'we need more growth,' he will be cheered. To an economist, the two go hand in hand, but not to the voters. That means the voters are either economically illiterate or selfish, probably both.

Hold on, you may say, it is possible to grow your economy without immigration. If you have high unemployment you can grow without importing any more people since you have a surplus of workers. Also, your current workers could improve productivity by moving up the technology curve. Both points are true in theory, but in practice there will never be full employment and Western democracies are already quite high up the technology curve. You will always need some burger flippers and manual labourers. So it is still generally true that more economic activity needs more people. And with birth rates in the developed world declining, that means immigration if you want growth.

The real reason immigration is such a political hot potato is not economic but cultural. Immigrants are different. They are not like us. They compete for our jobs and reduce our bargaining power. They turn a nation state into a multination state. This weakens the 'nation' component and strengthens the 'state' part. The state becomes more intrusive. Common sense has to be legislated because we have less and less in common. Implicit community values become explicit legal ones. These all seem like negative developments, no wonder immigration is a problem.

Let's turn the tables and look at things from the perspective of an immigrant. If you are in an economically impoverished area, you have two choices. Stay and wait for the jobs to come to you, or go where the jobs are. The latter is the normal choice. That accounts for the long term global trend from rural to urban living. There is also a natural filter mechanism working here. Those who go are likely to be entrepreneurial types seeking fame and fortune. Those who stay are likely to put a greater value on community, continuity and the status quo. Industrialisation is the trigger for migrants to move from countryside to city; from agricultural jobs to factory ones. Sometimes the move is from an agricultural job to another agricultural one but in a different country. The opening up of the American West sucked farmers from Europe across the Atlantic to the USA. The dynamism of the US economy is due to the entrepreneurial spirit of those immigrants. Europe's negative attitude to immigration may stem from the fact that it is full of the ones who stayed behind.

Who deserves a job more? Someone who has travelled halfway across the world to get it or someone who has been hanging around waiting for one to show up? You can make an argument either way. The energetic go-getter deserves a reward for his effort. The person who has been waiting has a sense of entitlement and may see the other as a queue jumper. Americans will have more sympathy for the first, Europeans for the second.

Europeans seem to have stronger locational ties, something that often astonishes American multinationals who have a far more mobile work-force in the USA. I remember the horrified face of a British colleague who had been told by his new American boss that he would have to move from London to Nottingham. It was mirrored by the puzzlement on the face of the American boss that someone could make such a fuss about a move of a mere 100 miles. In US terms that is still practically next door. But Europe has a far greater degree of cultural density. A 100-mile trip can take you through three different countries with three different languages.

Nation states still have a powerful control mechanism in the form of passports and work permits. But assume for the moment that these barriers are surmountable and that you are a bright graduate just out of university. You can effectively choose which country you want to work in. You will presumably choose a place with a vibrant and dynamic economy because that's where the opportunities are best. A big cosmopolitan city is good too, lots of different cultures and restaurants and a stimulating nightlife. London, Hong Kong and New York spring to mind. These cities are very different to the hinterland around them, almost like separate economies which are predominantly services based.

These cities form the new Hanseatic League of global finance. They compete aggressively but have more in common with each other than they do with their respective countries. They are also as welcoming as they can be to immigrants and foreigners. Money knows no boundaries and in the fluid world of global finance they need to be at the top of their game. That means getting the best people regardless of what their passport looks like. Maybe this is what the future holds: city states competing to attract immigrants in a national setting that is increasingly irrelevant.

Corporatism not nationalism

Let's go back to the four factors of production: land, labour, capital and technology. In medieval times, three of these were owned by the lord of the manor and the fourth, technology, was not much of a factor at that time. Fast forward to today. In an industrialised economy, technology becomes very important and land produces more than just agriculture. So we should substitute the word 'raw materials' for 'land'. Who owns these factors of production today? It is companies not countries. In fact, countries have very little control over them at all. Raw materials are freely traded, capital controls have been lifted, workers are free to go to wherever the jobs are and technology is disseminated globally by academic journals and the internet. It is companies who are in control of this flow, not countries. Power has been passed from the nation state to the multinational company.

It seems this fact has not dawned on the national consciousness yet. Consider a headline like this: 'British scientist discovers cure for arthritis'. Now, as we said before, newspapers are inherently nationalistic. They only publish stories that are relevant to their readers, and readers always have their nationality in common. So a jingoistic piece is an easy win. The only problem is that the nationality of the scientist is irrelevant. The only way the science in the lab is going to end up as a product for the masses is if a company picks it up and develops it. Let's dig a little deeper. What if the scientist holds a British passport but is working in a lab in Geneva? What about a Turkish national working for a British company in a facility it owns in Canada? What is it that makes it a 'British' success? Is it the passport of the scientist? The university where he is researching? The headquarter's location of the company that will commercialise it? Or the location of the factory which will mass produce it? The real news is just that a cure for arthritis has been discovered. That is good for everybody. The jingoistic spin is erroneous because technology knows no nationality any more.

For the general populace, technology still seems to be considered as a national asset. This thinking is stuck in the world of John Buchan novels or Hitchcock movies. A scientist makes a breakthrough. It's the chemical formula for a deadly nerve gas. Dastardly foreigners are lurking around trying to steal it. This triggers a chase through town and country as the hero escapes their evil clutches. Hitchcock used to call this plot device a 'macguffin': the object that everybody is searching for but the audience does not care what it actually is. It's just a catalyst for the thrill of the chase. The jingoistic technology story is a bit like that too. No one really cares about the scientific details, just that our guys are smarter than their guys.

Pause for a moment and consider how ridiculous this is. Ideas don't stop at geographic boundaries. The whole point of science is that it is universal. Newton published his *Principia Mathematica* in Latin, the common language of science in his day, so that everyone could read it. Science thrives through publication in journals and peer review, regardless of nationality. So 'national science' is a bit of an oxymoron, but governments still have 'national science' budgets. A cynic might ask: what's the point in training up all those scientists if there are no jobs for them to do? Wouldn't it be better to let other countries train them up and then give them good jobs here? Something that already happens in medicine – with the migration of doctors from the Third World (where they are needed most) to the First World (where they can earn most money).

The same erroneous nationalism can be seen in another 'ideas' industry: the film industry. During the awards season, the British press is full of articles about the success of various British films. But what is a British film? Is it that the director and actors should be British? In which case, Hitchcock's classic 'macguffin' movie *North by Northwest* starring Cary Grant[59] is a British film. Or does it need to be made in Britain? If so, then *Star Wars* and the Indiana Jones movies which were shot at Elstree are British; lovingly made by teams of British craftsmen. Or is it more of a finance issue? A Hollywood studio financed the Wallace and Gromit movie. Is it

59 Cary Grant, one of the greatest Hollywood stars of all time was British. His real name was Archie Leach and was born in Bristol in 1904.

still British? How about Scorsese's *Gangs of New York* which was financed by a British producer? It is hard not to conclude that there is no such thing as a 'British Film'. Films may have a language but do not really have a nationality.

National movies are a catataxic fallacy. Despite this, for many governments the nationality of a movie is still a hot topic. The movie industry was one of the first truly global industries, and the early Hollywood silent movies had a huge appeal worldwide. Not only was the dialogue on cards easy to translate, they told simple stories that were universally understood. And since almost everyone in Hollywood was an immigrant, the whole ethos was international from the start. As early as 1927, the British government introduced a quota system to restrict US imports and help its local industry. Screen quota systems still exist today in countries such as France, Korea, Brazil, Italy and Pakistan. In each case, there is a complicated set of rules that attempts to define what constitutes a local film. There are many things to consider besides just language: the story and subject matter, the location of the shoot, the nationality of the actors and crew, along with other elements of production, post production and distribution.

Taking a step back, you can see the same misguided nationalistic concerns in almost all industries. Take this transaction in the services sector: A Chinese tourist has his hair cut by a Polish stylist working in a London salon. Which country has benefited? Just as with movies, it's a moot point. An economist could map out for you how this export of services benefits the UK Invisibles[60] trade balance, and possibly Poland's too, if the hairdresser remits some of the money back to Poland to help his family. But the whole tortuous accounting process seems a bit pointless. It's a personal service that matters to the individuals, but it's never going to be the main plank of any national economic policy.

Governments tend to be more concerned with manufacturing: tangible goods rather than intangible services. Manufactured goods are visible symbols of national prowess. Think of German cars or

60 The UK has a huge trade surplus in invisibles; services such as tourism and banking. It is sometimes hard to conceive just what this is. The UK Invisibles Trade Delegation on a trip to China in the late 1990s was surprised to find itself being taken on a tour of a Braille printing machinery maker. The concept of 'no see' had got garbled in the translation.

Taiwanese semiconductors. But even here, the nationalistic sentiment is probably misplaced. Do industrial products really have a nationality any more? Where does the national label come from? Is it the designer? The parts manufacturer? The location of the assembly plant? Nike trainers are designed in Oregon in the USA and manufactured in Indonesia. Are those shoes an American product because they are designed in the USA? What about Apple's iPod? It has a British designer, working in California on a product that is manufactured in Taiwan. Does that make the iPod a British product?

Probably not. Most people would argue that the nationality of a product is determined by where the company is headquartered. But then again, company headquarters can often be relocated for tax purposes. Half of all publicly traded companies in the USA are incorporated in Delaware for tax purposes, even though their main offices are elsewhere. You might like to focus on ownership rather than location. After all, it is the shareholders who benefit in the end. They are the ones that the management of the company is toiling away to satisfy. Even here nationality is difficult to ascribe. Most publicly traded companies are owned by institutional share-holders; fund managers, like Fidelity or BlackRock, whose funds pool the savings of countless individuals around the world. It is hard to see beyond that institutional pool to the nationality of the individual savers. Typically, for a publicly traded company such as Apple or Nike, half of its shares will be held by foreigners. In Britain, over fifty per cent of the shares in publicly listed companies were in the hands of British individual investors in the 1960s. This has since fallen to around ten per cent. UK shares are overwhelming held by foreigners these days. It is the same trend in the rest of Europe. Those who think of Mercedes-Benz as a German company may be surprised to learn that seventy per cent of its shareholders are foreigners, a substantial proportion of whom are based in the Middle East.

The point is that companies are not national any more. They are multinational. Not just in where their factories are based or where their employees come from, but also in the pattern of their owner-ship by shareholders. Moreover, the four levers of economic control, resources, labour, capital and technology are no longer national but multinational. It is companies who control them these days. You can cast this as an epic battle between warring twins. The nation state and the joint stock company are both born at a similar time; two twins whose arrival heralds the modern world. Just as the Treaty of Westphalia ushers in the nation state, the creation of the English and Dutch East India companies in the early 1600s bring the concept of the corporation to life. At first, country rules company. These East India corporations are extensions of nationalistic enterprise and soon become the penetrative edge of a blade called colonisation. Then slowly nationalism gives way to multinationalism. In the end, destiny dictates that Romulus must kill Remus. Economics trumps politics. The company becomes more powerful and slays its twin, the nation state.

The bullying bond market

'I used to think that if there was reincarnation, I wanted to come back as the president or the pope. Now I would like to come back as the bond market. You can intimidate everybody,' says James Carville in 1993. He has just successfully run Bill Clinton's election campaign and is now his chief political advisor. He realises pretty soon that his boss, the most powerful man in the world, is less powerful than the forces of the global economy as expressed through yields in the bond market. Will future historians see this as the moment when economics trumps politics? . . . the moment that Remus dies? Or is it just the public acknowledgement of something long understood but unspoken. Maybe the key date is one year earlier, 16 September 1992, when the British Government was forced by speculators to withdraw sterling from the European Exchange Rate Mechanism (ERM). Or, maybe, it was the ending of the Bretton Woods system and the Nixon shock of 1971. We can leave that debate to the historians. What is clear is this: any governments that lack fiscal discipline will sooner or later have it imposed upon them by the global bond markets.

Look at modern Greece. No other country can lecture Greece, the birthplace of democracy, about the political arts. But when it comes to the economics, that is another matter. With the introduction of the Euro in 1999, the Greek Government is able to borrow money at a far lower interest rate than previously. As a result, it spends heavily and as a result runs up a substantial deficit. The rules for Euro membership set a limit for government deficits; they can be no more than three per cent of GDP. As early as 2003,

Greece has breached this. The figures then seem to improve slightly but this is only because Greece is hiding its true level of debt from the EU authorities. The 2008 global financial crisis hits the Greek tourism and shipping industries hard. GDP declines and the deficit soars to six per cent. In 2009, the government comes clean and announces that the deficit is in fact thirteen per cent. The yield on Greek bonds leaps to fifteen per cent, triggering a major crisis in the Euro zone and an emergency bailout for Greece which is effectively bankrupt. The Greek government is forced to impose a very severe set of austerity measures involving public sector wage cuts, tax hikes and pension reductions.

The point of the story is this. The bond market is able to do something that neither the Greek government nor the rest of the EU can achieve through political means. The Greek populace, through its elected governments, is unable to discipline itself financially. Anyone proposing an appropriate set of austerity measures in the years before the crisis is unelectable. Nor is the EU, despite its rules about deficit limits, able to impose any discipline through political means. If you have club rules, but rule breakers are still allowed to stay, then it's not much of a club, is it? No politician can get Greece to cut spending and live inside its means. The only mechanism that can force a Greek public sector worker to work longer hours for less money and retire later with a smaller pension is the bond market. Economics trumps politics. QED.

The non-nation state

Poor Nation State. It has lost its four levers of power. Capital is now its master, not its servant. Technology buzzes freely in the non-geographic realm of cyberspace. Resources are openly traded in global commodity markets and labour is increasingly able to move without restriction. It seems the Nation State is past its sell-by date. Is there anything left for it to control? Well, yes, there is still one thing: the rules.

Could it be that the future of the Nation State is to be stripped right back to its core: to be just a set of rules that operate in a particular defined region of geographic space. In fact, there may be more than one set of rules in that space. It is almost like a return to the overlapping authorities of medieval times. In those days, there was a multi-layered patchwork of city states, thrones, dominions and papal authorities all piled on top of each other. Maybe the future is a kaleidoscope of charter cities, special economic zones, monetary unions, trade blocs and supervising authorities, all competing for labour and capital in the international marketplace. Citizens get to pick and choose. Go to school wherever you can get the best free education, work in the country with the lowest taxes and retire somewhere where there is free health care.

Maybe the perfect state is so multicultural that it becomes culture neutral. It needs a strong and respected legal code, legislation to protect against discrimination, secure property rights, stable democratic government and plenty of land. Even better, and for good measure, a whole bunch of natural resources to gently exploit over the centuries. It can then compete aggressively for citizens, awarding passports to smart or wealthy immigrants to boost its economy. Welcome to the future; the culture free state. Yes, I am talking about Canada.[61]

Before I get lynched by my Canadian relatives and friends, I need to explain that I mean 'culture free' in the sense of being 'beyond culture'. In other words, a state that is not defined by its cultural identity, but by its legal identity: A country where the 'nation' part is no longer important. So you could maybe say that the future belongs to the non-nation state. Another way to illustrate this point is to contrast Canada and China. In effect, Canada is the 'Anti-China'. China is culturally distinct with weak legal institutions. Canada is multicultural with strong legal institutions. China is densely populated and resource poor, Canada sparsely populated and resource rich.

It is the legal institutions that are more important than the natural resources. Abundant resources, without rules, are a recipe for disaster. Just look at the Democratic Republic of the Congo. It is the most resource rich country on earth and also one of the poorest. That makes it a prime location for setting up some experimental charter cities. Canada, in contrast, has the full panoply of legally defined rights and, what is more, an efficient functioning bureaucracy to ensure they are properly exercised. It is bureaucracy that we turn to in the next chapter.

---

61 I could have picked Australia instead, or maybe even some of the Cantons in Switzerland.

CHAPTER 8

In Praise of Bureaucracy

Staffordshire, UK. Dr Peter Sackville is under pressure. He is the chief process engineer with a specialty chemicals company that has just won a small contract from a global food company. It's just a small order, more like a test order really. So it's important to deliver a high quality product on time. Because this little order could lead to much bigger things down the line. He is making Ethyl Heptanoate, a grape-flavoured food additive. It is an esterification reaction: combining an acid with an alcohol to form an ester. In this case, it is heptanoic acid, an oily liquid with an unpleasant rancid odour that he is mixing with ethyl alcohol. The result should be a clear colourless liquid with a fruity odour, a bit like green grapes. This reaction works fine in the lab, and the two-gallon test rig produced some excellent samples. But Paul is now standing in front of the big 750-gallon industrial reaction vessel on the factory floor scratching his head, because the bloody thing doesn't work, at least, not when it's scaled up to this size. It's the same chemicals, in the same proportions, put together in the same way but nothing is happening. All he can smell is that foul heptanoic acid. He has tried all the usual things; checked for impurities, changed the speed and size of the mixing blades on the stirring mechanism, tested for emulsions and all the rest. It still does not work. He has only three days before he has to deliver the final product. Time to call in the experts. He walks back to his office to phone a firm of consultants who specialise in scaling up chemical reactions . . .

Penampang, Malaysia. Chan Chew Lun, an amateur naturalist, is walking through the small village of Ulu Moyog. He is returning from a fruitful day spent pursuing his passion in the rainforest. Chan is crazy about stick insects, or Phasmida. He is an enthusiastic collector and has written a number of articles about these extraordinary insects. It is almost impossible to spot them in the rainforest canopy because they blend into the background so well. It's the ultimate passive defence strategy: hang around looking like a twig and hope no one spots you. There are over 3,000 different species of Phasmida, Some resemble sticks, others bark or leaves with an extraordinary variety of ingenious shapes. That is what makes them such popular pets. A local farmer sees the stick insects in Chan's collecting jar and beckons him over. Chan approaches him and the farmer beams with delight. He is holding something in his hands. It's a huge stick insect. The biggest Chan has ever seen. It's two foot-long. The farmer gives it to him with a smile and a nod. Chan's heart beats a bit faster. This is unlike any other stick insect in his collection. It might even be a new species. And it's enormous. It could be the longest stick insect in the world. If so, that would also make it the biggest thing in the whole insect kingdom: an insect as long as your arm. He had better send it to the Natural History Museum in London to make sure . . .

Tokyo, Japan. William Purcell is sitting in his twentieth floor apartment. He is looking at the concrete metropolis but dreaming of the desert. He works as a broker for an international investment bank and has just got a big bonus. He has been working hard all year and is looking forward to his holiday. Not just any holiday, but a very special one. William read the book *Arabian Sands* by the British explorer Sir Wilfred Thesiger last year, and it has inspired him to attempt his own desert adventure. Thesiger was exploring the Rub' al Khali, the empty quarter of Saudi Arabia in 1950. William plans to go this year to the Taklamakan desert in Western China: a huge expanse of sand skirted by the legendary oasis towns of the Silk Route. He can't wait to see the amazing rock paintings at Dunhuang and the bustling market of Kashgar. It's going to be expensive but he can afford it. All that sparse emptiness is the complete opposite to crowded Tokyo life; a perfect tonic. No, money is not the problem. His problem is camels. Not the getting hold of them, he can buy them in a local market when he gets there. The problem is how many camels to take. There is nothing at all in the desert, so the camels have to carry all the food and water for the expedition. But then the camels need to eat and drink themselves. That means more camels to carry the camel fodder. And more camels mean more herders. He has worked it all out on a spreadsheet. There is a clear upper limit. The longest the expedition can last is fifteen days. Taking more camels will not prolong that time, because most of the camels are already just carrying water for themselves. Still fifteen days in the desert is enough. This holiday is going to be fun . . .

The problems of scale

These three different stories are all about the same thing. They illustrate the problems of scaling things up because more of the same is different. This is the essence of catataxis. Within chemical engineering, there is a whole sub-discipline that is concerned with the problems of reproducing test-tube reactions in industrial sized kit. There can be any number of reasons why things don't work when they are expanded to an industrial scale. How can you ensure the two liquids are mixing properly together? You can't just shake it in your hand like a test tube any more. The size and design of the mixing paddles can make a critical difference. The viscosity and surface tension of liquids have different effects at different scales.[62] Maybe the two liquids will end up forming an emulsion. In other words, they might remain separate in a mayonnaise style suspension rather than reacting with each other. What about temperature? Is the chemical reaction at a larger scale generating too much heat? If it is a multi-step reaction then maybe the intermediate phases are combining with each other in a different way and end up going down a different path.

All these different types of problems with the scale-up of chemical reactions can be reduced to a single underlying concept: the surface area to volume ratio. As things get bigger, the surface area expands with the square but the volume expands with the cube. So the surface area to volume ratio decreases. It's a simple mathematical relationship. Imagine a sugar cube 1 cm long. It has six sides so its surface area is 6 square centimetres. Its volume is 1 cubic centimetre. So its surface area to volume ration is 6 (i.e. 6 divided by 1). Now let's double its size. The surface area is 24 square centimetres (6 times 4). The volume is now 8 cubic centimetres (2^3). The surface area to volume ratio is now 24 divided by 8, which is 3. So when we doubled the size of the sugar cube, the surface area to volume ratio halves.

Why does it matter? The surface area governs things like how

---

62 That's why pond skating insects can walk on water and you can't, despite what your adoring parents told you.

much heat can be lost or how much contact between chemicals there is. The volume controls how much heat is generated in the first place or how much of the chemicals you have. When you scale things up, the surface area to volume ratio goes down. So more heat is generated and less is lost. The whole thing runs hotter. Also there will be less contact between the chemicals. Both things can make a big difference to how the reaction progresses. This is best illustrated by the most famous chemical reaction of all: the chain reaction in a nuclear bomb. Once the surface area to volume ratio reaches a certain point – the critical mass – it explodes. A nuclear power station is a bomb that has not been allowed to reach critical mass. The surface areas and volumes are being carefully controlled so that the heat generated can be safely dissipated without exploding.

Surface area to volume is important for animals too. Christian Bergmann, a German biologist, noticed in 1847 that mammals in cold climates are generally larger than those in warm climates. For example, a Polar bear is four times bigger than a Black Bear. The surface area to volume ratio means that big bodies retain heat better, which is a useful trait in the Arctic. But there are other reasons why size is important to animals. Let's return to the stick insect story. Chan Chew Lun did send his phasmid to the Natural History Museum. It was indeed a new species and was named Phobaeticus chani or Chan's Megastick in his honour. It is the largest insect known in the world.

It is unlikely that we will ever find an insect much bigger, because there is an upper limit to insect size. This is because they have an exoskeleton rather than an endoskeleton. In other words, they have a hard carapace on the outside rather than bones on the inside. Beyond a certain size the hard exterior shell becomes excessively weighty; think of a knight struggling in heavy armour. In addition, insects grow by moulting, shedding the old shell and growing a new one. The bigger the shell, the more wasteful this is. A third issue is breathing problems.[63] Insects don't have lungs to pump air in and out of their bodies. Instead, they have a passive system that relies on diffusion through holes called spiracles in their exoskeletons. This

---

63 Of the three factors, breathing is probably the critical one. The fossil record shows larger insects when the oxygen levels were higher in the Carboniferous era 300 million years ago.

allows air to enter their tracheal tubes and deliver oxygen directly to their tissues. The bigger the body, the longer the tubes need to be, and it takes much longer for oxygen to diffuse down a long tube than a short one. So, the bigger the body, the harder it is to get oxygen to the cells.

This is the key point: the giant ants in the cheap sci-fi movies are a physical impossibility. Insects can never get bigger than Chan's Megastick. For a creature to get bigger than that, it needs to adopt a different body plan: an endoskeleton rather than an exoskeleton. Having made that design switch to internal bones, you can then grow to an enormous size. Let's take mammals as an example. One of the smallest is the Etruscan Pygmy Shrew at 3 cm long, similar in size to a large ant. The largest is the Blue Whale, which at 33 m long is more than a thousand times bigger. An insect could never get that big because of the limitations of an exoskeleton. So, just as with chemical reaction vessels, when things get bigger you have to do them differently.

Let's move from chemical reactions and insects to companies. A small company is different from a big company, as anyone who has worked in one knows. One of the most troublesome transitions in any company's life cycle is the growth from one to the other; from small local concern to big international company. It's the same as the switch from exoskeleton to endoskeleton. In order to get bigger, you have to completely re-invent the way you do things. That means defining things in a more systematic way; more admin, more red tape. Bureaucracy is the corporate endoskeleton.

Small companies seem more human. There is a much better team spirit. There is far less division of labour. Everyone seems to have two or three different things to do and generally people are happy to pitch in and help out where they can. Need a fire and safety officer? That can be you, Jim . . . Someone to write some bumf for the website? Edna, why don't you take a crack at that . . . Marketing Department? Ask Sarah, she is in charge of sales. The part that everyone plays is much more visible. It is easy to spot anyone who is not pulling their weight. In a small company there is not really anywhere to hide.

Small companies normally punch way above their weight. They can perform prodigious feats, just like insects. A grasshopper can jump twenty times its own height, a human less than two times and an elephant can't jump at all. So most small companies see the addition of more admin types as a big step backwards. All those extra bean counters and rubber stampers just soak up resources and get in the way. What do they do all day anyway? They just look like useless extra deadweight.

We are back in surface area to volume territory. Every company starts with at least one salesman, normally the owner. In its initial stages of growth, it expands by hiring more salesmen. The sales force, facing outwards to customers, is the 'surface area' of the company. All the other employees, with no client contact, are the volume. When small to big company switchover happens, the volume expands far faster than the surface area, the body plan changes from exo- to endoskeleton and suddenly there are a lot more administrators around. Whole new departments like HR, IT and Legal appear and start growing like Topsy. To front line staff this seems like madness. How can it be a good thing? The answer is that an ant can perform more impressively than a similar sized pygmy shrew, but can never get to be the size of a whale. In order to be bigger you have to be different. That is catataxis. More of the same is different.

The teeth to tail ratio

We have spent the last several chapters talking about economics and politics. Bureaucracy is the third leg on this stool. Both economics and politics are only possible with systems. It is the least glamorous of the three but maybe the most important. Most of us dream of being rich, famous and powerful but it is sometimes fun to ask your friends which of the three matters most to them. Would they prefer to be an anonymous millionaire, a bankrupt celebrity or an impoverished, faceless bureaucrat secretly running things behind the scenes? Be careful of the ones who answer the latter. They are the most dangerous.

We saw in the last chapter how the Roman Empire was so successful not because of its cultural excellence, but because of its bureaucratic excellence: its systems, infrastructure and laws. Romans were defined by their engineering; walls and roads that still exist to this day. These are control and communication structures. They are the physical manifestation of bureaucracy, the endoskeleton of empire. When they fell into disuse in the Dark Ages it is not because people suddenly forgot how to build and repair them but because they were no longer needed. It is not technological amnesia but the absence of a civilising bureaucracy. You no longer need big long distance roads because there are no large markets or forts to go to any more. No logistical imperative, so no main roads: Just local roads for local needs.

The armed forces understand the relationship between logistics and power very well. It is evident in the changing ratio of front line troops to support staff. This is called the 'teeth to tail ratio' or just T3R in military jargon. The soldiers in the front line with their rifles are the 'teeth'. Behind them is a long 'tail' of logistical and support units, like cooks, trainers, doctors, technicians, engineers and truck drivers. In the 1860s, during the American Civil War, the ratio stood at ten, in other words ten combat troops for each support person in the rear. By World War I this had fallen to three and in the Vietnam War, it stood at one (i.e., the number of combat troops was equivalent to the number of support troops). In the Gulf War of 2004, the ratio was only 0.6. A typical US heavy division of 22,000 troops breaks down like this: 8,500 combat troops, 6,300 logistical support and 7,200 in HQ and Admin. In addition, there are around 8,000 civilian contractors. In the past, these guys would have been part of the army but it's cheaper these days to subcontract these functions out. Including these contractors, there are three support staff for every one fighting man in the US Army today. The finest fighting machine on earth today has got a lot of bureaucrats.

The standard view of World War I is of 'lions led by donkeys'. Wave after wave of brave troops going pointlessly to slaughter, because the Generals are too stupid to change their tactics. The machine gun and barbed wire have changed the balance of power firmly in favour of defenders. Any attack is doomed to failure. It takes the invention of the tank and the aeroplane to swing the advantage back to the attacking side and break the deadlock of trench warfare. That is the most commonly held view of the tragedy of World War I. There is, however, another argument which goes like this: trench warfare is a stalemate not because of a failure of tactics but a failure of communication. Historians such as John Keegan have pointed out that the breakthroughs in the trench lines happen fairly often. The problem is not getting across No Man's Land to reach the other side; it is exploiting that breakthrough once you had made it. In a vast and confusing battlefield, twenty miles long, there is no easy way of communicating your success. So you don't get the logistical support and reinforcements you need and your fleeting gains are obliterated by a counterattack. The only form of communication is by field telephone, the radio has not been invented yet. This means talking over fixed land lines, not wireless. Just imagine how tough that is. Once you have captured part of the enemy trenches, someone has to run back across No Man's Land unreeling two thin copper wires to try and plug you into HQ. If a stray shell happens to break a cable, you have to start all over again.

So if you have a revisionist frame of mind you can argue that the stalemate in the trenches was not due to bureaucratic blundering and 'lions led by donkeys' but instead, because the admin and logistics functions were not powerful enough. Had there been a modern ratio of support troops, plus a reliable wireless communications system, things could have been very different. Look at the spectacular success of the second Gulf War. Combat operations last only three weeks and coalition forces lose only 200 men in the whole campaign. It is a stunning demonstration of what a modern army can achieve. Now look at the teeth to tail ratios. In 1918, it is three combat troops to one support; in 2004 it's the exact reverse. Yes, I know you cannot really compare the two; they are completely different types of war at different times with different technologies. At the same time, it looks like all those guys working in logistics and admin really knew their stuff and made a big difference. The point I am trying to make is this: more bureaucracy is not necessarily a bad thing. In fact, it's sometimes a very good thing. It can make the difference between winning and losing a war.

Hero with a clipboard

It's not just the army, it's the navy too. The historian Nicholas Rodger believes that the reason the British Navy was so dominant in the nineteenth century was the excellence of its logistical supply. The secret to exploiting naval power to its fullest extent is the ability to keep ships at sea for long periods with healthy crews. This is something that Britain excelled at, through the work of the Victualling Board at the Admiralty. Their system of fresh fruit rations gave rise to the mocking nickname 'Limeys' but it conveyed a serious military advantage. It was not really the heroic escapades of Horatio Hornblower-types that made the British Navy so powerful, but the daily toiling of a grey bureaucrat in a procurement office in London. It's hard to make an entertaining story out of that, though.

Here we get to the real reason why bureaucracy gets such a bad rap. In most popular fiction and movies the bureaucracy is the enemy. Bureaucracy is anti-heroic. It's an obstructive force that the protagonist must circumvent. The constraints of the narrative dictate it must be so. The hero is an individual battling against dark and sinister forces. He stands apart from the crowd and does things unconventionally. He is a man of action with contempt for pen pushers and paperwork. His boss bawls him out for not doing things by the book. All these clichés are meant to strengthen our identification with the hero. We are united with him against the common enemy: the bureaucrats. Procedures and paperwork are for pussies!

The problem is that procedures and paperwork are very important. A new technique has been introduced into hospitals in the last decade which has caused a dramatic improvement in surgical survival rates. This new, life-saving technology is a very old idea: a checklist. Surgical procedures have become increasingly complex over the last fifty years. In the USA, 80,000 people a year get infected while in intensive care which often ends in accidental death. Doctors looked across at the airline industry and its enviable safety record and copied the pre-flight checklist concept from them. Now hospitals that have introduced pre-surgery checklists have seen a major improvement in outcomes in the operating theatres. It's all pretty simple stuff. The surgical team introduce themselves to each other and then go through a simple checklist: Washed hands? Check. Cleaned patient's skin with antiseptic? Check. Surgical drapes? Check. The result of this seemingly pedestrian activity is that surgical infection rates fall by two thirds. Even the act of introducing themselves to each other makes a difference. Nurses who spot an error during the surgery are more likely to interrupt the surgeon and point it out if they know his name.

So there you have it. Clipboards and checklists save lives. As soon as there is enough complexity in a large project you need a proper process. If there is a long list of tasks that have to be done in precisely the right order, then it's foolish just to rely on human memory.

Project managers already know this. So do architects, supply chain consultants, construction engineers, software programmers and production risk managers. And there is a whole tool kit of Gantt charts, PERT networks and Critical Path diagrams that have been developed to help control the process. I know that these guys sound like the type to avoid sitting next to on a long flight. But just because you find it dull does not mean it's unimportant.

Spreadsheet to database

It all comes back to the problem of the camels at the start of the chapter. The natural first assumption is that things are simple and scalable. Need it done in half the time? Let's get twice as many people. Want your desert adventure to last longer? Then get more camels. But pretty soon you realise things are not scalable. Just as insects can't get bigger than a certain size, some projects will always take a certain amount of time. More camels won't prolong your trip because it's not a simple linear relationship, it's more complicated than that. Another good example is a large software project. Let's say you have ten programmers working on a complex piece of software. Your deadline is looming and you want it done in half the time. Should you hire another ten programmers? No. In fact, that might be the worst thing you could do. More people means it could take even longer. Since all the bits of code need to interlock with each other, everyone needs to know what everyone else is doing. The more people there are, the greater the coordination requirements. Pretty soon everyone is spending all their time telling all the others what they are doing, rather than just getting on and doing it.

You can see this catataxic shift most clearly when you go from a spreadsheet-based system to a multi-user database. Let's say Sarah in the sales department is keeping a list of which clients she has sent samples to. It's all on a little spreadsheet that she set up herself; a list of client names and a few boxes ticked in columns where samples have been sent. Sarah's colleague Jim sees it, and he likes it. He starts to keep a similar list himself. Then the boss has the bright idea that maybe they should use a list like that to keep track of the activity in the whole department. And not just samples, what about keeping track of client meetings too? Pretty soon his secretary is struggling with a big, unwieldy spreadsheet trying to keep track of everything. She complains its taking up so much time she can't do her other work. Maybe it's time to convert it into a proper database? That way everyone can keep their own stuff up to date, and they can just look up the summary data themselves without having to ask the secretary . . .

It's a fairly familiar story. The shock comes when the software company quotes for the bespoke client management system. It seems very expensive. All you want is a couple of interlinked lists of customers that everyone can look at and keep up to date. You don't need the new system to do much more than what you have cobbled together on the old spreadsheet. The functionality is the same: it just needs to do that more efficiently. Since the spreadsheet cost you nothing, why does the new system cost so much? This is the common complaint of someone facing an exo- to endoskeleton transition.

The spreadsheet is an amazing general purpose tool. You can create lists, manipulate data, perform arithmetic functions and create charts very simply. It allows you to design, specify, populate and test a little system in under fifteen minutes; so quickly, in fact, that you may not realise you have even done all those steps. It's an instinctive way of expressing some quite complicated things. It's also personal, so you get exactly what you want, how you want it. It's cheap and best of all, it works. And even when it does not, it's quite easy to fix. Using spreadsheets tends to set your expectations of software systems quite high. The spreadsheet is the grasshopper that jumps twenty times its own height.

Now contrast that with a bespoke database system. It could take you three days just to explain what you want, and another week for the software guys to interview prospective users to analyse their requirements. Then you have to sign off on the functional specifications that have to be converted into code by programmers. You have to create dummy data to test the system functionality, and then populate the system with real data. Then comes user-acceptance testing, and rollout. What a palaver. No wonder it costs so much. And at the end of all that, you just have something that does the same as the old system. The pygmy shrew is unimpressive compared to the grasshopper. Apart from one key difference; the database is scalable, the spreadsheet system is not. In moving from spreadsheet to database, you have just crossed a catataxic boundary. From a single user tool to a multi-user system.

Cloud computing and catataxic crime

In the world of computing, there are many hierarchical levels. We already discussed some of them in Chapter 2. A personal computer has a whole set of hierarchies, from memory chips and mother-boards to operating systems and software. Each can only be understood in its own terms. You can't edit a word document by tweaking things at the memory chip level. Even if you ignore all the hardware, there is still a complex hierarchy just within software. The latest trend of cloud computing extends this into the realm of services. In essence, anyone sitting at a PC connected to the internet can avail himself of many different types of services 'in the cloud'. It does not really matter whether the programs are running on your machine or somewhere else. You don't really care about the physical location or the configuration of the system so long as you are getting the services you need. So cloud computing is a bit like the electricity grid. It does not matter very much how or where the electricity is generated or how it gets to your house. You just want a constant supply at the right voltage coming out of your socket.

A good example of cloud computing is Google Docs. This is basically a word processor 'in the cloud'. I have written this whole book in Google Docs. I could have used a word processor on a computer at home saving copies of my draft on my own hard disk. But by using Google Docs, my draft is available to me anywhere in the world at any time on any computer I like. I can be sitting in an internet cafe near the beach, in a hotel room on a business trip or sitting in my friend's house using his computer. I just log in and pick up writing where I left off. Both the programme I use to write with and the manuscript are up there in the cloud. And best of all, it's absolutely free. Sounds like an advert for Google Docs? Well, I guess it is. I'm a fan and I have used their service extensively for two years without paying a cent. But there are plenty of other cloud computing programmes besides Google. In fact, the most popular category is client account management systems. The story I told earlier about the database is so common that there are now a lot of off-the-shelf solutions in the cloud.

With cloud computing, the user is sitting at the highest conceptual level of the hierarchy and ignoring everything underneath. She may be ignoring it, but others are paying close attention. Hackers exploit the weaknesses of the system because they are below the visible horizon. They attack from beneath like *Jaws*. Computer hacking is a catataxic crime because it operates one or two levels lower down, at the operating system level. Computer viruses, like their biological counterparts, are far smaller in scale than the host systems they infect. In the military, they call this asymmetric warfare. The combat operations of the Second Gulf War were over in three weeks. What followed was years of asymmetric warfare as the complex high level machine of the US military struggled to cope with individual insurgents and suicide bombers. Terrorists, hackers and viruses in this sense are all the same. They are catataxic aggressors, operating at a lower level than their target and harnessing the hierarchical complexity to their advantage.

The future that wasn't

Terrorists . . . hackers . . . computer viruses? That was not the vision of the future in the 1940s. The future back then was all to do with the progress of science and how labour saving devices would change the way we live. Some of that came true. It is possible to argue that the washing machine has changed society more profoundly than the internet has, by liberating women from the drudgery of housework. But one key part of the 1940's fantasy future has not come true: robots. The dream was that robots would do all the work while we all led lives of indulgent leisure. A bit like an antebellum plantation owner in the South, but with mechanical slaves.

Things are certainly more automated today but if anything we are working harder than before. What happened to all that leisure time? Well, the flaw in the argument is that an economy is not a closed, static system but an open, dynamic one. If you think about the robot fantasy in more detail you can see that it assumes two things: the amount of work is fixed and some form of benevolent dictator is there to distribute the benefits. If there is only a certain amount of work to do then there is a clear choice; either the robot does it or you do. But if you don't do any work why should you get any rewards? You need a benevolent dictator to freely redistribute the products the robots make. Without him, your 'leisure time' should really be called 'unemployment'. If you look back at the public films of the 1940s extolling the benefits of automation, leisure time and the robotic future, they seem a perfect distillation of the capitalist dream. In fact, they are implicitly socialist. The 'leisure dividend' story requires a closed economy and a bureaucracy to carry out an egalitarian redistribution of goods. Sounds just like communism, doesn't it.

In the modern world, economies are open and dynamic. The robots may be doing the work you used to do, but you are now doing other more productive work. Mechanisation means less people are involved in manual labour, and more are doing white collar work. A combine harvester in a wheat field can do in one day what it took fifty men to do a few generations ago. It's the same story with assembly robots on a car line, or the cranes and containers in a busy port. Meanwhile, humans have increasingly become office workers; wearing suits and doing marketing, design or administrative work. The productivity has increased dramatically as a result. The benefit has not come in increased leisure time but in cheaper goods and more consumer choice. It's all about added value and price. So we are all office workers now; we have become bureaucrats because we add more value that way.

The death of modernism

A bureaucrat is, literally, someone with a desk job. It comes from 'bureau' the French word for desk or office. Maybe we need to draw a distinction between two different types of bureaucrat. There is the top down central planner that you might find in a Stalinist regime. Then there is the administrative office worker; maybe a sales coordinator or someone on an IT help desk. One dictates things from above, the other responds to requests from below.[64] The first type imposes the same solution regardless of circumstance, the second tailors things to the customer's needs. The support troops in an army division are the second type. Sure, they have their own way of doing things, but it is a way that has been sculpted by bitter experience. Software engineers developing a database are the second type too. They spend a long time trying to figure out exactly what the customer wants. In fact, corporate bureaucracy is generally of the second type because it is honed by the discipline of the market.

---

64 I will refrain from making a mean joke about the responsiveness of 'help' desks here. Those guys do a thankless task and are cruelly under appreciated.

A good example of the first type, aside from anyone in a communist regime, is a town planner. At the beginning of the twentieth century, modernist architects believe they can cure society's ills by designing better cities. They see buildings as 'machines for living' and think by planning towns properly they can do away with urban problems such as crime, traffic jams, poverty and squalor. A number of new cities are designed and built along modernist lines. The main principle is strict functional separation: industrial, commercial and residential zones kept apart and the citizens housed in tall apartment blocks at widely spaced intervals. Often they are capital cities, such as Brasilia (Brazil), Canberra (Australia) and Islamabad (Pakistan). They are built on brand new sites to avoid contamination from the old and to give the architects a blank canvas for their utopia. Half a century later they are seen as sterile, experimental failures. 'Suburbs in search of a city' is a common jibe. There is little economic activity in any of them apart from government workers who are forced to be there. None of them pose any real competitive challenge to the vibrant, raucous, unplanned cities they were supposed to usurp. It is hard to find anyone who, if given a free choice, would not prefer Rio to Brasilia, Sydney to Canberra or Karachi to Islamabad.

On a smaller scale, the failure of modernist architecture is best encapsulated in the story of the Pruitt–Igoe housing project. In 1950, town planners in St Louis, Missouri, clear local slums to build thirty-three residential tower blocks in an urban renewal project. Following the best modernist principles, the apartments are made deliberately small and the elevators only stop at every third floor. Why? The planners want to force residents to use the stairs and other communal facilities. This will promote community interaction. Sadly, the only community interaction that develops is muggings in the stairwells and laundry rooms. Despite winning several architectural awards, twenty years later the Pruit–Igoe tower blocks are virtually abandoned and have deteriorated into a crime-infested, decaying, dangerous neighbourhood. In 1976, the complex is finally demolished; an act that is now interpreted as the moment that modernism died. The bulldozers clear away not just the rubble, but also the utopian dreams of top down of urban planning.

Cities are an emergent phenomenon, they accrete from the bottom up. There is no better, or more literal, example of this than the Basilica di San Clemente in Rome. At ground level, you see a beautiful eleventh century church. It is one of the most richly adorned in all Rome with shrines to St Clement and the tomb of St Cyril, who invented the Glagolitic alphabet.[65] This church is built on the ruins of an earlier fourth century basilica. Then beneath that is a first Century mithraeum; a sanctuary to the cult of Mithras. At the very bottom is part of the Cloaca Maxima, the main sewer system of Ancient Rome. So by walking up from the basement of this building you pass through a thousand years of history to arrive at street level in a building which is itself a thousand years old.

The great cities of the world, like Rome, have grown through the actions of lots of individuals over a long period of time. They have evolved, through cycles of sacking and rebuilding, to become a rich and complex accretion of history and human enterprise. That is what makes a city great. A stimulating place to visit and to live. You can't plan that. It has to arise slowly and spontaneously through time. Today's town planners recognise this and take a much more collaborative approach. No longer dictating from above, they seek to influence development from the side. They are mainly concerned with transport infrastructure, services and environmental concerns. They set certain guidelines and constraints, but allow the private sector to design and build their own buildings inside those general rules.

The overpaid curator

The mistake modernist architects made was to reduce the multiple meanings of a city to a single one. To focus only on the configuration of space, misunderstanding the importance of place. Cities are complex systems that do not respond well to a reductionist approach. Cities are more than the sum of their parts. Their value is not dissectible. It emerges from the interaction of elements many layers beneath. They are a cataxic triumph. This leads us to pose a more general question. Is it ever possible to impose value by top down planning? Or to put it another way: does the curator of an exhibition add any value?

---

65 The Glagolitic alphabet is a Slavic alphabet with 41 letters. It was superseded in the Middle Ages by the simpler Cyrillic alphabet with 33 letters, named in honour of the original saint.

Let's take a hypothetical art gallery. A new show has been curated with pieces by many different artists. Has the value of the pieces been changed by being gathered together? Is it greater than the sum of the parts? The answer is yes for the viewer, but no for the owner. We can examine this in more detail. The value of an individual painting may go up if it is shown in a gallery. Greater public recognition will make it worth more. But that is because it is in the gallery and not because it is in the collection. There is also a value in juxtaposition. The physical proximity of two pieces implies a relationship between them. An Old Master displayed next to a modern abstract painting might highlight unexpected resonances. This could deepen the appreciation of both works, illuminating them in a new way. This can be called the 'Shakespeare in modern dress'[66] argument. By putting a classic text in a new environment, new layers of meaning are uncovered. Same old words, new context. But the value lies with the beholder; the value of the object itself is not increased.

There is one way that a curator can add value. It is through the classification and categorisation of pieces. Identifying a piece as by a particular artist can make a big difference to the price, something we will examine further in the next chapter . In other words when a curator acts as a taxonomist he adds value. In everyday life, there is a similar phenomenon. Most people have a pile of old, unsorted junk in their attic. Sorting that stuff out, photographing it and putting it on eBay will turn that pile of junk into a pile of cash. In your attic it is worth nothing; properly labelled and in a marketplace it is worth something. Taxonomy and the proper context adds value; the effort bureaucrats expend in filing things is not a waste of time.

If an art enthusiast has spent years acquiring pieces for a personal collection, is that collection worth more than the sum of its parts? Probably not. That's why the collection ends up being sold off in an auction piece by piece. If it is kept together and bought by a museum 'for the nation', the price paid is likely to be a discount to its true value. Each individual piece may be more valuable having

---

66 I am not picking on curators. Most ideas have already been thought of by someone else. So authors like me are really just reorganising them so that they can be seen from a different perspective. In other words, this book is also a 'Shakespeare in modern dress' exercise.

been previously owned by a famous person, but the whole is less than the sum of the parts. It's the same economics at work when antiquarian books get broken up. The engraved prints inside them are worth more when framed up and sold individually. The text is junked. The pictures are worth more than a thousand words.

In financial circles, breaking up collections of things and selling the parts is known as asset stripping. We can illustrate this by looking at investment trusts which are a popular financial vehicle in the UK. An investment trust is a closed end fund. It works like this. An initial sum of money is raised and invested in assets like stocks and bonds. This lump of money is incorporated as a company. The company does not do anything except own those assets. Investors buy shares in the company to get exposure to the fund's assets. The prices of the stocks and bonds that the company owns change every day. As a result, the share price of the company changes to reflect the fluctuating value of the underlying assets. This is the key question: is the whole worth more than the sum of the parts? Is the value of the holding company greater or less than the assets that it owns?

The answer is less. Investment trusts normally trade at a small discount to asset value. In other words, the whole is less than the sum of the parts. There are exceptions. An investment trust that specialises in exotic or illiquid stocks can sometimes trade at a premium. This happens when investor enthusiasm for a particular theme, say China or Green Energy, exceeds the investible universe. But this is a short term phenomenon and the funds soon end up back at a discount again – but not too much of a discount. If the difference between the value of the company and its assets becomes too great then someone can buy up the whole company, break it up and sell off the parts at a profit. This is called asset stripping. It can be done, equally effectively, to companies, antiquarian books or art collections.

It is easy to see if it is worth breaking up an investment trust. The share prices, both of the company and its holdings, are listed every day. So it's a simple sum to see if the discount is so great that it has become a good break-up target. This information is available to everyone, so people buy in the expectation that someone else might break it up. As a result, investment trusts normally trade in a discount range of three to twenty per cent. If it is any more than this, it becomes a takeover target.

Do companies add value?

An investment trust is a company that does nothing except hold shares or bonds. What about a normal company that actually makes things? We can do the same calculation that we did with the investment trust. A company's share price is quoted every day. The value of its assets is regularly given in its quarterly and annual accounts. Is the whole greater than the sum of the parts? The answer is yes. Companies normally trade at a premium to their asset value. So why is a normal company worth more than its parts but an investment trust less? It must be because it is not just a holding company, it is actually doing something. Companies, in general, do add value.

There is an old joke about economists that goes like this. Two economists are walking down the street. The younger man spots a £20 note lying on the pavement, and points it out to his colleague. The elder, not even bothering to look, says, 'You are mistaken, dear boy. It cannot be a £20 pound note. If it were, someone would already have picked it up.' Using the same logic, companies must add value otherwise they would not exist. Someone would have already bought them out or asset stripped them.[67] But there is a deeper issue here that I want to explore.

Companies come in many different shapes and sizes. At one extreme is a single person company; at the other is a vast conglomerate. Let's look at the former first. An individual freelancer going about his business is called a sole trader. He may wish to set up a company with one director and one employee, both of which would be himself. This company is different from a sole trader set-up, because the law recognises the company as a legal person. It's one individual but two 'people'; one is flesh and blood, the other a legal construct. The company exists on a different hierarchical level. So here we have the first potential area for catataxis: a self-employed businessman and his accountant doing their tax returns. How much of his spending on taxis and lunches can be claimed as business expenses? Should the costs be borne by the individual or by the

---

67 Strictly speaking this is only true of listed companies whose shares are freely available to buy in the stock market. For a private company, the owner can decide if he wants to sell or not.

company, one level up? The accountant's job is to resolve this level confusion.

The law sees the company as a separate entity. If anything goes wrong, it is the company that is liable and not the individual. This leads unscrupulous businessmen to set up companies and operate through them. When things get too hot, they shut down that company and open another, leaving the mess to be sorted out by the receivers in the bankruptcy proceedings. This behaviour has become more prevalent in recent times. If a company has done something grossly wrong, is it fair that the directors should be able to get away with it scot free?[68] This is the second area of catataxis, sometimes known as 'piercing the corporate veil'.

Imagine a talented architect is leaving a firm to set up on his own. He wants to take a bunch of clients with him. He has previously signed a no-compete clause and wants to get around it. So he sets up a new company just to employ himself. His old firm tries to sue him. He claims that he is not competing. It is the new company that is doing the competing and it has not signed any agreements. In a case like this, most courts would still find the architect guilty. The court would pierce the corporate veil and view the new company as a sham.

Piercing the corporate veil is more common in the USA than the UK. It normally happens with small companies where there is a lot of overlap between the shareholders and the company's activities. Larger companies have a greater degree of separation between the employees and shareholders. Coming back to the original topic, they are more likely to create value. Let's look at three types of company: a small firm of consultants, a medium sized manufacturing company and a large multinational conglomerate. Taking the first one, a corporate structure offers limited benefits to the consultants in the small firm. There is no expensive plant and machinery required. The only advantage is the shared office overheads. The consultants don't interact with each other much and there is only a loose connection between them. They have their own clients and could do pretty much the same amount of business on their own as freelancers. The value of the whole is similar to the sum of the parts.

---

68 The individual and the company may be jointly liable under Tort law, in which case there is no need to pierce the corporate veil.

The best indicator of a setup where the individual is adding more value than the company is big bonuses. Investment bankers or footballers are good examples. The bargaining power of the individual is high because it is his activity rather than corporate know-how that is creating the value. The recent public outcry against 'obscene' bonuses at investment banks is a cataxic fallacy. The investment bank has no centralised system that enables it to regularly make money trading the markets. It relies on the individual flair of its traders and investment bankers. Likewise, there is no secret instruction book that guarantees winning a game of football.[69] It is highly dependent on the reactions and skills of the players on the field. That's why in the UK football clubs regularly make losses while paying enormous amounts to their players. It is all about relative bargaining power, both in sport and in banking.

Investment banks and High Street banks are different creatures. When mergers combine them together, a tectonic fault line remains between the two. The main difference is in the attitude towards risk. Investment Banks are risk-seeking because that is where the rewards are. High street banks are risk averse because that is where the problems lie. High street banks put great faith in their systems. The bank's know-how is encapsulated in their complex loan approval process. That means staff are fairly lowly paid because they just need to follow the system. Individual flair and creative imagination are more of a liability than an asset. Systems and processes add the value, people don't. An investment bank is the complete opposite of this. Deals are won through personal relationships with clients or the finely honed instincts of an individual trader. People add the value, system and processes get in the way. Of course, investment banks will often claim that they have a fine set of systems and processes, particularly when they are talking to a banking regulator. But if their success was institutional rather than individual, then why are the staff paid so much? The staff, clearly, have the upper hand when it comes to bargaining.

69 American football with its frequent stoppages is more play-book dependent than soccer. But the point is still the same. If the secret of success is all in the book, then why are the players paid so much? And why do American Football stars generally earn more than those in European Soccer.

High Street Banks also understand bargaining power. One of the best examples of how 'more of the same is different' is the loan conundrum. If you owe the bank a small amount of money then it is your problem. If you owe the bank a large amount of money then it is their problem. If your debt is so large that defaulting would bankrupt the bank then you have a lot of bargaining power. The scale of the debt is the key factor. When it comes to loans, size matters.

So far we have been looking at service companies. In manufacturing, it is much more evident that the value is created institutionally. There is a factory full of expensive machinery and a complicated, sequential manufacturing process. The larger the company gets, the higher the degree of specialisation and division of labour. The workers on the factory floor execute their eloquent teamwork. Then there are all the other departments such as sales, accounts, legal, R&D and so on. Each performs its own specialist role. This is a complex system with a large number of people. It creates value as an emergent phenomenon. Here the whole is more than the sum of the parts.

At the other extreme is the big multinational conglomerate. Conglomerates have many different business lines and many different companies under their umbrella. Conglomerates can exploit synergies between these companies. They can benefit from economies of scale. There may be cross selling opportunities, for different products to the same client. But beyond all these benefits, there comes a time when the sheer size of the conglomerate becomes a negative. It becomes more of a holding company than a dynamic value creator. At this stage, the multinational begins to suffer from a conglomerate discount implying the company would be more valuable if it was broken up. If the discount gets big enough, corporate raiders will do just that.

The termite CEO

At this point, some readers may raise an objection. There may seem to be an inconsistency here. We have argued that top down planning does not add value. We have also argued that a company *does* add value. Surely a company is planned from the top down? It is not a spontaneous emergent phenomenon, is it?

The objection argument goes something like this. A termite mound is an emergent phenomenon. There is no grand termite architect planning the whole thing, it arises from the collective activity of thousands of termites. A company is different. A car does not spontaneously arise from workers aimlessly milling around on a shop floor. The whole thing is designed and planned. It is driven from above and not below. Termites don't have a CEO, companies do.

In my view, companies *are* emergent. I think you can reverse the causality of planning and growth. The conventional view is that companies plan, therefore they're successful and grow. But you can equally argue that companies are successful and grow, therefore they plan. Bureaucratic functions, such as planning, emerge at a later stage when a company switches from exoskeleton to endoskeleton.

The link between cause and effect is notoriously difficult to make. A common logical fallacy is best summed up in the Latin phrase *post hoc ergo propter hoc*. This means 'after this and so because of this'. Just because an event happened before another, it does not mean that it caused the other. The appropriate analogy here is the egotistical rooster. He notices the sun always rises after he crows in the morning. Therefore, he believes that his crowing causes the sun to rise.

The argument here is similar to the discussion about the unit of selection in biology in Chapter 4. Cell enthusiasts point out that the number of single cell organisms is vastly greater than the number of multi-cell organisms on earth. Life is predominantly a single cell phenomenon. Theories of evolution have focused too much on large creatures: finches, wombats, lizards and humans. Microbes are generally ignored.

Now look at the corporate world. Small companies vastly outnumber the big ones. Of the five million companies in the USA, eighty per cent have less than ten employees. Small businesses generate half of the country's GDP. Most management theorising focuses on the large, successful companies since that is what everyone aspires to become. This is a distortion of the corporate universe. Typically, a consulting guru will pick a successful multinational and then illustrate what game plan they followed to achieve that success. The script goes something like this: This was their plan, they were successful. If you use this plan, you will be successful. In my view, this approach suffers from the 'post hoc' fallacy. There are so many potential weak links. Was that really their plan at the time? Did they actually apply it? Was their success due to that plan or some other fortuitous macroeconomic event? Can it be applied elsewhere? Is it appropriate today?

Small companies tend to try many things and then just focus on the products that are popular. Their 'planning' process is better described as 'suck it and see'. They evolve in a complex environment created by the wishes of customers, the actions of competitors, the shortcomings of suppliers and the idiosyncrasy of employees. Most of these are only half glimpsed through the fog of incomplete data. Small companies are just doing their best by muddling through. They are successful not because they dictate the environment but because they adapt to it.

A big company is just a successful small company. So the CEO of a big company, explaining why his firm has done so well, is like the arrogant rooster who believes he caused the sun to rise. Companies are pragmatic. They don't start with a theory and then execute it. They do what works and then let management consultants theorise about it. Companies are anti-academic. Their credo is, 'It works in practice. Now tell us why it's OK in theory.' Most company management is reactive, not proactive. Company strategy is the logical outcome of a set of constrained choices. Cars may have a designer, but they still end up looking pretty much the same. That's because, as we know, they all use the same wind tunnel to test the design. They all look similar because that's the best answer to the design constraints. So in my view companies are like termite mounds, more shaped by pragmatic responses to the environment than a top down central plan. The 'plan' is a post hoc rationalisation of what has already happened. It exists because it is the grammar of bureaucracy. It is an effect rather than a cause; an output not an input.

Bureaucracy adds value.

How can you tell if a company adds value? My answer is that it depends on their size. It should be large and complex enough to have division of labour. There needs to be a bureaucratic endoskeleton so that it is more than just a bunch of talented individuals: The whole must be worth more than the sum of the parts.

This may come across as a glib oversimplification of a complicated topic. There is a vast amount of literature and an established analytical framework that addresses this question in a different way. The traditional way, which establishes if a company is worth more than the sum of its parts, is to look at the Price to Book (P/B) ratio. This is the market value of the company divided by its total asset value. In other words, what the stock market says it is worth, compared with what the accountants say it is worth. The stock market is valuing the whole. The accountant is valuing the parts.

A second way to examine value added is to compare inputs with outputs. A company takes in raw materials and puts out finished goods. If the value of what comes out is greater than what went in (including labour) then it has added value. There are several different measures of profits but all are indications of added value. A third way is to look at investment returns. A company is said to be value creating if it makes a return to shareholders above its cost of capital. Companies borrow money and invest it in their activities. If the returns from that investment are greater than the cost of borrowing, then the company has added value. So there are several different established ways to answer the value question. You can take your pick between them: a sum of the parts calculation, a profitability measure or an investment return analysis.

I think all of these methods are missing something. They focus on a narrow definition and not the bigger picture. Each one has its flaws. First, the Price to Book ratio is based on tangible assets like plant and machinery. The creative genius in an advertising company is not valued as a financial asset because he is not owned by the company. He is not a slave even though he may complain that he is treated that way. So the P/B ratio for a consultancy firm looks artificially high because the denominator is understated.[70] I contend that a company composed of a loose collection of freelancers is worth less than the sum of its parts, even if the P/B ratio is greater than 1. This is because the accounts struggle to value the intangible parts. Likewise, profitability measures are easy to manipulate. In effect, you are subtracting two very large numbers (sales and costs), so very slight changes in either can have a dramatic effect on the difference. A company's 'profits' are quite subjective and often depend on the intended audience. Most companies have different

70 Unlike investment trusts, it is very rare to find a listed company with a P/B less than 1.

sets of accounts; the management accounts will have a different profit figure to the tax accounts. The third analysis compares return to shareholders with cost of capital. If financial output is greater than financial input then value has been created. The trouble is that it is tricky to evaluate the input. This method uses the Capital Asset Pricing Model (CAPM) to calculate the cost of equity. The CAPM assumes that risks are normally distributed and that investors are rational, both of which are doubtful as we discussed in earlier chapters.

The linking theme for all three points in the debate is the meaning of the word 'value'. It has a precise definition for accountants and financial analysts. In the sense that I am using it, that definition is too narrow; too focused on shareholder value and not on stakeholder value. I am not able to offer a financial definition of my own. I am using the word 'value' more in a conceptual way than a monetary way. Oscar Wilde famously observed that 'A cynic knows the price of everything and the value of nothing'. Even in financial circles there are several different theories of value, each espoused by a different economic school. So I will summarise my view below.

Corporate value is emergent. It arises when the whole is more than the sum of the parts. It is greatly influenced by company size and the operating environment. When there are enough employees to have division of labour and operational complexity, value is created by the company. A company's value is embedded in its systems and know-how. Every company has its own way of doing things, a culture that has evolved through hard won experience. That core remains even though the employees may change. That core is a bureaucratic endoskeleton which is the repository of corporate value. If a company is too small, then the value lies with the people and not the corporation. If it's too large, the companies under the conglomerate umbrella may be more valuable on their own. A curator's approach, collecting unrelated companies under a single umbrella rarely adds value. Value arises from below and is not imposed from above.

Fat is good

One of the common exercises that company management conducts to increase value added is outsourcing. It involves a detailed analysis of which parts of the company are adding value and which are not. It there is a particular part or component that another company can make more cheaply, then it could make sense to outsource it. That way the company can focus on the core activities it does best, and let subcontractors do the same in their areas of expertise. The auto industry today is an interesting example of how far this process can go. Car makers are traditionally seen as symbols of large scale, monolithic manufacturing. But decades of outsourcing by car makers in search of higher profit margins means that you could now almost start a car company from your bedroom if you have enough money. You can find a subcontractor for almost every step in the process. You can start by commissioning a well known designer to come up with a great looking car; then run his ideas past a firm of auto engineering consultants. There are plenty of independent auto parts manufacturers, 10,000 of them in the USA alone. So every conceivable item you may need can be outsourced to them. Then there are assembly subcontractors who will happily bolt it all together for you, and independent distributors who will sell your cars in their showrooms. Sitting in your bedroom, you just need to fund it and coordinate it all. Congratulations, you are now a luxury car maker.

It's a fanciful example, but theoretically quite possible. What it illustrates is that the only bit that can't be outsourced is the money and the admin. So if you strip away all the non-essential activities you are left with the real essence of a company: finance and organisation. In other words – bureaucracy. That must be the bit that adds the value, everything else is optional. Of course, few companies would ever go quite that far, because there is a downside to outsourcing which is loss of control. If you outsource too much you become vulnerable. We can generalise the issue like this: there is a trade-off between redundancy and resilience.

The demands of the market drive organisations towards efficiency. There is a constant need to eliminate waste, reduce costs and find economies of scale. Look at modern supermarkets. To maximise profits, you need really good inventory control; the minimal amount of produce in your stores and depots but still enough that the customer gets everything he wants. Your stores are supplied through distribution hubs. These central warehouses take in goods from around the country and ship them to stores on a 'just in time' basis. Economies of scale mean that the bigger and more central your distribution hub the more efficient it is. Over time your hubs get bigger and the number of hubs gets smaller. The logical conclusion of the trend is to end up with just one big hub. But this is where the second factor, resilience, kicks in. If something goes wrong in that big central warehouse then you are really in trouble. Since it supplies all your stores, your whole retail empire will suffer. So maybe it's best not to put all your eggs in one basket, or all your dairy produce in one big distribution hub. Better to have a few extra hubs; they may be redundant from a pure efficiency standpoint but they make the network more resilient to shocks. That is the redundancy *v.* resilience trade-off.

A similar phenomenon is seen in biology. As an organism evolves, it is shaped by the environment and there is a tendency to drop redundant features. Why invest energy in something you don't need? But when catastrophe comes, those redundant features may be the ones that save you. Who knows? Maybe nipples on men will come in handy some day, though whatever catastrophe might require that is too ghastly to contemplate. Even at a genetic level, there seems to be a lot of redundant code whose purpose is unclear. This may be some type of evolutionary safety net. If the environment changes dramatically, these redundant genes may be switched on allowing us to quickly adapt to those changes.

Another example is languages. There are around 6,000 languages in the world today. That number is falling fast and there may only be half as many in a hundred years time. There is a strong trend to standardise because the more people you can communicate with the better. The most diverse linguistic region of the world is Papua New Guinea, with 832 different languages in a tiny population of only four million. Steep mountainous terrain has kept the tribes apart. In contrast, there are 400 languages spoken in Europe and North America, with a population of one billion. Social interaction kills diversity. There is strong economic and social pressure to speak the language of the most dominant culture. This is another form of the 'economies of scale' argument for supermarket warehouses. Of the 300 original Native American languages only 160 survive today, and of those only eight have more than 10,000 speakers. But even here there is a resilience argument too. It can sometimes be an advantage to speak a language no one else can understand. Bilingual speakers of Choctaw, Cherokee and Navajo[71] have regularly been used by the US military as radio operators. No need to encrypt your messages if you speak an obscure language.

The more interconnected the world becomes the more vulnerable it is to unexpected shocks. Capitalism drives the slack out of the system creating a super-efficient distributed global network. To begin with, this network helped to reduce risks, acting like a shock absorber. A network is better than a single supplier. But it is possible to be *too* networked. It now seems that the drive for efficiency has pushed the global network beyond the optimal point. The network now transmits and amplifies shocks like Nero's lyre, tuned to the harmonics of crisis. A tsunami in Japan has an unexpected economic impact in the North of England because car parts don't arrive in time for the Nissan assembly plant there. A volcano in Iceland has a knock on effect in Disneyland, Paris. The ash cloud shuts European airports and cuts off the flow of tourists. Cause and effect are linked in hidden ways that only emerge when crisis strikes. They are accompanied by gyrating prices in the commodity markets and sudden shortages in the supply chain. The food distribution network in developed economies is so efficient that there are only a few day's supply in the chain. A major external shock and suddenly the supermarket shelves become empty. Most western cities exist only a few days away from starvation. The network is too efficient; we need some more shock absorbers in the system. Maybe, a bit more redundant bureaucracy to make things more resilient. Goodbye, lean and mean. Hello, chubby and happy.

Still waters run deep

Shock absorbers are checks and balances. Things that slow down the transmission of messages and dampen energetic vibrations. This is traditionally seen as one of the vices of bureaucracy: a dead hand that crushes innovation. A huge inertial mass of status quo. It is beautifully

---

71 The movie *Windtalkers* tells the story of how Navajo speakers were used by the US marine corps in the Pacific.

illustrated in the TV comedy *Yes Minister*, when Sir Humphrey Appleby explains the four steps in a bureaucratic response to a crisis. When a crisis first looms the first response from the bureaucracy is that nothing is going to happen. Then, a little later, as the crisis gets worse, there comes the second response: something is going to happen but nothing should be done about it. This soon moves to the third response: something is going to happen but nothing *can* be done about it. Last, comes the argument that something should have been done, but it's too late now. Using these four arguments, events can come and go but the bureaucrats remain inactive and unruffled.

This mocking portrayal of bureaucratic inertia is largely true. On the other hand, just because something remains in the same place does not mean that nothing is happening. It may be in dynamic equilibrium. The net result of two strong opposing forces is that they cancel each other out. A swan, gliding calmly on the water, disguises a lot of hasty paddling below. Still waters run deep.

In the corporate world, the story goes something like this. A new employee comes bouncing into your department full of energy. She questions everything and wants to put things right. She is full of enthusiasm and looking for better ways to do things. But in the end she ends up just like everyone else, not wanting to rock the boat. Her individualism has succumbed to teamwork. Her energy has been absorbed into the collective. Since everyone's individual impulses are to move in different directions, they all cancel each other out and the net effect is stasis. Can an individual make a difference? Libraries full of business books say 'yes'. CEOs are convinced of their ability to 'lead' but maybe they don't make any difference at all. They are neutralised by the shock absorbing properties of the bureaucracy.

Maybe this is a good thing. As you get bigger the conflicts between different departments slow down the company's ability to act. There are so many contradictory impulses. The sales department wants more customers but the legal department is risk averse. The production guys need new equipment but finance says they can't afford it: So many differing opinions that the net result is close to paralysis. A big company is like a super tanker; inertia keeps it on the same slow course. Maybe that is how it is supposed to be. If you look at stock markets then dramatic moves are more the exception than the rule. The market is busy resolving all those buyers and sellers, so it looks like nothing is happening but in fact it is working very efficiently. Lots of individual dramas below, average themselves out into some gentle ripples on the surface. The only time you will see a dramatic move is if the environment changes radically, otherwise it is pretty humdrum. In the same way, a big company has internalised all those arguments. In effect, it has become a marketplace for clearing the opinions of its different managers. It is efficient. It is doing nothing because often that is the best thing to do.

If this is sounding too much like a paean to torpor, then it may be worth pointing out that there are things that a big bureaucracy can do that individuals can't. The elephant may not be able to jump but that does not make it powerless, far from it. Take the EU. It is often held up as the worst example of bloated bureaucratic inefficiency. It may be inefficient and it probably is too large but it has managed to do some good things too. The European food chain is reasonably safe, free of harmful chemicals and spoilt produce. The environment is clean, quality of life is good and individual human rights are strongly guaranteed. Most importantly, it has managed to stop war in what has historically been the most bellicose continent on earth. The EU has managed to internalise those arguments, replacing physical fighting with bureaucratic wrangling. Or take the UN. Through the World Health Organisation, it has managed to eradicate infectious diseases such as smallpox and polio. It would have been impossible for any individual or country to do this by themselves.

The key question to ponder is this: If bureaucracy is as bad as everyone thinks, then why is there so much of it? You hear plenty of people complaining about it and rarely any praise. The next time you hear someone grumbling about 'too much red tape' consider the principle of the economist and the £20 note: bureaucracy must be necessary, otherwise it would not exist. If it was useless, it would have already been eliminated. Once things get complicated enough, bureaucracy spontaneously arises. It is an emergent phenomenon, like snowflake patterns or termite mounds. To complain about bureaucracy is to make a catataxic error. Your interaction with something that exists on a different level is making you frustrated. But that bureaucracy on level two does not exist to serve you. It has its own logic and concerns. When you scratch your head because its actions make no sense to you, consider this: maybe it is not supposed to make sense to you.

Is bureaucracy immoral?

'Man is the measure of all things,' says the Ancient Greek philosopher Protagoras. According to him, when considering the virtue of something, you must consider it in relation to yourself. In this sense, he was the first relativist: there is no absolute truth, only what is true for you. Moral relativism has become the dominant view in Europe, rejecting religious absolutism. All views are seen as valid and morality is seen as a subjective and personal issue. So there has been a progression from: 'I am right because God says so,' to: 'Everyone is entitled to their own view.' This can be seen as a horizontal moral dispersion, from single perspective view to multi perspective view. I call it 'horizontal' because it still only concerns people at the individual level; a human viewpoint, rather than the view from one rung up or down the cataxic ladder. But what about the vertical axis for morality? Are genes moral? Is a biosphere moral?

It seems a ridiculous question at first, because morality implies some sort of conscious decision between right and wrong. Genes are not conscious entities; they express themselves according to their own rules. So asking if genes are moral is a non-question. Considering genes is stepping down the hierarchical ladder. It gets more interesting when you start to step up. Is bureaucracy moral? It is a structure one level above the individual. It seems incomprehensible at times: that's why you scratch your head at the idiocy of the bureaucrats. Should it be governed by moral rules from the human level? Or is bureaucratic morality a closed book to us, just as ours is to our genes? To put the question another way, should we expect companies to be ethical?

A company is composed of employees but is more than just those individuals. It sits one level higher in the conceptual hierarchy than its staff. Let's look at the friction at the boundary between the two. Are the rules that apply to a company different from the rules that apply to an individual? We have covered some of the legal aspects of piercing the corporate veil. What about the moral aspects? Morality is a personal attribute. The courts view a company as a legal person. Is it level confusion to expect a company to be moral? Does a company have human rights?

The answer of the US Supreme Court is 'yes'. In January 2010, the Court ruled that companies have the right of freedom of speech. The issue concerned the engagement of companies in the public debate of political issues. This was previously restricted but the new ruling opens the door to a flood of corporate spending in future elections. If we push this argument further we soon arrive at some absurdities. If a company drives another out of business, is that murder? In a corporate sense, another 'legal person' has been killed. Is it wrong? Of course not. It is not morally reprehensible for a company to outcompete its rivals, even if it makes them extinct. Some would say that is the purpose of a company. Murdering other companies is what a company should do.

Applying moral codes to the interaction between companies is a cataxic error. Morality is a code of behavioural conduct that applies to humans. It requires consciousness. From this comes the ability to feel emotions like guilt and the understanding of the impact of one's actions upon others. Companies are complex organisational structures, but are not self-aware.[72] Individuals inside companies should have moral codes, but the companies themselves cannot. It is good business practice for company employees to act in an ethical way when dealing with others. An employee is a representative of the company, but he is not the company. The company is composed of moral individuals but in itself is beyond morals.

Company to company interaction is inherently amoral. At that level, morality is an empty concept. What about across levels? Does morality apply to the interaction of a company with an individual? There is a huge body of corporate law that defines the rules in this area. Companies can be held guilty of fraud and manslaughter. But this is a legal requirement not to cheat or kill, rather than a moral one. Most company directors wish their company to be perceived as ethical; to be a good corporate citizen. This is an extension of the principals of the individuals that run the company. It is a 'Level 1' projection of ideals. On Level 2, the corporate level, it makes good business sense. Consumers prefer ethical brands. A company can be 'ethical' without being moral. The 'ethical' label is applied from level 1 to level 2. So an 'ethical company' is an example of cataxis.

---

72 At least, we don't think they are self aware. There is always the possibility that they are self aware in a way we don't understand. Maybe the global economy is a self aware life form beyond our ken.

In 2009, an online 'Honesty Lab' experiment is set up by Dr Finch and Dr Fafinski. It attempts to find out the consensus of opinion of the general public to certain moral conundrums. One interesting result is that two thirds of respondents do not view stealing stationary from work as a crime. There is a clear moral distinction between stealing from a person and stealing from a faceless organisation. This is bottom up evidence that moral rules don't apply at the corporate level. The majority opinion is that stealing from work is not dishonest.

There are other examples of moral hierarchy. They show a friction between morals at the individual level and the societal level. Consider the white lie. A good example is telling your hostess how delicious her food is. Or answering the question, 'Do I look fat in this dress?'. It is a conflict between two moral precepts: 'Don't tell lies' and 'Don't be rude'. The first acts at the individual level, the second at the societal level. So which is worse; lying to a person or causing social disharmony? Different cultures have different answers. In the Far East, social disharmony is the greater sin which is why people are normally told what they want to hear. Some would claim that putting society before the individual is a sign of civilisation. In which case, the more you lie the more civilised you are.

Dark woods, grey suits

Is it too much of a stretch to argue that putting bureaucracy before the individual is also a sign of civilisation? To many, that may seem a step too far. They could convincingly argue the opposite; that protecting the individual from the bureaucracy is the true sign of civilisation in our modern world. For me, the question has no resolution; it is an inevitable catataxic friction to be observed, but never solved. Against the Hollywood-style hero all forces must be ominous and sinister. The dark woods of Grimm's fairy tales have transmuted into grey bureaucracy in modern fables. That is where the baddies lurk. In a story of individual heroism, the bureaucratic collective is the perfect opposing force. The hero is active, it is inactive. The hero has a face, it is faceless. The hero is pure, it is corrupt. The hero is flesh and blood, it is an abstract concept.

Such dramas play on our natural distrust of powerful organisations. Our normal view of bureaucracy is therefore biased. This chapter has tried to redress that balance. Bureaucracy should be praised for a number of reasons. It is the clipboard checklist that saves lives. It is the value adding core of all companies. It is the shock absorber that protects against dangerous perturbations. It is the elephant who can't jump but who can slowly and quietly flatten troublesome problems. Bureaucrats do a lot of good without getting much credit. They need a better PR consultant to help improve their image. It's time to hire some spin doctors, and that's the subject of the next chapter.

CHAPTER 9

The Necessity of Spin

The whale, the dragon and the pipe

New York. Mr Hogan is sorting through old books in his uncle's house. His uncle, Frank Hogan, has recently died and he is helping his aunt to sort out the deceased man's affairs. He comes across a book with a black cloth binding and gold lettering on the spine. It's called *The Natural History of the Sperm Whale* by Thomas Beale, Surgeon. It was printed in London in 1839 and has some quite nice engravings. It could be worth something. He decides to take it to a second-hand book dealer to get it valued. The only trouble is that some idiot has scribbled all over it. There are all sorts of annotations in the margins, underlined sections and marked passages. Luckily, they are only in pencil. So Mr Hogan gets an eraser and diligently rubs them all out. He does not want to try and sell it until he has cleaned it up a bit. The good news is that he can erase them all so well that you can hardly notice them. The bad news is there is one part he can't erase, because it's in ink. Right there on the half title page at the front of the book is someone's signature. It says 'Herman Melville. New York, July 10th 1850'. Herman Melville? That ring's a vague bell. Hasn't he heard that name somewhere before . . .

London. Graham Ogilvie has slipped out of his City job at lunchtime to pursue his secret pleasure. He is going to the College of Arms. It is an institution that dates back to 1484 when it was incorporated by Richard III. The Heralds' College was given a royal charter to grant coats of arms and to oversee any disputes about these heraldic family symbols. Today it is housed in a beautiful seventeenth century brick building in Queen Victoria Street, just to the south of St Paul's Cathedral. Graham is passionate about local history and there is a Coat of Arms on a tomb in his local church that he wants identified. He asks the receptionist if there is anyone who can help. 'Yes,' she replies, 'We always have an officer in waiting to help with enquiries.' Graham is impressed. He knows about doctors on call in ER and consumer help lines, but emergency heraldry services? That's a new one. The receptionist shows him to the most exquisite room; dark antique oak floorboards and panelling and a single oak table with chairs. It's like he has stepped back in time three hundred years. He sits down to wait. A few minutes later the door opens. An immaculately dressed middle aged man enters and walks over to shake his hand. The handshake is weak and curiously lopsided. Was that a secret handshake? 'Welcome,' says the man conspiratorially, 'I am Rouge Dragon Pursuivant. How can I help?' . . .

Los Angeles. John Baldessari, a conceptual artist based in California, is designing a new show about surrealism for the Los Angeles County Museum of Art. The surrealists were trying to blend dream images with reality to create a super reality;[73] hence the name surreal, 'sur' meaning 'over' or 'above' as in surcharge. Surrealism is all about changing people's perceptions. He wants to turn the normal visitors' experience upside down. So the floor will have a carpet patterned with puffy white clouds on a blue background and the ceiling will be papered with images of road junctions. Visitors will enter through a door with a hole cut in the shape of a human silhouette: a non-door. The show will be called 'The Treachery of Images'. There will be a six-foot high hair comb leaning against the wall and a stainless steel rabbit by Jeff Koons. And then, right at the very far end, the painting that started it all off. You approach it slowly and with reverence. It is one of the most famous and subversive paintings of the twentieth century. It's a painting of pipe with a wooden bowl for the tobacco and a black Bakelite mouthpiece to inhale through. This common household object is painted with almost cartoon-like simplicity. Something any smoker will be very familiar with. There is nothing remarkable about it at all, apart from the inscription which reads 'Ceci n'est pas une pipe'. In English, 'This is not a pipe' . . .

This chapter is all about spin, which is the linking theme for these three short illustrations. Spin is the attempt to control the way that

---

73 In this sense, surrealism is a cataxic art movement. It tries to blend two lower levels to create a third higher one. To convert the subconscious into the super real.

things are interpreted. Spin doctors try to manipulate the press. Spin is a level three phenomenon. On level one are the facts and on level two is the story made from those facts. Spin exists one level higher than that; it's the story about the story, or the meta-story. Although spin is all about shaping public opinions, it does a very bad job when it comes to itself. Surgeons smoke, the painter's house is the worst decorated one in the street and spin doctors have a terrible reputation. Spin doctors are seen as slimy, underhand, manipulative bullies. Along with bureaucracy, spin is one of the most loathed phenomena of our modern world. But just like bureaucracy, you need to ask this question: 'If it is so unpopular, why is there so much of it?' The answer must be 'because it is necessary'.

The annotations in the margins of Mr Hogan's book are a type of 'story about a story'; a level three phenomenon similar to spin. We could call it a meta-level commentary, which in this case is extremely valuable. Herman Melville, as I am sure you know, wrote *Moby-Dick*, seen by many critics as the greatest American novel ever written. Much of Melville's novel about the quest for the legendary white whale is based on Beale's scientific book about those creatures. Beale's book has lengthy chapters on the anatomy and behaviour of sperm whales, along with descriptions of how they are hunted, killed and caught. So to find Melville's actual copy of that book, filled with his notes in the margin, is a literary bonanza beyond compare – like finding Shakespeare's rough notes for *Macbeth*. The book is now in the Houghton Library at Harvard, with all the erased marginalia revealed through specialist photographic techniques.

Heraldry is about spin too, in several different ways. Heralds were the original spin doctors, proclaiming status-enhancing messages about their noble masters. They wore a tabard embroidered with the appropriate heraldic symbols to show who they spoke for. This coat of arms itself is a form of spin; a way of advertising who you are. Originally, it was set of specific symbols on your shield to identify you in battle. These days it is more likely to appear on headed notepaper or be carved into the mantelpiece above a fireplace in a stately home. A self-made businessman who wants to increase his social standing can apply to the College of Arms and be granted a heraldic family crest. But heraldry is a form of spin in a more subtle way. When the coat of arms is granted it is given in written form: words not pictures. Heraldry dates back to a time when there was no easy way to reproduce images. A time before faxes, before photography, even before printing: A time when the most convenient way to record things was by writing it down. There is a whole arcane vocabulary of heraldic terms. Here is an example: *argent on a fess sable three bezants above lion rampant reguardant gules.* Give that to a competent local artist and he will be able to reproduce the picture for you. He will paint the background silver white (argent), put a black band at the top (fess sable) with three gold circles on it (bezants). Then below the band, he will draw a red (gules) lion rearing up and looking backwards over its shoulder (rampant reguardant). So the heraldic description is meta-level commentary that allows you to reproduce the picture one level below. Pure spin from which you can reproduce the 'story'.

Ceci n'est pas une pipe.

Which lead us to Magritte's enigmatic meta-level comment, 'Ceci n'est pas une pipe'. The point he is trying to make is that there is a difference between reality and a representation of reality. It is not a pipe, it is a picture of a pipe. Magritte's picture can be seen as an artistic version of Cartesian Dualism. Descartes drew a line between mind and matter. Magritte's line is a similar one, between an object and its illustration, between facts and the story, between reality and perception. Spin is the attempt to control perceptions. Now, the central question of this chapter is this: Why is there so much spin these days? To which the answer is 'because it is necessary'. And why is it necessary? Because, in the modern world there is no difference between perception and reality. Perception *is* reality. This blending together of two levels is caused by changes in scale as we shall see. So if Magritte was painting today he should write, 'This is a pipe,' or better still, 'This has become a pipe.' Perception has become reality. This is catataxis.

Perception is reality

Here is a popular psychological game, much beloved of chat up artists on a blind date. It starts by asking someone to name the first animal that comes into their head. Quick, what are you thinking of? Okay, now name a second one. And now a third. Your partner will have rapped out the names of three animals in quick succession, as they bubble up from their subconscious. Maybe tiger, tortoise, rabbit. You then reveal that the first animal represents how they see themselves. A tiger: rapacious, fierce and elegant. The second animal is how others see them. A tortoise: cold and hiding in a shell. The third animal is who they really are. A rabbit: cuddly and with great reproductive prowess. It's all a gimmick of course. You just make up flattering characteristics about any animal they mention and hope they don't pick 'dog'. Pretty soon they will be happily chattering away about the 'real me' while you nod and smile attentively. What an insightful and caring person you are!

Which of the three animals is the most important in the modern world? It's number two; how others see you. Perception is reality. No one really cares about the 'real you', and few people will ever have the time to find out. You are who people think you are: Once the media has drawn its caricature of you, that's who you are. Not just the media, your family has its own caricature of you too. Many extended family gatherings, at times like Christmas, end in tantrums and tears. Families are quite hierarchical, everyone has a function and a place. When families meet up again after some time apart, everyone is expected to be the same as they were before. How they are remembered rather than who they are now. This can be a joyous celebration of past shared experiences, or it can feel like a straight jacket. If you are forced to be who others think you are it may be an uncomfortable fit.

The dominance of perception over reality can be seen everywhere: in art, sport, the work-place, news, politics and business. We will look at each in turn in this chapter. The underlying reason for the change is a shortening attention span. First impressions may be the only impressions, because nobody has time any more. There is just so much stuff out there demanding your attention. Both the number of people in the world and the amount of digital information swirling around has grown exponentially. Perception is now reality because of this change in scale. As the world gets bigger, we get shallower. In earlier times, living in a village, you would know all your neighbours well, but the king and other nobles would be distant figures you might never even see. Today, this has been inverted. You know public celebrities by their first name and read all about their lives in the media, but hardly know your neighbours at all. Your opinion is based on what you read in the press rather than your own first-hand experience. Your information input about the outside world is no longer direct but indirect. Perception has become reality.

Art and craft

The difference between perception and reality has long been a theme in the art world. Magritte's pipe is just one stop on a long journey of exploration. The discovery of the techniques of perspective in Florence in the fifteenth century is a good place to start. Before this, artists showed that one object was further away by overlapping it with another. But the realisation that if it is further away then you must draw it smaller required a conceptual breakthrough. You have to draw what you see and not what you know to be there. Take two people who are the same size. Put one in the foreground and one in the background. When you draw this, you must make the one in the background smaller, even though you know there is no difference between them. To make it look realistic, you are reproducing what you perceive and not reality. Drawing on the work of Arabic mathematicians, artists such as Lorenzo Ghiberti and Filippo Brunelleschi developed the geometric principles of perspective which are used to this day.

The techniques of perspective produced such startlingly realistic images that they soon spread throughout Europe. At this moment, painting was as much craft as it was art. The technique was more important than the technician; the painting more prized than the artist. Pupils were made to copy paintings by masters. This helped a studio to keep a consistent style, but it was quite normal under the guild system of the time for these copies to be sold as the work of the master. By the seventeenth century, famous painters had numerous pupils working alongside them in their studios. These enterprises were more like industrial workshops, churning out popular paintings for an eager public. That makes it very hard these days to identity which paintings are by an Old Master and which by a student. In 1968, the Rembrandt Research Project was set up in Amsterdam to review the works of this Dutch Old Master. Of the 610 paintings originally believed to be by Rembrandt, over half have been reattributed, either as copies by students or as fakes.

A more interesting question than 'fake or not?' is 'why does it matter?' Under the Guild system, it clearly did not matter. It was the beauty of the final object that was all important. But in the twentieth century it does matter. It matters so much, that a team of experts spends forty years in painstaking research trying to resolve the problems of attribution just for a single artist such as Rembrandt. Imagine two antique paintings. The images are identical; the same composition, painted in the same studio, at the same time and with the same materials. The only difference is one is painted by Rembrandt and the other is a copy by a pupil. As a result there is a vast difference in price. One could be worth 100 times more purely on the attribution of the famous name. Pieter Brueghel's *The Bird Trap*, painted in 1565, is worth maybe US$40m today. A copy of this painting by a pupil from his studio is valued at around US$400,000. A modern copy painted by an artist in China costs US$40. So you can see there is a huge price range for what is, functionally speaking, the same thing. The paintings all look identical. There is a premium for age and rarity; the modern Chinese copy is far cheaper than the copy that is 450 years old. But the difference in price between the original and the pupil's copy is purely down to name. After all, if Brueghel had painted two identical pictures himself they would both have the same value.

For paintings, it is not the object itself that is valuable but the attribution of the name. Once a picture is perceived to be the work of a famous painter its value changes dramatically. The perception of who painted it is more important than the painting. So this is another example of perception trumping reality. This transition occurs at the tipping point between craft and art. A craft object is about the skilful execution of technique and the quality of the object itself. An art work is all about the vision of the artist himself; a summary of his experiences expressed in the grammar of emotions. Art is personal, and who that person *is* matters. The individual transcends the object. So painting was originally a craft activity, executed under the supervision of a guild, but with time became a fine art.

With art in the modern world, the value is in the name and not the object. But this is not always so. Master potters in Japan still leave their ceramics unsigned, in the belief that the piece should speak for itself. A Japanese potter is expected to have technical mastery over all aspects of the craft. He will dig the clay himself, excavate a kiln in the hillside, choose and then personally cut the wood for the fire to heat it. The interaction of the glazes with the flame and ash from the fire produce beautiful, spontaneous patterns: cracked and burnt finishes that are part designed and part emergent. The resulting piece is a harmonious fusion of materials, processes and techniques. Not a showy, virtuoso performance but an under-stated naturalistic masterpiece. The skill required to produce it is not evident on the surface. This is the acme of craft: pure, exquisite and self-contained. Signing your name would draw attention away from the object and towards the craftsman. By doing so, a name would defile it.

Contrast this with the piece that is seen by many critics as the most influential artwork of the twentieth century.[74] It is a piece of signed porcelain submitted to an exhibition in New York in 1917. Not a pot, a plate or a vase but a commercially manufactured urinal bearing the signature R. Mutt. The artist is Marcel Duchamp, a Dadaist, and this piece is titled *Fountain*. Nothing could be further from a Japanese pot. It is signed rather than unsigned. It is not made by the artist but on an industrial production line. A common object, there are thousands of identical ones like it. The artist required no skill or craft, he merely chose it, signed it and entered it in a show. Hence the name: 'Readymade' or found art.

As we noted in Chapter 2, concepts in the art world often have a simultaneous parallel in science. There is a linkage in 1910 between the Cubist painters and Einstein's relativity: they both deny the integrity of mass. For Duchamp's readymade art there is a parallel with Quantum Physics: the transforming effect of the observer. Schrodinger's cat illustrates how the mere act of observing a quantum event effects the outcome. Likewise, it is the act of observing a readymade object in an exhibition that makes it art. Screwed to a wall in a gent's lavatory, a urinal is a purely functional object.

74 The BBC reported on 1 December 2004 that Duchamp's Fountain topped a poll of 500 art experts as the most influential modern art work of all time.

Displayed in a museum exhibition, it becomes art. The spectators who gather to view and interpret it are part of the creative process, just as the scientists in a lab are an inextricable part of the quantum experiment.

Marcel Duchamp's urinal and Magritte's pipe are making the same point: art is not the object but something at a higher level. Magritte's painting of a pipe is not a pipe. Duchamp's urinal in a museum is no longer a urinal. Art is about concept more than the tangible object. This is taken to extremes in so called 'conceptual art' where there may be no object at all. Here are some examples. An artist buys another artist's work and erases it, exhibiting an empty canvas (Rauschenberg, 1953); A display of 'invisible' paintings in an empty room (Klein, 1958); A barricade in a Paris street – the resultant traffic jam is the artwork, not the barricade (Christo, 1962). An artist sits in an empty room communicating his art telepathically (Barry, 1969). A one kilometre vertical brass rod buried in the earth; since you can't see it you must imagine it to be there (De Maria, 1977). All these artworks are playing with ideas and, of course, causing controversy and outrage. The public's angry reaction is caused by a catataxic friction; they expect a beautifully crafted object on level one, not a philosophical concept on level two. This type of art is still controversial after almost 100 years. There is a direct line from Duchamp's urinal to Tracy Emin, winning the Turner Prize in 1999 for exhibiting her unmade bed.

Modern art relies on context; an unmade bed at home is not art, but in the museum it is. With postmodernism, this is even more true. Postmodernism rejects modern art's seriousness. If almost anything can be art, and everyone's viewpoint is valid, then it is not possible to earnestly expound a single view. The only acceptable stance is an ironic one. Parody, mockery and humour are the tropes of postmodernism, along with the conflation of high art and low art into pop art. All this knowingness and irony is completely dependent on context. You have to understand what is being referenced in order to 'get it'. Take an ironic statement out of context, and its meaning becomes the opposite: 'Root canal surgery? That's really going to be fun'. Depending on how you say it, you are either joking or a masochist. Your tone of voice indicates whether you think it is fun or not. Without that context, your meaning can not be understood.

Maybe this is the key difference between art and craft in the modern world. One requires context, the other does not. A Japanese pot is pure craftsmanship. Its beauty is self-contained and can be understood in any context. A postmodern work of art requires a particular set of cultural concepts in the mind of the beholder in order to be understood. Without that context to anchor it, no one will 'get it'. Craft exists at level one, art at level two. Craft is about reality, art is about perception. In today's world, second seems to be more highly valued than the first.

The value of branding

The attribution of a particular name can make a huge difference to the value of a work art. The same is true of commerce. We discussed branding briefly in Chapter 5, but it is worth returning to the topic because branding is all about perception *v.* reality: Branding is spin. In our Rembrandt example, two paintings made at the same time, in the same place and from the same materials had vastly different values depending on whose name was on it. In the commercial world, the same is true. Take two bottles of wine, made at the same time from the same grape variety in vineyards only a mile apart. They are both from Pauillac in Bordeaux. One is a Croizet Bages, worth £14 a bottle, the other a Chateaux Lafitte is worth £1,000 a bottle. The reason for the price difference is the name, and the value of that name comes from marketing. As a friend, who owns a lesser known Bordeaux vineyard, ruefully tells me, 'It's not about making wine, it's about selling wine.' In other words, perception is reality.

The same is true of most luxury goods. Shoes made in same factory in China could be worth fifty times more if they have a Nike label attached. The raw materials and labour required to make a handbag cost a tiny fraction of what it will sell for if it is branded Louis Vuitton. These goods are not being valued on the basis of their function but on the brand associations: a set of perceptions and feelings that the company has established, through marketing, in the mind of the consumer.

One of the most extraordinary success stories in branding is the bottled water business. Companies have persuaded consumers to pay a premium price for something that is freely available from a tap. Bottled water is 10,000 times more expensive than tap water but has no discernible difference. This is a master class in spin. Take Nestlé's 'Pure life' brand of bottled water. Unlike some European waters like Evian or Perrier, this does not even come from a specified source. Tap water from any location is purified by distillation and then selected minerals are put back in. And then, through a marketing campaign, a whole raft of positive perceptions are also introduced, working around the themes of purity, hydration and healthy living. Hey Presto! You have just made a branded good out of the most basic and plentiful commodity on the planet. Pass straight to Go and collect £200.

Branding is the lifeblood of a company. Some may view it as an immoral exercise; duping consumers with outrageous mark-ups. But it could also be seen as a necessary corporate defence mechanism in a Darwinian struggle. If goods were purely valued on a functional basis, then pretty soon comparison shopping would erode all profit margins to zero. This is the equivalent to corporate death. The purpose of a company's existence is to make a profit. The only defence a company has against comparison shopping is to differentiate itself so that comparisons are no longer valid. Who is the villain in this story? The company attempting to brand and mark up its goods, or the rapacious, comparison shopping consumer? Both are locked together in an eternal conflict: An arms race that pushes both sides to greater excesses. Spin, in the form of branding, is necessary. If you want to know why then consider this: Have you ever compared the price of two objects in a shop before buying one of them? Yes? Then spin is necessary, because of your activities. It is you that is causing it.

Managing upwards

Companies use spin externally in the form of advertising, but spin also has an important role inside the company. This is particularly true for large companies where internal politics is rife. Just how important spin is can be gauged by answering this question: Does your boss really know what it is that you do? In a small company, or a traditional industry, the answer is probably yes. She may have spent ten years doing your job and so knows it backwards. On the other hand, in a bigger company she may have been transferred across from another department, or your industry may be changing so fast that the job today is not what it was previously. If this is the case, then she may not really know what you do. The key to success in a big company is to manage upwards. Focus on keeping your boss happy, not your underlings happy. You need to keep telling your boss what a great job you are doing. Go ahead and blow your own trumpet. Be your own spin doctor and take credit for everything you can. That's how you get pay rises and promotions. Competent and modest will get you nowhere. It's the squeaky wheel that gets the grease.

Enlightened companies try to eliminate the distorting effect of this self promotion by using some type of performance measurement system. If so, you need to make a different person the target of your spin: the person who looks after the numbers. Management information systems purport to be objective, but there is normally a lot of subjective leeway about how the numbers are booked. Wily political operators make friends with the accounts department to make sure that any spinning of the numbers is in their favour. Even accountants will admit that their field is as much art as science. The annual accounts, by law, must represent a true and fair picture of the company. But accountants can chose what angle that picture is taken from to produce a flattering or unflattering portrait. There is plenty of room for manoeuvre in the details of accruals, timing differences, revenue recognition and exchange rates. This means that the profits can be pretty much whatever the finance director wants them to be. Normally for listed companies, the numbers are smoothed out to give a slightly flattering account. This type of spin is necessary to keep investors happy. They want to see a track record that shows smooth, predictable growth. When in doubt, the temptation is to err to the positive. After several years of this, the gap between the published results and reality is getting a bit strained. Then comes a bad year when the accountants can 'kitchen-sink it'. Under the cover of an external economic shock, the finance director can reset the clock. He unwinds all those positive adjustments, and dumps out all the bad stuff, including the proverbial kitchen sink. The numbers end up shockingly bad, but the poor economic environment can take the rap for that. He now has plenty of leeway again for positive massaging in the future.

The throne and the man

Using external bad news as a cover to disguise some bad news of your own is a classic spin doctor technique. Companies do it all the time, as you can see if you follow their results through a cycle. But the real masters of this technique are the political spin doctors. The most appalling example is the internal email Jo Moore sends on 11 September 2001, just as the Twin Towers are collapsing. It reads: 'It's now a very good day to get out anything we want to bury. Councillors' expenses?' This shocking cynicism causes a public uproar and costs this press officer for the UK Labour Government her job. She is caught red-handed doing something that is fairly common practice.

Politics is the natural home of spin. Image and perceptions are the life blood of politics; the difference between being in power and not in power. Controlling how you are perceived is a requisite skill. Spin is basic necessity for a politician. This may be why politicians are so unpopular, because the public believe they are pretending to be something they are not. As masters of spin, politicians fall in the same category as hustlers, flim-flam artists and con men. Many people assume that any politician that they meet is a self aggrandising liar; the team of spin doctors and PR officers they employ proves it. There is, however, another side to this argument. Maybe they hire spin doctors because you demand it of them. Just as with comparison shopping, spin in politics is caused by your expectations.

A popular TV format is the list program. I saw one recently called '50 Most Annoying Pop Moments'. It was the usual line-up of talking heads discussing irritating videos and award show gaffes. But in the top ten of the most annoying was David Cameron's appearance on *Desert Island Discs*. This is a UK radio show where celebrities are asked to name the eight pieces of music that they would take with them to a desert island. The host plays the music while the celebrity in question explains why they have such personal emotional resonance. David Cameron's list includes bands such as Pink Floyd, The Smiths and Radiohead . . . nothing unusual here; typical introspective middle-class schoolboy fare. Why does this qualify as an 'annoying pop moment'? The talking heads give several reasons such as: 'It spoils a song for the rest of us if it's a favourite of someone we don't like.' Hearing a British Prime Minister extolling his love for a Radiohead song[75] does cause a frisson. It's partly because rock is supposedly anti-establishment, while a Conservative Prime Minister *is* the establishment. But behind that, there is a deeper cataxic reason. When someone emotes about their favourite song it makes them human, just like us. We don't want our leaders to be too human. We want our figureheads to be authoritative, commanding and separate from us: symbolic, not flesh and blood. There is the role of Prime Minister and then there is the human being who occupies that position. These two things exist on different levels. One is conceptual, the other real. So when they collide together in a cataxic mash-up we feel uncomfortable.

Bill Clinton is a gifted politician and achieved an impressive amount in his two terms as President of the USA. But these achievements are overshadowed by the Monica Lewinsky affair. His name will always be linked to the story of his romp with the White House intern. Adultery is immoral but not criminal, nor uncommon. People do it all the time, but you don't expect the President to do it. The real crime was to bring the Office of the President into such disrepute. The official Starr report gave a sordid account of the affair in such minute and graphic detail that the public were sickened. This was too much information. It was the disconcerting feeling of watching a cataxic crash between the man and the office.

Why do politicians pretend to be something that they are not? Because the public wants them to. Someone who occupies an important political office is expected to transmute into something else; something higher, more moral and on a different plane. It is the spin doctors who help that transmutation. This is not a new phenomenon. Rudyard Kipling's poem, *The Disciple*, points out that the great religious leaders did not actually write anything themselves. Their sayings were compiled and interpreted by their followers. It is the gospel writers who were the original spin

---

75 Margaret Thatcher, a previous Conservative party leader, claimed her favourite song was 'How much is that Doggie in the Window', to the great relief of all rock journalists. An appropriately untrendy choice, by someone from a different world. Imagine the irony and uproar had she chosen something by Iron Maiden . . .

doctors.[76] Chairman Mao did not write his famous little red book. It was written by the Gang of Four, the senior party officials who were closest to him. In every age and creed, leaders need spin doctors to promulgate an appropriate image to the public.

It is expected that leaders be something more than human. But there is a second unrealistic belief that the public holds dear; another reason why spin doctors are necessary. This is the requirement for a consistent government message. Governments get elected on the basis of a set of policies and, to begin with, everyone on the Government team believes the same thing. Time passes, events progress and the government needs to respond to a new situation. A debate over policy is held behind closed doors and the new party line emerges. All the members of the team have to take collective responsibility for this decision. They may privately have doubts, but publicly they need to look united. We demand that they appear united. So our expectations create the lie. They must all pretend to believe the same thing when, of course, they all have different views. This is a catataxic friction between the collective view and the individual view.

Now imagine a government minister being grilled by a journalist on TV about that new policy. He has to pretend that the party line is his own, personal, firmly held belief. The journalist is asking difficult probing questions, pointing out inconsistencies with his previous viewpoints. The minister is lying for our benefit. He will be judged on how well he presents and sells government policies even if he does not fully believe them personally. He has already decided before the interview what he is going to say. He will merely push his sound bite across, regardless of what question he is asked.[77] Now look closely at the journalist. He has something in his ear. It's an earpiece through which he can hear his production staff. Researchers are feeding him useful facts and his editor is guiding him in for the kill. Suddenly you realise that this whole

76 It might be more accurate to say that the Bishops at the Council of Nicaea in 325AD were the first spin doctors. It is they who decided which texts belonged in the New Testament and formulated the Nicene Creed.

77 A TV journalist I know once joked that the best opening question for a politician would be: 'What is the answer to my first question?' since it would highlight that the reply will always be a pre-packaged sound bite regardless of what is asked.

interview is a sham. It is staged like a discussion between two people, but it is two institutions at war up there. The politician is the mouthpiece for the collective view of the government, and the journalist is the mouthpiece for his media conglomerate. The two people are merely the visible part of a confrontation between two organisations. If it was just two normal people, they could have a civilised exchange of views about what they really think. In fact, they probably will do, once the cameras are turned off. But right now it's a catataxic conflict staged for our benefit. And the directors of the show are the spin doctors. Are you not entertained?

You are your sound bite

A TV interview is a live show where people actually respond to questions. When it comes to the written word, things are a bit different. Here the spin doctor has complete control over the message with a well crafted press release. It does not need to be delivered through a third person verbally. As a result, PR professionals can practically write the content of newspapers themselves. The first press release ever issued was by the Pennsylvania Railroad in 1906 about a train crash. Today, there are thousands of press releases issued daily which has changed the nature of journalism. Where previously journalists went out looking for stories, cost issues and time pressures mean it is easier to cut and paste a press release. This process is known as 'churnalism' and is surprisingly prevalent in the UK press. A 2008 research project by Nick Davies and the University of Cardiff showed that eighty per cent of the stories in the quality press were recycled press releases. Newspapers have changed from being active news gatherers to passive information processors.

Sometimes this information processing introduces distortions. Readers' attention spans are short and so there is a need to get the essence of the story across as quickly and briefly as possible. A complicated issue needs to be reduced to a brief, catchy headline. That condensation process inevitably warps the truth somewhat. The headline is a meta-level version of the story and there is catataxic friction between the two. Sound bites can be deadly when they misconstrue the intent of the speaker. Here are some examples:

In 2008, the Archbishop of Canterbury gives a speech at the Royal Courts of Justice. It is an intellectual and technical argument about the limits of a unitary, secular legal system in a religiously plural society. He observes that: 'Some aspects of Sharia law are already recognised in our legal system.' The headlines in the press say 'Archbishop backs Sharia Law', which triggers a huge furore in the general public with many demanding his immediate resignation. It's a great controversial headline which will boost circulation, but it is a complete misrepresentation of what the Archbishop actually said.

Later in 2008, Professor Michael Reiss, an eminent biologist and member of the Royal Society, gives a lecture at a science conference in Liverpool. His talk is about the scientific method; how alternative views must be evaluated by examining the evidence. He says that creationism should not be dismissed out of hand. It should be discussed in classrooms to demonstrate its lack of scientific basis. Teachers should point out its flaws rather than just ignore it. The headlines in the press interpret it like this: 'Leading scientist urges creationism in schools.' Again, there is a popular uproar and the professor is publicly vilified.

Now Sharia Law and Creationism are both hot button issues, and controversy sells papers. But in both these cases the speaker is being castigated for what he seemed to have said, rather than what he actually said. The reaction of the public demonstrates that perception is reality. You are your sound bite. Many commentators feel that the fault lies with these two elderly intellectuals. They are clearly out of their depth in the modern media world. Some point out the need for them to hire better press officers. This is an unusual case of an argument calling for more spin.

Sometimes the media distorts not what is said, but the context in which it is said. Consider the case of Lord Triesman, former Government minister and the chairman of the UK Football Association (FA). In 2010 he meets an ex-colleague, a civil servant called Melissa Jacobs, for dinner in a local restaurant. He does not know that she is wearing a concealed tape recorder. In two hours of conversation, the only newsworthy comment he makes is that the Spanish football authorities may be trying to bribe World Cup referees. Highlights of the tape transcript are published in the press.[78] The next day, Lord Triesman is forced to resign from the FA.

78 *Mail on Sunday* (May 16 2010)

What exactly did he do wrong? Had he called a press conference and made formal accusations that were later shown to be false then he might have had something to apologise for. He could have been sued for libel. But he was making off-hand comments in a private conversation in a restaurant at the weekend. These were to a close friend who had no links to the world of football. How is that malicious? I'm sure we all say things privately that we would not say publicly. Was he stupid? Overly trusting? Reckless? Should every official always assume that close friends are taping their conversations and out to get them? Maybe his crime is just to get caught. The verdict of the public is that the Chairman of the FA should not go around saying such things. This is a cataxic error: A conflation of the official with the private man. Surely the fault lies with the press for publishing it, or with the unrealistic expectations of the public.

These are all examples of PR gaffes. What happens when you don't have a spin doctor on your side. When you do have one, the results can be spectacular. The celebrities that we see across our newspapers and magazines are all there through the work of publicists. Celebrities are often known by just their first name: Brad and Angelina, Britney, Oprah and Beyonce. Movie stars and singers have always been famous, way back to the days of Charlie Chaplin and Caruso. A more modern phenomenon is the celebrity who is famous just for being famous. There seems to be little discernible talent, nor much to admire: Paris Hilton, Zsa Zsa Gabor, Katie Price and Peaches Geldof. This cult of celebrity is sometimes held up as a symbol of the degeneracy of modern society. But it can also be seen as a natural progression and a triumph of the art of the publicist. Through their efforts, we know more about their lives than we do our neighbours'. We are on first name terms, know their likes and dislikes, collect their photos, know their opinions and follow their exploits on TV and in magazines. It is the same set of activities as with your best friends, although only in one direction. Your real friends are unlikely to be exceptionally talented but you are still friends with them because, well, you just know them. It is familiarity, not talent, that is the glue. Celebrities are your cyber-friends, why do they need to be talented?

The art form with no author

The rise of the cult of the celebrity is linked to reality TV. This is where ordinary people are given exposure and the publicist gets the first grist for the mill. There seems to be a strange confluence of different entertainment strands at work here. Drama, news and sport all seem to be converging on the same point, and that point is reality TV. They are all turning into each other. Let's take drama first. The most addictive type of drama is the soap opera; a continuous story form that is never fully resolved. Modern TV shows like *Lost*, *24* and *The Wire* have been hugely successful by using this format. Set up a group of characters that resonate with the audience and then weave in a number of plots and sub-plots extending over several shows. Make sure you end each episode on a cliff-hanger and the audience will be back next week because they want to find out what happens.

There is a strong human desire to see resolution. There is a story, probably apocryphal, about a famous composer who torments his gay lover by playing a piece on the piano, but stopping just before the final chord. Hours later in the middle of the night, the lover cannot stand it any more. He gets out of bed, runs down stairs and plays the final chord on the piano. It has been irritating him all this time and finally he gets resolution. It is that same suspense that makes drama shows so compulsive. We want to know how it ends. How are all the strands of the story tied up in the finish of it all. Where is that grand-resolving chord?

In news, you see the same thing. In the past, TV news would be a man in a studio telling you what has happened. Now it is more likely to be a reporter at the scene speculating about how the story might resolve itself in the future. It is a fairly regular occurrence these days for the anchorman to intone ' . . . and now we go live to our reporter on the ground . . . ' More often than not, the reporter has nothing much to report. So he just gives some impressionistic colour about what the atmosphere feels like and then speculates about what may be about to happen. Again, we hunger for what happens next: the resolution to the story.

That news reporter on the ground is like a sports commentator. At the half-time break in the game, the pundits discuss what the play has been like so far and who is going to win. Sport is the ultimate entertainment because it is meant to be unscripted. Events happen but you can draw the causal links between them any way you like. You are free to join the dots up as you wish. Everyone's point of view is valid. The team's play is not as fluid as normal? Did the coach make a mistake in his selection? Why are they passing so badly? These may just be random errors but the desire to fit a narrative to them is irresistible. In sport, you are guaranteed a resolution, but you have to supply the story yourself. Sport is the art form with no author.

Reality TV combines both of these strands together. It is both unscripted and unresolved. You have the hunger to find out what happens next while supplying the story line yourself. Does this seem like the end of the road? A sterile dead-end like modern art? You have got rid of the scriptwriters, you have got rid of the stars. You just have cameras running full time on a bunch on nonentities for eternity. It seems like there is nothing left to deconstruct. But that view misses an important point. A reality TV show may be unscripted, but it is not unedited. All the skill and art is in the editing. The story arises from the selection of clips you are shown. No one is telling actors what to do. They are not speaking scripted lines, but there is a still a narrative being sculpted in the cutting room.

If you ask the question, 'What is the dominant art form of the twentieth century?' the answer must be the movies. Films have had an enormous impact on society and have transformed the face of popular entertainment. But if you consider what is really new about them, you struggle to identify something. Is it the directors and actors? No. They have been around since Shakespeare's time. Is it the scriptwriter? No. Storytellers have been around for even longer, probably since the Stone Age. So has music in the soundtrack. Okay, then maybe it is because they are films; captured on celluloid. Again, no. Photography is a nineteenth century invention. The more you think about it, the more you realise the special thing about movies is the editing. In fact, you could say that the art of movies is the art of editing. This is the only revolutionary change. The ability to alter the sequence in which people experience things. To decide what they will see and what they won't see. To manipulate their perception.

The editor is the unsung hero of the movie world. You know the names of the stars and the directors. You may even know the names of some producers and a cinematographer or two. But can you name a famous editor? Probably not. Because a good editor is invisible, like his editing. Once you become conscious of the cutting, you are no longer able to suspend your disbelief and the cinematic illusion comes crashing down. Does that remind you of someone else? An editor is just like a spin doctor. A spin doctor should be invisible too. It is a well known saying that when you become aware of the spin doctor, when he becomes the story, it's time for him to go. A spin doctor is an editor, not of film, but of events in the real world.

The social media revolution threatens the power of the traditional media. YouTube challenges the power of the TV controller. You watch what you like, not what he has chosen to put on TV. Blogging and tweeting produces a torrent of news and views which usurp traditional print media. Podcasts do the same to radio. So the traditional role of the editor is becoming obsolete. You no longer need someone to decide what should or should not be published. Everything is published. Let the public decide for themselves what is interesting and relevant. If editors are on the way out, and spin doctors are editors, does that mean spin is obsolete too?

The answer is no, because there are two types of editors. Consider the old Soviet Union. There were plenty of economists constructing five-year plans; trying to anticipate what the citizens wanted. Sadly, this proved to be an impossible task and they were all swept away when Communism fell. Does this mean that there are no economists any more? No. There are just no central planning economists. There are more free market economists than ever. Likewise with editors. The newspaper editor is like the central planning economist. The spin doctor is the free market economist.

Things are changing for sure. The main tool of the spin doctor, the press release, may be on its last legs. Formal press announcements are becoming anachronistic in the world of blogging, Facebook and Twitter. But these new social media channels are already being co-opted by PR companies. And there is also a whole new bunch of potential customers. Imagine someone starting up a new blog. How is he going to get his voice heard in that maelstrom of chatter. Hopefully, the sheer quality of his blogs will attract a few readers and he will gradually develop a groundswell of support. But he is probably going to need some sort of publicist too, working unseen in the background, helping to mould perceptions. Getting readers is just like getting voters. That is very familiar territory for a spin doctor.

The right amp

It is 1973, the golden age of vinyl, and there is one topic of heated discussion for all music lovers. You can hear the same type of argument everywhere in pubs, clubs, schools, and at work. The debate is this: which is the most important part of the hi-fi system. Some argue that you should spend the most money on the turntable. After all, that's where the sound originates from. Invest in a good pick up for the deck because if the signal is no good there, it will just get worse further down the line. Others hold that the speakers are key. That is where the signal is actually turned into sound. So for audio nirvana you should buy the best and biggest speakers you can. But the cognoscenti know both these arguments are wrong. The most important part of the hi-fi system is the amplifier. That is the heart of everything. That is where the sound is processed and expanded. That is what gives the sound its colour and warmth. Buy yourself the best amp you can and you will be fine, son . . .

Why is spin necessary? Because everyone needs a good amp. The amplifier may not originate the sound, nor deliver the sound, but it does make it audible. For sound, isn't that the most important thing? Culture arises from below and coalesces to form a common narrative which we use to define ourselves. Life is a swirling mixture of exposures to art, advertising, office politics, news, real politics, celebrities and TV. Spin is at the heart of all these things. That cocktail of ephemeral contacts is our modern life. Social life is about shared perceptions; perceptions that are moulded and amplified by spin to form a collective culture that nourishes us. Without spin, there is no culture. It is not a symptom of the degeneracy of the modern world but of its health. It's the most important part of our hi-fi system. There is only one remaining question and that is the question of scale. Has the amp got too big for the speakers? That is the topic for our final chapter.

CHAPTER 10

Catataxis in Practice

Splitting the rainbow

It is 1671. Isaac Newton is doing experiments in optics. He shines a white light through a prism and notices that it is refracted into a whole spectrum of colours. This is an exciting discovery. Light itself is made up of component parts. The trouble is that Newton's own colour perception is not that good, so he calls a colleague to come into the room. Newton asks his friend how many colours he can see in the rainbow. 'Six', the friend confidently replies, 'I see red, orange, yellow, green, blue and violet.' Newton frowns. 'You are mistaken' he says 'there must be seven.' After some persuasion, the friend succumbs and includes the colour indigo, between blue and violet. Newton smiles happily. Now the spectrum of colour matches the seven notes in a musical scale and the seven days of the week. There is pattern and harmony again in the physical universe. His hermetic beliefs are upheld. As above, so below . . .

Of course, there are an infinite number of colours in the rainbow. It is a continuous spectrum. You can break it up into as many different parts as you like. For Newton, it was important that it was seven because that fitted in with his world view. The divisions between the levels that I have made in this book are the same. At times, I have decided to label the rungs on a ladder in a particular way, because that fits my world view. You are free to label them however you like. There are an infinite number of ways to divide up a spectrum. But in drawing the dividing lines, what we both have in common is an understanding of scale. And also that, on different levels, different rules apply. So we are out of tune with Newton's hermetic beliefs. Catataxis means 'as above, *not* so below . . .'

Jumping up one level

There is a topological trapdoor that allows you to escape from any puzzle. Topology is the study of shape and dimensions and the mathematics of topology can often provide a way of resolving a conundrum by invoking a higher dimension. For example, string theory in physics tries to reconcile quantum mechanics with relativity by invoking an eleven dimensional space time. We can only experience three dimensions of space as humans, but some suggest these other dimensions could be curled up at a subatomic scale. That is all far too complicated for this book. It is easier to explain the topological 'get out of jail' card by looking at a very limited number of dimensions.

Let's start with one dimension. Consider an ant crawling along a string. The ant is constrained to only one dimension; it can only move forwards or backwards. When it meets a blockage or barrier it must stop. It can only get past the barrier by leaving the string and climbing around it. But, climbing around something means moving sideways; in other words, crossing into the second dimension. So the solution to the problem involves moving up a dimension. Now let's consider a two-dimensional problem. The ant is constrained to crawl over a surface bounded by some sort of encircling fence. The only way the ant can escape from this corral is to climb up and over the fence; moving vertically in the third dimension. Again, it escapes by using a higher dimensional trap-door. What about a three-dimensional problem? Imagine a prisoner locked in a cell with no doors or windows. How can he get out? The answer is to invoke a higher dimension, in this case time. He can travel back in time to the moment before he was placed in the cell. Of course, time travel is impossible because we are three-dimensional creatures. Likewise, vertical movement is impossible for a two-dimensional creature. I am just using this as an illustration of the dimensional escape route: the solution to an intractable problem can often be found by moving up one level.

The world's problems are problems of scale.

Two theoretical examples is not a very good start for a chapter called 'Catataxis in Practice'. From now on I will keep it practical and conclude this book by pulling together all the different themes, with some real life examples. Let's start with the major problems facing the world right now. First, there is global warming. In a rare moment of global togetherness, the Kyoto Protocol for reducing CO_2 emissions was signed in 1997. Developed countries pledged to reduce their greenhouse gas emissions by an average five per cent by 2012. Sadly, this agreement has failed to produce any real reductions in emissions of greenhouse gases in the last fourteen years. This is partly because the treaty was not ratified by everyone, the USA and Australia being notable exceptions. It was also because the treaty was not legally binding in any way, there were no penalties for missing targets and there were plenty of loopholes and offsets that could be used to avoid any dramatic action. The Copenhagen Summit in 2009, which aspired to replace the Kyoto Protocol with a more substantive and comprehensive agreement, ended in failure. Some 198 different countries attended the summit but no agreement was reached.

The real issue with global warming is that the scale of the problem is bigger than the scale of the institutions trying to tackle it. Both the Kyoto and Copenhagen meetings were organised under the auspices of the UN. But that organisation lacks the teeth and the legal status to enforce anything meaningful. It is quite good for drafting a bland communiqué or a statement of intent but it does not have the muscle to push any substantive changes through. At the moment, sovereignty stops at the national level, and few nations want to pass sovereignty any higher. Global warming is an intractable problem for which we need to invoke the dimensional escape route: move up one level. In this case, pass sovereignty upwards to a global organisation that could impose serious penalties for carbon polluters.

Global warming is one example of an issue that can't be fixed at a national level. There are plenty of others. Let's look at overfishing in the oceans next. A recent report[79] predicts that ninety per cent of the edible fish in the sea will have disappeared by 2048. In fact, twenty-nine per cent of all edible fish species have already collapsed because of overfishing. Factory fishing fleets trawling the oceans are taking unsustainably large catches. Technological advances like larger ships, flash freezing and fish-finding radar have transformed the fishing industry, much to the detriment of fish stocks. The Newfoundland cod fishery is a good example. This area of the Grand Banks off the coast of Canada was reliably yielding 200,000 tons of cod a year for several hundred years,

79 paper by Boris Worm, published in the *American Journal of Science*, 3 November 2006

providing a staple food stock for North America and Europe. In the 1970s, technological advances mean the catch goes up four-fold, but only for a brief period. The fish stocks soon collapse and in 1992 the Canadian Government close the fishery to give the cod a chance to recover. This is meant as a temporary measure, but twenty years later they are still waiting. The cod stocks have not recovered and the fishery is still closed. A similar story can be told for the anchovies off the coast of Peru and for sole in the Irish Sea.

In some ways, the Newfoundland cod fishery is not a good example because it is under the control of one government. Most of the Grand Banks falls inside Canada's Exclusive Economic Zone (EEZ), the 200-mile area off a country's coast for which it owns fishing rights. The real worry is in the deep oceans where no law prevails and fishermen can take what they like. If a developed country such as Canada is unable to protect its own fish stocks, what chance is there in the lawless ocean? This situation is some-times known as the 'tragedy of the commons'. The term stems from the land shared by peasants in medieval times. All villagers had the right to graze their livestock on this common land and, as a result, it was normally disastrously overgrazed. For a peasant there was an incentive to keep putting his cow on that land because any benefit came solely to him, while any damage was shared by every-one. Likewise, for fishery in the oceans. Any catch you make benefits you personally, any damage you cause is shared out amongst the whole world.

The overfishing problem is a problem of scale: finite resources overexploited by a much larger demand. People have been fishing in the sea since the dawn of man. In the past, it has always been assumed that there is an inexhaustible supply of fish in the sea. But now, with six billion people on earth and major advances in fishing technology, we face a future where there may be none. There is a real risk that our children will have no fish at all, just an ocean full of jellyfish who will move in to usurp that ecological niche. Can anything be done about it? Well, the normal solution to a tragedy of the commons is privatisation. Once there is a legally defined ownership, property rights and some established boundaries there is a strong incentive not to over exploit the resources. The eighteenth century saw a wave of Enclosure Acts in the UK which converted common land to private ownership.[80] In order to apply this to the high seas and the fisheries problem, there needs to be some supranational authority able to enforce property rights over free swimming fish in the deep blue ocean.

Applying law to the high seas is a tricky business and leads into the next global problem: piracy. In the last decade, piracy has grown alarmingly off the coast of Somalia and to a lesser extent near the Strait of Malacca. Hundreds of ships are attacked by pirates each year. The vessels are captured and ransomed along with the crew. Losses due to piracy are estimated to be US$15 billion a year. The problem is that the pirates operating on the high seas do not fall under any clear legal jurisdiction. This means that if they are apprehended, there is no court in which to try them, so they end up just being released. Commercial vessels are loath to have guns or armed personnel on board as it leads to complications with insurance and port procedures. So commercial ships can only defend themselves with passive measures such as barbed wire or water hoses. Most are just relying on an avoidance strategy; travel fast and keep out of known risk areas. Naval ships on patrol can only engage with pirates if they are fired upon first, or if they can make a clear positive identification. It is hard to tell the difference between a local fishing boat and a pirate craft with concealed weapons. All in all, the odds are stacked in favour of the pirates, which is why it is such a growth industry. The financial returns in piracy are so high that it is attracting investment as an emerging market in its own right.

In previous centuries, piracy was stamped out by firm policing from a strong national navy. But that was a different era, where human rights were less of a concern and the captain of a Royal Navy ship could do as he pleased. Now it falls between the inter-jurisdictional cracks and will only be solved by some form of global anti-piracy task force which could only claim legitimacy from a supranational body. Again the solution depends on appealing to a higher level. There are other examples of global problems which require the same sort of solution. In financial services, banks are

---

80 Enclosure benefited the aristocracy at the expense of the peasantry. The peasants displaced by these clearances emigrated to the USA, where they in turn enclosed the land of the American Indians. Enclosure may solve the tragedy of the commons but it brings its own tragedies too.

now bigger than the nations that are supposed to supervise and guarantee their losses. They are 'too big to fail' and are able to hold national taxpayers to ransom when they need bailing out. After the global financial crisis of 2008, a number of solutions were suggested such as a global banking regulator, or a 'Tobin tax', on speculative currency trading. In practice, little has actually happened. Nations can't act unilaterally; global banks are free to move to any jurisdiction. Any action needs to be globally coordinated, but there is no institution that is able to do this and few nations wish to pass the sovereignty of national banking regulation up to a higher body. There is a Basel Committee on Banking Supervision which produces global banking accords but it cannot enforce them, that is left to the national governments still. It was set up in 1974 and, just like the Kyoto Protocol, has had little real impact. CO_2 emissions are still going up and international banking crises still happen every decade or so. For a similarly ineffective international agreement, consider the nuclear non-proliferation treaty. This was signed in 1968. Since then India, Pakistan, North Korea, South Africa, Israel and Iran have all acquired a nuclear weapons capability and Iraq and Libya both came quite close.

Community solutions one level down

All these examples, global warming, overfishing, piracy, global banking and nuclear proliferation require stronger institutions on a higher level to solve issues. But there are also problems whose solutions require stronger institutions one level down, at a community level. The move from village life to city life has broken down many traditional local support mechanisms. The percentage of the world population living in cities has grown from thirteen per cent in 1910 to fifty per cent in 2010, and is predicted to be seventy per cent in 2050. For the average global citizen, his grandfather lived in the country and his grandchildren will be city dwellers. In the developed world, where the process of urbanisation is already pretty much complete, national governments struggle to deal with a number of social issues that are essentially local problems. These are issues such as housing, crime, congestion, poverty, anti-social behaviour and recycling. National level policies have been launched many times, and to great fanfare, in order to address these problems. They have had little impact and the problems stubbornly persist.

The more recent trend is a move towards localism and the recognition that they can only be solved by moving down one level and focusing on community solutions. Community structures, destroyed in the urban migration, need to be rebuilt.

Part of the trend to localism is explained by ecological concerns. Consumer tastes have begun to swing back to favour locally grown, organic food, again prompting the growth in farmers' markets. The food is fresher and 'greener' in that it saves on food miles. But more important than this is the community dimension, because there is always a glut of whatever is in season. Anyone whose hobby is growing their own vegetables always ends up giving half of them away to neighbours, because nature's bounty gives us too many tomatoes at harvest time for any one person to be able to eat. Vegetable growing is a natural community activity. Some activists believe that persuading city dwellers to grow their own vegetables will solve many of society's ills: fewer food miles, less carbon emissions, more recycling, friendlier neighbourhoods, less crime.

Some green energy schemes are more economic on a community basis. Wind and solar power installations are more efficient when servicing a group of houses rather than a single dwelling. Co-generation schemes are another good example here. These reuse the surplus heat from power stations to warm homes in the local vicinity. This is a community scale project that would not make sense on a national or individual basis. Those steaming manholes in Manhattan, so commonly seen in gritty New York movies, are part of a cogeneration scheme whereby Con Edison heats domestic buildings on that densely populated island. It brings to mind another island, in Greece this time. In the village where I was staying, the houses did not have ovens in their kitchens. The villagers would take their stew pots filled with raw ingredients to the baker in the morning. His large communal oven would slowly cook everyone's food, using the left over heat from his early morning bread-baking. They would pick up their hot meal along with some bread from the baker in the evening. An elegant community-based solution to the shortage of firewood on the island.

Some academics believe the best solutions to the tragedy of the commons problem are community based. Elinor Ostrom won the Nobel prize for economics in 2009 for her analysis of this issue. She studied traditional societies in Africa and Nepal where scarce resources such as water and grazing are effectively managed on a community basis. The solution still involves clear boundaries and private ownership, but in this case it is ownership by the local group. The resource in question appears like a private good to an outsider but a public good to an insider. It all hinges on a strong sense of local community. This may solve the tragedy of the commons, but the downside is that it promotes xenophobia.

A discussion about strong, differentiated local communities brings us to our last global problem area: terrorism. This is seen as a worldwide problem, as in the 'global war on terrorism' but it is more of an omnipresent local problem than a global one. Most terrorist attacks come from disgruntled nationals in local communities rather than international criminal masterminds: Minority not Moriarty. There was a cruel irony to the London tube bombings on 7/7. British troops were fighting in Afghanistan, ostensibly to keep the world safe from international terrorism, but the suicide bombers were home-grown militants from Leeds. The Madrid train bombings in 2004 were also the work of radicalised locals, as were many of the attempted bombings, e.g. the shoe bomber, that have been successfully thwarted. It seems as though terrorism, though inspired by a global sentiment, is a local emergent phenomenon arising from minority communities who feel excluded. The solution to the problem probably lies in local community engagement rather than wars in foreign countries.

The train model of power

Governments look beneath them and fear the threat of al-Qaeda. They see an international terrorist conspiracy lurking in the shadows, one level below the national. It is a difficult foe to combat because the battle is not nation *v.* nation but nation *v.* radicalised individuals. Individual conspiracy theorists look upwards and see secretive government organisations running everything. There are many versions of this mythical 'government plus big business kombinat'. Take your pick from the list of usual suspects: the Bilderberg Group, the Freemasons, the Illuminati, the Priory of Sion, the Templars, the Rosicrucians or even Skull and Bones! These fears are mirror images of each other. Each is looking to a different level that it does not understand and populating it with ghoulish fantasies.

Who is really in charge? Who is pulling the train? Is it a loco-motive at the front? Or is it a shunting engine at the rear? In this metaphor, you have to imagine turning the hierarchy of power on its side; the locomotive is the government and the shunting engine the individual. The debate is about the pull or push between the elected and the electorate. The answer is neither and both. Trains have changed in modern times. The power is no longer all con-centrated in one engine driving a bunch of free-wheeling carriages. In modern urban electric trains, every carriage has its own power source. The train is an assemblage of self-propelled units. In other words, everyone is pulling the train. The romance of the famous locomotive, such as Stephenson's *Rocket*, or the *Flying Scotsman*, is over. They have been replaced by the glamour-free, but functional, 'electric multiple unit'. Likewise in politics there are no leaders any more, just an assemblage of interlinked units; carriages with names such as media, markets, bureaucracy and consumers. They are coupled to each other, but driven by their own motive power.

Let's turn the metaphor back upright again and look at the vertical hierarchy of levels rather than a horizontal string of carriages. The appropriate way to understand the modern world is to isolate the different levels and recognise the exclusive rules that apply at that level. Catataxis is the erroneous application of rules at the wrong level. Take, for example, the issue of right and wrong. At the state level we have laws, at the community level, cultural ethics, and at the personal level, morals. Each level has its own mechanism of virtue. The mistake is to mix them up. Political correctness is a catataxic fallacy, because it attempts to legislate respect for others' feelings. State laws are an inappropriate rule to use at this personal level. Let's look at a financial example. At the state level we have taxes, at the community level, charitable giving, and at the personal level, tipping. They are all different methods of redistributing wealth. When you are accosted in the street by a charitable fund-raiser (or 'chugger'[81]), that is catataxis. Tipping is a person-to-person transaction, normally for a service rendered. You tip your waiter or a street busker. You may even give money to a beggar, for no service rendered, out of compassion: But a chugger is an institution, raising money on the street; level two intruding into

81 A chugger is a charity mugger

level one. That is why it is often so resented. At the state level, income tax is a fairly recent invention. In the nineteenth century, the poor were supported by optional philanthropy. But anyone who dreams of a return to those days, with taxes being replaced by optional charitable giving, is living in a catataxic fantasy world. You can't turn back the clock.

Shopping to save the world

Globalisation and the rising threat of terrorism? We have all been here before. Cast your mind back to 1900. The world's economy is truly global with little hindrance to the flow of goods and people. Western investors are pouring money into emerging markets: Brazilian rubber plantations, Chinese railways and African mines. Passports do not exist and emigrating just means catching the next ship to anywhere in the world to seek your fortune, whether you are an Irish farmer, an Indian shopkeeper or a Chinese labourer. This globalisation exists because most of the world is under the control of European empires.

At the same time, many heads of State are being killed by anarchists or, as we call them today, terrorists. In a few short years around the turn of the century the Austro-Hungarian Empress Elizabeth, King Umberto I of Italy, the King of Serbia and the US President, McKinley, are all assassinated. A decade later, the assassination of Archduke Franz Ferdinand of Austria triggers World War I, a nationalistic war between empires.

Recognising the dangers of nationalism, the first supranational organisation, the League of Nations is set up in 1919. Sadly, this is too weak to prevent the even more destructive nationalistic conflict of World War II. The second attempt in the form of the United Nations has a longer shelf life. It still exists today, as do other supranational organisations such as the EU, the IMF and the International Court of Justice. But consider this. If it took the horrendous, destructive conflict of World War II to create these dysfunctional, toothless, supranational paper tigers, just how bad must things get before sovereignty is passed up to an entity that can really fix today's problems. How bad must the ecological catastrophe get before a global organisation is empowered to fix it?

Maybe the answer lies in a different direction. In the past, external threats have often been overcome by banding together to make a bigger entity: principalities merge to become kingdoms, local tribes to empires and city states to nations. But there is also a case to be made that the trend of history is for sovereignty to be passed downwards and not upwards. As discussed in Chapter 7, the seat of sovereignty has passed over time from god to king, then from king to the land-owners represented by parliament, and finally from the land-owners to the individual with universal suffrage. So the individual is more powerful today than at any time in history. At the same time, the current version of globalisation is driven by companies and not nations. In the battle of the twins, the multinational has defeated the nation state. Globalisation 2.0 is a corporate affair. So the answer to the problems of our world may lie with individual wishes being channelled through the behaviour of multinationals, sidestepping outdated national structures. This is a bottom-up solution rather than a top-down one. Solve global warming by voting with your money and not in the ballot box: Shop ethically to save the world.

There is one problem with this: ethics and globalisation rarely seem to go hand in hand. Once you inflate personal ethics to a global scale, something seems to go wrong, which is just what you should expect if you believe in catataxis.

Let's look at some supranational entities that, unlike the UN and the EU, are remarkably effective. How about starting with FIFA, the *Federation Internationale de Football Association*. Soccer is the world's favourite sport and it is governed by FIFA, a supranational body which is notionally headquartered in Switzerland but, in effect, exists outside the laws of any country. FIFA has been spectacularly successful and the global soccer market has grown to be worth US$25 billion a year. With so much money washing around, it is also spectacularly corrupt. But since it exists beyond the purview of any country it can do what it likes.[82] Or consider the global foreign exchange market, where average daily turnover is US$4 trillion every day. This is a completely unregulated, over-

---

82 For evidence that soccer is more important than nations, consider the UEFA Cup Final in 2008 between Chelsea and Manchester United in Moscow: two UK clubs playing in a foreign country. British fans could turn up at Moscow Airport clutching only a ticket to the game and be waved through immigration without a passport.

the-counter market. There is no institution that oversees it, although different countries have regulations for their national banks. It is a truly global, supranational phenomenon that does not 'belong' to any country. Is it effective? Yes. Is it successful? Hell, yes. Is it ethical? Well, what do *you* think? Have you ever *not* felt ripped off whenever you exchange foreign currency?

So these look like the two options: some ghastly, global cataclysm, far worse than World War II, that ushers in a single, top down, world government or a set of bottom up emergent institutions outside national control that are effective but unethical. It would be nice to find a middle path between these two extremes. This would seem like a return to the medieval system of overlapping authorities. Different entities having ultimate authority over some clearly defined slivers of the global cake. Sovereignty passed upwards, but only for a limited band of the governing spectrum. For example, imagine an armed and powerful global maritime agency empowered to protect fish and eliminate piracy, funded by individual and corporate donations: Greenpeace of the high seas with guns. Nations states might be persuaded to pass sovereignty over to a global entity in a very limited field once they acknowledge they are unable to fix that specific problem on their own. Another alternative is to limit the number of nations at the top table. The trend in recent years has been one of inclusion; the G7 group was expanded to G10, and then again to G20. Maybe it would be easier to sort things out if it went back to being a G3 (USA, EU, China) or even a G2. If the world's most powerful country and the world's most populous one just ran things in a joint hegemony, you might see some astonishing progress on global issues. Probably the best answer, if you follow the train model of power, is for each level to do its own thing. Individuals, communities, spin-doctors, governments, multinationals and the UN all have their part to play. They don't even need to be co-ordinated. If each just focuses on what concerns them and what they can do at that level, the result may surprise all of us.

Catataxic sound bites

This book is meant to be descriptive and not prescriptive. Its purpose is to illustrate the different viewpoints attached to the different layers. No one layer has the monopoly on the truth. The view of bottom up reductionists is as distorting as that of the top down holists. The unit of selection does not permanently reside on any one rung of the ladder. The point of this book is to persuade you to step off your favourite rung and get some perspective of the ladder in its entirety. That makes a conclusion quite hard to write. There is no list of things that I propose that you should do. There is no manifesto that I can exhort you to execute. But at the same time, I don't want to leave you with the feeling that all the hard work of reading this book has been for nothing. So I will conclude with a set of deliberately provocative sound bites. I don't present them as being necessarily true, or a reflection of my deeply held beliefs. They are there to entertain you: Contentious ammo that you can use to enliven a boring conversation. Here are some catataxic themes with which to shock the complacent, or the certain:

London is more important than Britain

The nation state is past its sell-by date. The pendulum is swinging back towards cities again. London, as a global financial capital, is more important to the world than Britain is. Multinational companies are more powerful than countries, and they place their headquarters in global cities like London. Cities are cool, countries are not. That is why branded goods list cities (e.g. London, Paris, New York) where they have outlets and not countries. In time, the EU will make national distinctions as irrelevant as county distinctions. Distinguishing between German cars and British cars will sound as pointless as differentiating between Berkshire cars and Buckinghamshire cars. Cities will become more important inside the EU as beacons of culture, trade, excitement and opportunity, just as they were in medieval times. Nationalism will be seen as a rather unpleasant and destructive transitory phase. Cosmopolitanism, centred on multicultural 'world cities' such as London, will be the new paradigm.

Democracy is the opposite of consensus

Democracy is a pugnacious system in which the winner takes all. Those who are outvoted just have to put up with it. A consensus model, more common in Asia, tries to find a compromise that all parties will be happy with. Democracy does not necessarily reflect the will of the people, and often not even the will of the majority of the people. The only way to make democracy truly fair would be to have more than one government at the same time. In such a scheme there might be three parties in power concurrently and the voters are governed by whichever party they individually picked at election time. Workers in the same office may pay different taxes and receive different services depending on who they voted for. The ballot is no longer secret, and you only get free healthcare if you voted for the right party. There again your taxes are likely to be higher. Such a system already exists on a local level in metropolitan cities that cross state boundaries. New Yorkers pay different taxes depending on which state they live in. The same is true in London boroughs. The 'vote' is cast by deciding where to live. This type of democratic scheme is the only way to ensure that everyone gets exactly what they voted for. But it can only achieve this by fragmenting the sovereignty of the state. If the unity of the government is paramount, then there are just two opposing options: find a compromise that everyone can agree on (consensus model) or subjugate the minority to the will of the majority (democracy). Which one do you think is more civilised?

Today's groups are tomorrow's individuals

The story of life on earth has several transformative steps. Two key ones are the development of the first cells and, later, the emergence of multicellular organisms. The first life forms on earth were the prokaryotes; bacteria and archaea which were little more than a strand of DNA in a bubble of cytoplasm. Complex cells, with a nucleus, mitochondria and other organelles are known as eukaryotes and emerged at a later stage. Quite how the eukaryotes developed from the prokaryotes was a subject of much controversy. It is only recently that the radical theory of endosymbiosis, first put forward by Lynn Margulis, has moved from scientific heresy to general acceptance. This proposes that complex cells arose when a cell engulfed a number of different types of bacteria to form a communal organism. So a single cell amoeba is, in fact, a colony of diverse bacterial forms interacting in a symbiotic way. Likewise, at a later date, multicellular creatures first emerged when several single cell creatures began interacting collectively. More recently, social animals such as ants, bees, wolves and humans have taken the next step up the ladder with their colonies, packs and tribes. The history of life on earth has a common vector; things that are seen as a group at one point in time will later be viewed as a single organism. The mechanism for this transformation is the shift in the unit of selection: the basis of evolution sometimes moves up one level. Competition between groups becomes more important than competition inside the group. The unit of selection shifts from the individual to the group. Physics has its underlying laws of thermodynamics which state that entropy always increases. Biology now has a profound underpinning doctrine too: today's groups are tomorrow's individuals. If you extend this line of thinking to human society, it implies that the Federal States of Europe is an inevitability at some time in the future, as is the United States of Earth, once we discover some alien life forms to compete with.

To win, embrace mediocrity

If you are running a company, then you probably would prefer that your employees' energies are directed at beating the competition rather than internal office politics. Following on from the previous paragraph, you therefore believe that the unit of evolutionary selection belongs at the corporate level and not the employee level. Competition between companies is more important than competition inside companies. For the group to succeed, individualism must be suppressed. Strict egalitarianism is a hallmark of hunter gatherer societies, which provide the best window in time to view our early evolution. A good example is the ritual 'insulting of the meat': a successful hunter apologises for the inadequacy of the carcass he brings home even if it is huge, to avoid appearing boastful. The Plains Indians embraced a cult of mediocrity. The best hunters were expelled from the tribe, as well as the worst, in the interests of social harmony. Huntsmen training a pack of dogs know this too. Both the leaders and the stragglers are killed, in order to bind the remaining dogs into a more cohesive pack. Our success as a species is partially explained by the teamwork and group thinking that this egalitarianism promotes. Carrying this across to the corporate world leads to a startling conclusion. Rather than rewarding your top performers with huge bonuses, you should fire them instead. They are probably just taking credit for other peoples' hard work anyway. If you want a large successful company, then hire team players and embrace the cult of mediocrity.

Atlanta airport is bigotry in concrete

Here is the bigot's paradox. In your own group, you notice the differences between individual people. It is those very differences that make them individual. When looking at outsiders, you just see the group. You make them different by being blind to their individual differences. You make them different by treating them all the same. There is no place in the world that makes you feel more like an inconvenient foreigner than Hartsfield Jackson International Airport in Atlanta. For domestic passengers, it is a miracle of efficiency, but international passengers feel very unwelcome. There is an unusual procedure that foreign travellers must go through. Having just come off an international flight and picked your baggage off the carousel, you then need to check your baggage back in again whilst undergoing a full security search. You are not getting on a plane, but on a train which you must take for eight stops just to get to the exit terminal. The fear is having made your way safely, 4,000 miles across the Atlantic and been reconnected with your luggage, you might lose it again somewhere inside the enormous airport. The whole process says 'you are foreign, you are different, you are a problem'. Contrast that with Singapore airport, which is a joy for domestic and foreign passengers alike. City States rule OK!

The World Wide Web is dying

The World Wide Web is in terminal decline. Its principles of information shared to all, accessed by browsers on a level playing field are under threat. They are being replaced by private-gated communities such as iTunes, Facebook and Skype. The Web is only one layer of many in the nested hierarchy of levels that make up the internet. At the bottom level are the IP and TCP protocols that move packets of information around. At this base level, things are still growing extremely fast. But traffic at the WWW level is declining. The familiar view of the internet, that you see through your browser window, is a shrinking domain. Browsers deliver HTML data over the http protocol. This was once the major data channel, but it now makes up only a quarter of the traffic on the internet. Other levels are now dominant and they are in private hands. Level 2 is dying, level 3 is growing. When you use apps on your mobile phone, make a Skype call, watch a streaming video or communicate with your friends over Twitter or Facebook, you are not using the World Wide Web; you are in a private-gated community. Communitarian ideals are being replaced by private ownership in an inevitable process of commercialisation. The open plains of the native Indians are being fenced and homesteaded all over again, in cyberspace.

Take votes away from pensioners

The aging population is causing a growing disconnect between the economy and society, between the body politic and the body fiscal. Retirees are the fastest growing demographic group in most countries. They are politically active but, economically speaking, they are a drag on the system since the working population is paying their pensions. As the elderly become more numerous, and therefore a more powerful political lobby, politicians pay them more attention than is justified by their contribution to society. Pensioners vote for politicians who promise better pensions, all paid for by the hard working middle-aged. This threatens a breakdown in the social contract. The motto of the Boston Tea Party – 'No taxation without representation' – was a protest against being forced to pay taxes without having a political voice. This can be inverted to say, 'no representation without taxation'. In other words, if you are economically inactive, then you don't deserve a vote. Tax-paying employees are the only people who should have a voice in how their money is spent. If, on the other hand, you argue that the economically inactive do deserve a vote, then maybe a mother of three should get three extra votes to cast on behalf of her kids. Married middle-aged mums and dads would get a far stronger political voice. Such a system is known as Demeny voting, after the demographer Paul Demeny, and would go some way towards countering today's growing gerontocracy.

CEOs are glorified sports commentators

Sports commentators are experts at 'post hoc' rationalisation. They do it on the fly. Here is the half-time score. A good pundit can immediately explain to you why it is what it is. Had the score been completely different, he could have explained that too. Sports commentators are inventive, plausible, eloquent and knowledgeable. As a result they are quite well paid. Now consider the CEO of a big multinational. He is hostage to the whims of the global economy and presiding over a corporation of such complexity that as a single individual he can make little difference. He will, of course, take the credit for any success and find an appropriate scapegoat for any failures, but is he actually doing anything? If he was not there, would it make any difference? If you apply the economist £20 note principle, he must be doing something because he is paid a lot of money. If you think that he is just a cipher, reacting to events that he cannot control then the only conclusion you can come to is that he is just like a sports pundit. He can give you a plausible 'post hoc' explanation of the strategies that delivered the growth.

The railway is the deadliest weapon of all

Consider these two famous battles, Waterloo and the Somme. They take place 100 miles and 100 years apart. Waterloo lasts one day and results in 50,000 casualties. From one vantage point, it is possible to see the whole two-mile front of the battlefield. The Somme, on the other hand, has a front that is twenty miles long. The battle lasts four months with a million casualties: ten times bigger, twenty times more deadly. But it is a mistake to consider the Somme just a scaled-up version of Waterloo. Something fundamental has changed; a cataxic boundary has been crossed. Just as the change in scale from insect to elephant requires a change from exoskeleton to endoskeleton, so the slaughter of World War I requires a transformation in internal organisation. It needs the revolution in logistics, triggered by the invention of the railway. Napoleonic armies live off the land and so when there is no food or forage for horses available locally, they starve. Russian scorched earth tactics defeat Napoleon's Grande Armée. In the retreat from Moscow in 1812, some ninety-five per cent of the French army die, mainly due to lack of supplies. Railways change all that. One railway line in the US Civil War keeps General Sherman's 100,000 strong army well enough supplied to defeat the Confederate states. To do the same by road would have taken 36,000 wagons, with six mules each; an impossibly large number to manage, even if the roads could have taken that amount of traffic. At the beginning of World War I, a million men and half a million horses are delivered by the French railways to the front line in only two weeks. By 1916, the French are running 230 trains a day to keep the front line supplied.

Without the logistics of this railway network, it is impossible to continue fighting: no food, no ammunition, no artillery shells, no war. The railway is the endoskeleton of war. Some may explain the appalling increase in casualties of modern war to the invention of deadlier weapons such as howitzers, machine guns, grenades and mortars. But the deadliest invention of all, the thing that enabled slaughter on such a huge scale, was the railway train.

Evil is the root of all money

My Latin teacher drummed in to me a particular Latin tag, *radix malorum est cupiditas*: money is the root of all evil. But with a Wildean playfulness you can reverse this motto to get something equally true. Paper money was invented in China to get around the problems of fake coinage. Coins were often adulterated with impure alloys, or clipped to make them underweight. Confidence in the currency got so low in seventh century China that the Song emperor issued paper money backed by his authority. For the first time, a piece of paper with no intrinsic value was given value through an act of faith. Money moves from the physical to the conceptual level. This is the birth of money as an abstract idea and since it was introduced to stamp out cheating, you can say that 'evil was the root of all money'. It was an inspired idea, but it did not work so well in practice, at least to begin with. The first Chinese paper money devalued by seventy-five per cent in fifteen years because the bureaucrats could not resist printing extra sheets. Confidence in paper money plummeted and it was then replaced by silver bullion. Since then governments have learned to manage confidence better and restrict the printing of money. Most money today is in electronic, rather than paper form. The global economy is more conceptual than real. An idea supported by nothing more than confidence, one level above the tangible world.

Your subconscious is more valuable than you are

When commerce on level three looks down at you on level one it sees a set of irrational but interlinked choices. This data is highly valuable. Supermarkets with their loyalty cards are tracking all your purchases. Google is looking at the pattern of your web browsing and selling your attention to advertisers. Amazon is suggesting books you might like to read based on what you liked in the past.

When you twitter on your mobile phone you are sending two messages into cyberspace: where you are and how you are feeling. This vast pool of geo-located emotions is a valuable dataset for multinationals to mine. The internet for social scientists is like the invention of the telescope for astronomers; it allows the observation of movements and linkages that were previously invisible. It allows their exploitation too. To the commercial world you are not much more than a set of inchoate preferences; a fuzzy bundle of prejudice and instinct. All this is happening at a subconscious level; your purchasing choices are more emotional than rational. They don't want to know what your considered opinion is; what you actually do is more important that what you say you will do. They want to talk to the boss, the one that makes the decisions: your subconscious. They observe what your instincts are driving you to do and then use that data to predict your future behaviour patterns. It's a direct interaction between the corporate world and your subconscious: Level four talking to the basement garage level.

Reptiles don't exist

In the biology lessons at school you were probably taught that there were five classes of vertebrates: birds, mammals, reptiles, amphibians and fish. But in the new cladistic-based taxonomy, the reptiles are not a single clade; in other words, this category no longer really exists. Some reptiles share a common ancestor with mammals, other reptiles share one with birds. So the category of reptiles now consists of several parts of different branches and part of the trunk too. Of course, all three, mammals, reptiles and birds, have a common ancestor further back in time. They all fit into the clade called amniotes; creatures whose embryos develop inside an amniotic sac. So the correct term these days for reptiles is 'non-avian, non-mammalian amniotes', but that is so clumsy that most people still just use the term 'reptiles'. Using this word is a cataxic error, because you have selectively assembled a number of items from the level below and presented them as if they were a coherent higher level entity.

Microbes drive your vote

Most people will be willing to concede that your economic environment can influence the way that you vote. If you grow up in a poor neighbourhood, you are more likely to be left-wing. At a stretch, you can also make the case that the political landscape is influenced by geographic landscape. The wide open prairies in the USA were settled by pioneering individualists. The descendants of these home-steaders have an in-built right-wing bias. Shortage of arable land can create the opposite effect. The crowded paddy fields of Asia require group co-operation and consensual sharing of resources. The collective outranks the individual – so much for the economic and geographic environment, but what about the microbial environment? As discussed in Chapter 4, recent studies show a strong correlation between collectivism and the prevalence of infectious diseases. The greater the threat of catching something nasty from a stranger, the greater the likelihood that the society is collectivist: xenophobic, conformist and respectful of authority. The correlation holds for human transmitted diseases but breaks down when examining animal to human diseases, like rabies. The relationship is also consistent if you look back in history. You may believe that politics drives health policy but, in truth, it may be the other way around. Individualism and democracy flourish in the absence of infectious diseases. Microbes on level one affect politics on level five.

The internet makes geography more important

Popular opinion holds that the internet makes geography irrelevant. If you can be friends online with anyone anywhere in the world then your local neighbourhood is obsolete, right? If we are all networked together, then geographic space (level one) is trumped by cyberspace (level two). Barriers to information flow disappear and online communities subsume physical ones. So goes the traditional argument anyway. But just as the 'paperless office' prediction proved to be 180 degrees wrong, the internet actually seems to be making geography more important. In the post industrial knowledge economy, hubs of creative people clustering together in specific locations is becoming even more prevalent. Urbanisation is increasing, villages are denuded and cities with a creative, entrepreneurial buzz are blossoming. The knowledge economy is a confluence of technology, money, marketing and speed. These are city attributes. No need for vast horizontal acres for production lines, what you need is vertical glass towers of creativity. These communities thrive when they are close-coupled physically, making centres of urban excellence where the different skills and disciplines reinforce each other in an upward spiral of virtuous circles. Sure, you can email in from home and online conference from the boondocks, but it's still not the same as being there in the centre of things, is it?

The pig wants to be eaten.[83]

I am sure you have, at some time, debated the ethics of eating meat with your vegetarian friends. One of the carnivore arguments runs like this. A symbiotic relationship has developed over millennia between humans and farm animals. We have bred them over many years and they would not exist without us. From the animal's perspective they have thrived and prospered from their association with us. They are far more numerous, having outcompeted their wild cousins. We provide them with food and shelter and they give us their flesh. Therefore, we are morally justified in eating them because they consent to this deal. This idea of 'animal consent' goes back to hunter gatherer days. The Eskimos believe the whale gives itself up to the people. The Ancient Greeks would sprinkle water on the heads of sacrificial animals. When the beasts nodded their head to shake it off, it was taken as a sign of consent. But generalising this concept of animal consent to all farm animals is a cataxic fallacy. In theory, it may possible for an individual to consent but how can that be applied to a whole class of creatures. Also, selective breeding has altered the genes of the herd to make them more appetising to humans. It is hard to see how genetic manipulation at level one can be used to justify a moral argument two levels up. The pig wants to be eaten? What if he changes his mind? Will you set him free?

Don't bother learning anything that can be taught

The rising costs of university education and widespread graduate unemployment have prompted many to question the value of a degree. There is a cataxic angle to this debate. We can call practical knowledge, level one and theoretical knowledge, level two.

---

83 Douglas Adams in his *Hitchhiker's Guide to the Galaxy* had a pig that introduced itself to diners explaining which part his body would taste best; a satirical take on 'guilt free' carnivorism.

The academic method, as taught at university, is to examine the facts, to abstract them into some general principles and then reapply this theory back to the real world. In catataxic terms, this is a return trip from level one to level two. From the specific to the general and then back to the specific again. The trouble is that a lot of real world problems do not succumb to this method. They fall at the first step; the abstraction step. By abstracting to the general level, you often leave most of the problem behind, because the devil is in the details. By attempting to create a simple, abstract summary, you end up with a facile, unrepresentative snapshot that will only give you facile answers. The non-academic approach to problem solving is to muddle through on level one, trying almost anything to see if it works in practice. Which approach is best? The answer must be that the more complex and fast moving a problem is, the more suitable the non academic approach becomes. And since the vector of the modern world is towards increasing complexity and speed, level one problem solving is becoming more favoured. That is what the marketplace seems to be telling us. Graduates have to work as unpaid interns before they can get a job. That implies experience is more valuable than a degree. Practical, specific knowledge is worth more than theoretical ability. Level one is more important than level two.

All words are lies

Here's an old joke: How can you tell when a politician is lying? His lips move! Maybe we should extend that principle beyond just politicians, because it potentially applies to all of us. Language is a logical construct which exists one level above our thoughts and feelings. So the process of trying to explain our emotions through a grammatical structure will inevitably introduce some distortions. By linking a level one thought to a level two word, we cross a catataxic boundary: in short, we lie. There are non-verbal languages that are more truthful. Body language is one example; research suggests that eighty per cent of communication is non-verbal through gesture, facial expression and posture. We can sometimes lie with a fake smile, but fidgety hands and feet are a giveaway. Then there is visual language of movies. For me, Nick Roeg and Terrence Malick are the masters here. If you look at their films, you will often be confronted with visual sequences of such staggering power that you understand what they mean without being able to articulate it in words. Picture an old man plodding slowly on a white horse, half glimpsed through trees in the moonlight. Or a couple making love on the rocks by the sea, while beneath the waves a shark savages a shoal of fish. These images are both mysterious and truthful in the same way that a dream is. They speak directly to the subconscious with the vocabulary of reverie; the ancient argot of imagination. This is what Keats meant when he said: 'Beauty is truth, truth beauty'. In other words, the truth is that which cannot be put in words.

And that, dear Reader, seems an appropriate place for me to stop.

Bibliography

When writing a broad ranging book like *Cataxis* it is sometimes necessary to reduce a deep and complicated argument to a few sketchy lines. So I would heartily recommend the following books, all of which are personal favourites, which deal with their respective subjects fully and at the appropriate length. They have all stimulated my thinking, opened my mind to new ideas and helped me in considering how more of the same is different.

Ball, Philip, *Critical Mass* (Heinemann, 2004)

Boorstin, Daniel, *The Discoverers* (Vintage, 1985)

Buss, Leo, *The Evolution of Individuality* (Princeton, 1987)

Chua, Amy, *World on Fire* (Arrow, 2004)

Clover, Charles, *The End of the Line* (Ebury Press, 2004)

Davies, Nick, *Flat Earth News* (Chatto & Windus, 2008)

Davies, Paul, *The Fifth Miracle* (Penguin, 1999)

Dawkins, Richard, *The Selfish Gene* (Oxford, 1989)

Dawkins, Richard, *The Blind Watchmaker* (Longman, 1986)

Goldacre, Ben, *Bad Science* (Fourth Estate, 2009)

Goldberg, Jonah, *Liberal Fascism* (Doubleday, 2007)

Gawande, Atul, *The Checklist Manifesto* (Metropolitan Books, 2009)

Kahn, David, *The Codebreakers* (Scribner, 1996)

Keegan, John, *The First World War* (Pimlico, 1999)

Keegan, John, *A History of Warfare* (Vintage 1993)

Langewiesche, William, *The Outlaw Sea* (North Point, 2004)

Levy, Stephen, *Crypto* (Penguin, 2002)

Lipton, Bruce, *The Biology of Belief* (Hay House, 2005)

Lovelock, James, *The Revenge of Gaia* (Allen Lane, 2006)

Morgan, Elaine, *The Aquatic Ape Hypothesis*, (Souvenir Press, 1999)

Ormerod, Paul, *Butterfly Economics* (Faber & Faber, 1998)

Peters, Edgar, *Fractal Market Analysis* (John Wiley, 1994)

Rodger, N. A. M., *The Command of the Ocean* (London, 2004)

Surowiecki, James, *The Wisdom of Crowds* (Little, Brown 2004)

Taleb, Nassim Nicholas, *The Black Swan* (Allen Lane 2007)

Acknowledgements

I have been thinking about writing this book for many years and a lot of the ideas have come from discussions with a large number of different friends and family members over that time. I would like to thank my father for helping me to come up with the title and my mother for giving me her boundless curiosity. Thanks also to my three brothers, James, Angus and Alex, for the many hours spent discussing catataxis while drinking or walking and sometimes even drinking *while* walking. Who says men can't multitask?

In particular, I would like to thank the following for their support and help: Dominic Armstrong, John Baldwin, Paul Boateng, Haresh Balani, Pilar Camino Alcon, David Clapham, David Charters, Jennifer Christie, Donald Crawford, Tim Colman, Martin Dixon, Kanjana Ferns, Lawrence Heyworth, Simon Hookway, Steve Jarrett, Marcus Kiggell, Kevin Lapwood, Tim Moe, Graeme Marsh, Stephen Mitchell, St John Mound, Bruce Packard, Alan Payton, Martin Porter, Paul Satchell, Nick Webb, Julius Welby, Bob Zielinski.

Lastly, thanks and much love to my wife, Yoko, and my daughters, Flora and Rosie, for putting up with my bad temper and general grumpiness while writing this book.

Index